W9-CNY-793

CURRENT RESEARCH IN HYPNOPAEDIA

CURRENT RESEARCH IN HYPNOPAEDIA

Edited by F. Rubin, B.Sc.

Research Officer, Sleep-Learning Association

AMERICAN ELSEVIER PUBLISHING COMPANY, INC.

New York

American Edition Published by
American Elsevier Publishing Company, Inc.
52 Vanderbilt Avenue
New York, New York 10017

Library of Congress Catalog Card Number 68–19319

Printed in Great Britain

To Annette and the Children

PREFACE

In recent months Sleep-Learning has been given more frequent publicity in the Press in Great Britain and other countries owing to various reports on experiments and courses going on officially behind the Iron Curtain.

In scientific circles Sleep-Learning, or to use the Greek term, *Hypnopaedia,* is nowadays a subject giving rise to controversy between physiologists, psychologists, educationalists and linguists in respect of the two major aspects involved, namely sleep and learning.

Intensified research on the physiological nature of different levels of consciousness, from alertness to deep sleep, is being carried out in many laboratories all over the world. In the past twenty years there has been an upsurge of interest in sleep, leading to many new and sigificant discoveries. The central questions are the cerebral dynamics of sleep, the electroencephalograph (EEG) records of different stages of sleep, physiological and behavioural responses to external stimulation during sleep and, finally, mental activity during sleep. External events experienced by apparently sleeping persons and the recollection of dream images from certain stages of sleep led to the birth and development of hypnopaedia. Distinguished Russian scientists, followed by the Czechs and Hungarians, are thoroughly investigating hypnopaedic phenomena and they already apply their findings to improving memorisation techniques of rote material in education. This has been developed into hypnopaedically programmed language courses under the direction of Professor L. A. Bliznitchenko, Director of Linguistic Studies, Ukrainian Academy of Sciences, Kiev. His technique has been adopted by several other institutes and colleges in Moscow, Leningrad, Ivanovo, Voronezh and Dubna.

Responses to auditory stimulation during various stages of sleep have been investigated by the following: P. A. Davis, A. L. Loomis, E. N. Harvey and G. Hobart (1939); I. Oswald, A. M. Taylor, M. Treisman (1960); H. L. Williams, J. T. Hammack, W. Dement, R. L. Daly and A. Lubin (1964). Retention of material presented during sleep was experimentally investigated by C. R. Elliott (1947); B. H. Fox and J. S. Robbin (1952); C. W. Simon and W. H. Emmons (1954, 1955, 1956); and finally by A. M. Svyadoshch (1962), whose Master's thesis, 'The Assimilation and Memorisation of Speech During Natural Sleep' was the foundation stone of practical hypnopaedia in Russia.

Sleep seems to have different meanings according to the way it is viewed from behavioural angles or from the physiological (EEG) point of view. The attempt to define explicity what sleep is and what it is not has produced paradoxical views between the analysis of physiological arousal and behavioural awakening response to external stimuli, which is a decisive factor in establishing matters of fact in hypnopaedia. This can be seen in the controversy between some American and Russian data. Problems involved in the learning aspects of hypnopaedia or conditioned response behaviour during sleep seem to be less controversial, as physiological and behavioural conditions during the more explicitly described stages are being progressively clarified by further research. (U. J. Jovanovic, *et al.*, 1965.)

In this symposium I present a selection of more or less highly informative papers on experiments conducted in the United States, Russia, Czechoslovakia and France, followed by short contributions of my own. A relevant physiological basis for hypnopaedia, although it has no direct connection with it, can be presumed from experiments conducted in the Walter Reed Army Institute of Research (Washington, D.C.) referring to the continuation of higher mental states based on observations of organised behaviour of humans during EEG sleep. Therefore, I have decided to use this paper to introduce the symposium. The remaining papers, with the exception of Chapter 9, follow in sequence of chronological order of their publication. This sequence is also intended to form a logical development, and the reader is therefore recommended to read the papers in the order in which they are printed.

The Rand Corporation test, designed by Simon and Emmons (1956), scrutinising the EEG and other electrophysiological monitoring of the experiment, did not intend (with unaided recollection of one syllable nouns and answers to questions) to produce those results which are claimed to be achieved by the Russians, referring to the learning of texts and foreign expressions, during behavioural sleep. Although I agree with the complaints of Western scientists concerning some ambiguity as to how the Russians present their data generally, I believe that the work in this field, done in Kiev, Moscow, Karaganda and Ivanovo by major scientific establishments, cannot be ignored, when taken as a whole.

Hypnopaedia seems to be more a behaviour term than a strict physiological term, because the stimulus used in this new science (which branches from physiology, hypnology, psychology, paedagogy, philology and acoustics) is speech. Psychologically speaking, practical hypnopaedia seems to be also related to learning on the basis of the dynamics of original learning (during the nocturnal hours) by hypnopaedic sessions and re-learning during the analytical part of day-time study. This procedure can reduce the time required in conventional tuition, accelerating the process of learning. The terminological confusion, involving several branches of contemporary science, has not yet been overcome, but research on the problem is in full swing as a major scientific project in Russia and other countries. Learning and performing under classically induced hypnosis seems apparently linked with hypnopaedia, as shown in the early experimental work of the Russians. The term itself (hypnopaedia) is also misleading, but in practical sleep-teaching procedures, classically induced hypnosis is *not* applied.

Experimental work on learning and performing under classically induced hypnosis also produces very interesting results but this belongs to a different category of learning. The internal conditions of certain stages of hypnosis (rapport—emerging of 'alert points') appear also in hypnopaedia but *not* as a direct result of hypnotising the students prior to hypnopaedic sessions. The Pavlovian paradoxical and ultraparadoxical states may occur in both cases as a sustained transitional stage between different levels of awareness. (To provide a clear picture between the difference of learning under hypnosis and by the aid of hypnopaedia two monographs on learning in hypnosis are also presented in the symposium.) It is not surprising that scientists conducting hypnopaedic experiments seem unable yet to produce an unequivocal answer to the questions involved.

However, in Russia, Hungary and Czechoslovakia the first experimental night courses for teaching languages and other subject material have already been conducted in the dormitories of several military and educational institutes, and lessons were broadcast via local radio stations, involving several thousand participants.

I wish to express my gratitude to Dr. M. N. Pai, M.B., B.S., M.R.C.P., D.P.M., to the Sleep-Learning Association; and to the Society for Cultural Relations between the U.S.S.R. and Great Britain, whose co-operation helped to make possible my visit to Russian institutes and the obtaining of these papers.

The translations from Russian into English have been made by Dr. A. Scott of Intercontinental Translators.

F. RUBIN
October 1967

CONTENTS

PART III

PART I

I

OPERANT BEHAVIOUR DURING SLEEP

Allen M. Granda *and* John T. Hammack

Abstract: *Operant conditioning techniques were employed to produce organized behaviour during sleep as defined by the EEG record. Patterned responding was found in so called 'light' and 'deeper' EEG stages as well as in the awake records. Results suggest that the use of the EEG record as a reliable indicator of the sleep-awakefulness continuum should be re-examined.*

The numerous investigations of the role of the reticular formation (1) and single unit responses (2) in the modification of on-going behaviour, led to several speculations about how the central nervous system subserves sleep. *Of equal interest has been the problem that operative functions normally thought to be characteristic of waking behaviour alone are present also in the sleep state—functions such as discriminative responses* (3), *integrative behaviour, and control of on-going activity.* The problem appears to be in the inadequacy of traditional behavioural and physiological indices to define a state of sleep. This report shows that complex behaviour can be produced while physiological indicators, such as the electroencephalographic record, signal what has been defined as 'deep sleep'. [Editor's note: B. W. Levinson, Johannesburg, South Africa, reports patients' recollection of speech presented during anaesthesia when the EEG record consisted entirely of irregular slow high voltage waves. See page 194].

The experiments were done on five subjects ranging in age from seventeen through twenty-eight years. The subjects were tested weekly. The normal routine was for subjects to report to the laboratory on the night preceding the testing night. Suitable activities were provided during the intervening period, and the testing session was begun as closely as possible to each subject's normal bedtime hour. All subjects were thus deprived of sleep for about 36 to 40 hours.

Operant conditioning techniques (4) were employed in the following manner: A microswitch was taped to each of the subject's hands, and two electrodes for administering shock were attached to the lower leg. Whenever three seconds elapsed without a response on the left hand microswitch, a pulse was delivered to the leg. By responding at a rate greater than once every three seconds the subjects could not avoid all shocks. A schedule of 'time out' periods, each of which followed a fixed number of responses (fixed ratio), was programmed on the right-hand key. During a time-out period, lasting either five or eight minutes, all electrical equipment was turned off and the subject was allowed to sleep. The time during which avoidance and ratio-key responding were programmed constituted the scheduled activity period. Ten seconds before the end of a time-out period, a loud buzzer was sounded continuously for ten seconds and terminated with the appearance of the signal light mounted in front of the subject's head, initiating the next scheduled activity period. The first shock was delivered three seconds after the onset of the signal light unless the avoidance key was operated. This cycle of events was reported continuously throughout the session.

Continuous EEG records were made from several scalp placements. The bulk of the data reported here was taken from bipolar placements of electrodes on the occipital centre line. Parietal and frontal monopolar recordings were also obtained and were used in substantiating the various stages of sleep.

The scoring of the sleep stages followed a classification suggested by Dement and Kleitman (5) with some modifications. Stage 1A was taken as that portion of the record still exhibiting alpha bursts; stage 1B covered that part of the record between the last alpha bursts and the appearance of the first 14 c/s spindle and consisted mainly of 3 to 6 c/s activity; stage 2 was characterized by spindle activity with low voltage background, including some 3 to 6 c/s activity together with biparietal humps and K-complexes; stage 3 was signalled by the appearance of high-voltage slow waves (greater than 100 μV) with some 14 c/s spindling; stage 4 covered that part of the record where waves larger than 100 μV in the 1 to 2 c/s range occurred at a rate greater than two per ten seconds sample of record.

The results showed in general that all subjects displayed an EEG sleep record and learned to respond appropriately on both microswitches without returning to the EEG waking state. Moreover, the data indicated that patterned activity could occur when the subject was in any EEG sleep stage, including stages 2, 3, and 4, although most of the evidence was accumulated from stage 1B.

Of particular interest is the occurrence of responding during the time-out periods. Such respondings occurred in sequences lasting from two to twenty seconds and resembled the performance of the subject during normal activity periods in rate and pattern. All subjects exhibited this behaviour, although its occurrence was relatively infrequent and was seen only in the early sessions. The corresponding EEG stage was classified as 1B or 2 in all cases but one. Behaviour of this type may have occurred because the experimental conditions appeared ambiguous to the subjects in the early trials. In keeping with Jasper's notion, it may very well be that the subject must learn not to respond to 'irrelevant' stimuli.

These observations of organized behaviour during sleep, together with studies involving discriminative responses previously reported, lend support to the idea that the 'higher mental states' continue to operate at some level of the nervous system even during deep sleep. Perhaps such complex behaviour does not require an alert and active brain as defined by the EEG record, but perhaps it may be that our means of assessing levels of sleep and concomitant activity need to be re-evaluated.*†

REFERENCES

1. H. H. Jasper, in *Reticular Formation of the Brain,* H. H. Jasper *et al.,* Eds. (Little, Brown, Boston, Mass., 1958), p. 319.
2. E. V. Evarts, *Federation Proc.* **19**, 828 (1960).
3. I. Oswald *et al., Brain* **83**, 440 (1963).
4. B. F. Skinner, *Science and Human Behaviour* (Macmillan, New York, 1953).
5. W. Dement and N. Kleitman, *Electrophysiolog. and Clin. Neurophysiol.* **9**, 673 (1957).

* Editor's note: The views of the authors here support Pavlovian theories concerning cerebro-dynamical functions during 'partial sleep'.

† Editor's note: Hypnopaedia is revealing increasing proof of what is suggested by the authors.

2

EXTRACTS FROM AN EXPERIMENTAL STUDY OF THE RETENTION OF AUDITORY MATERIAL PRESENTED DURING SLEEP

Charles Ray Elliott

PROBLEM

The electroencephalograph studies of the past decade have been building up a substantial body of data. These studies indicate that definite cerebral results from auditory stimulus material presented to a sleeping subject, and that such cerebral activity can continue without wakening the subject. Other studies give rise to the suspicion that such auditory stimulation can affect the subject in a later waking state. It is clear then that retention in some form must occur. The exploratory investigation of this possibility, under controlled operations, is the problem of this study.

SUBJECTS

Contact with the subjects was made by the author appearing before psychology classes and asking for volunteers. A brief explanation of the EEG was given to arouse interest, but no reference was made as to the nature of this experiment.

Some sixty students from the University of North Carolina, and seventy-five from Duke University were contacts for the preliminary and final work in this experiment.

The final group of subjects consisted of forty adult, male, undergraduate students of Duke University, in good health, and free of hearing impairments. Twenty were used as experimental subjects and twenty as controls.

An additional group of nine subjects was put through the entire experimental procedure but were disqualified at some step due to a violation of some procedural criterion.

APPARATUS

Record Player: A specially built, portable, electric phonograph was used in this experiment. It was a Brown Ray Phones, type SE, input voltage 115 V, frequency 60 c/s, power 30 W, set at voice frequency level.

All learning was done from lists of words presented through a 3 in. permanent magnet dynamic speaker which was held by the subject at any comfortable distance from his ear.

An automatic playing device was not used, all records being played manually by the author. The built-in electric clock was used for timing all procedures.

Volume control knobs were used for discreet control of the intensity of the volume of the record delivered to the subject. An effort was made to keep the volume approximately the same by marking tape indicators at the place to which the knobs were turned for the playing of the record during the sleep period.

Electroencephalograph Machine: Two small, silver, bipolar disc-electrodes, fastened to an adjacent area, from 4 to 6 cm apart, over the right occipital lobe, were used to lead off the brain potentials.

The brain potentials were led off to a six-channel Grass amplifier having a voltage gain of from five to fifty million. Our entire electroencephalograph machine provided for six line polygraph record of the brain potentials of a subject placed in bed in an electrically shielded room such that the noise level was less than 5 microvolts, which is barely perceptible on the record. The responsiveness amplifier and pen-writing combination is practically linear from 2 to 30 c/s.

MATERIALS

Records A and B: Two records were prepared for presenting the material to be learned in this experiment. A different list of fifteen three-letter, one-syllable words was transcribed on each record. Each list was developed from preliminary trials. The words for each list are given in Table I. The record prepared for presentation at the first learning period was called Record A; that made for presentation at the second learning period was called Record B.

Each list was put on a record five times at the rate of one word each two seconds, with a pause of five seconds between lists. The original transcription was made at a local radio station. The words were pronounced in a moderate voice with as clear an enunciation as possible. Several copies were made of each record so that a fresh copy would be available for presentation at any learning period.

These lists were not equated as to difficulty.

Questionnaire: A questionnaire was drawn up for presentation to the subject the morning following his second night's sleep. It contains questions asking for pertinent information, interspersed among irrelevant questions to obscure their significance. The questionnaire was as follows:

Instructions: Write the answers to the following questions about your sleep last night—using as much space as you desire or need. Give as much detail as you can. Number your answers.

1. In general how well did you sleep last night compared with your average night at home (or dormitory room)?
2. Describe in detail any dreams you had.
3. Do you remember awakening at any time last night? If so, state what made you awaken, if you can; what you heard, felt, saw, when awake.
4. Add any other relevant comment that you think might be helpful—for example, what your usual hours of sleeping are, etc.
5. Put down your name and date.
6. Had you heard of any of the details of this experiment from any other subject before coming for the night?

Table I

List of Words Presented on Learning Records A and B

	Record A	*Record B*
1.	SIX	BOY
2.	HAT	EGG
3.	ARM	SAY
4.	NOW	ART
5.	FAT	RUN
6.	JOY	NOT
7.	DID	SIR
8.	HOT	LEG
9.	BIG	BAG
10.	HOW	ROW
11.	LAW	ICE
12.	DOG	OUT
13.	BUT	AGE
14.	LET	BOX
15.	WAS	EAT

PROCEDURE

Learning Record A: All subjects were scheduled for afternoon appointments thirty minutes apart. Record A was presented in a large basement room of the psychology building at Duke University. It was reserved for such studies as this and its interior was held constant for all subjects.

The subject sat in a plain chair, in front of a table on which was the record player. Behind the subject sat the experimenter who recorded at the table.

The subject was asked if he knew any details of the experiment. Then these instructions were read to him:

> On this record is a list of three-letter, one-syllable words. I am going to play the list over and over again to you. You are to learn it as soon as you can.
>
> Whenever you think you know a word you should try to anticipate it, that is, say it ahead of the record. For example, if on the record were the words 'red, white, blue', when you heard the word 'red' come over this speaker, you would immediately say 'white' then as the 'white' came over the speaker you would say 'blue' and so on, each time saying the next word before it came off the record.
>
> You need not learn the first word in the list as it is a cue to start you on the others.
>
> Only anticipate one word ahead at a time.
>
> Always try to anticipate every word you think you know on every trial.
>
> When you can anticipate the words correctly all through the list once, you will have learned it, and I will cut the record off.
>
> Are there any questions?
>
> Remember, try to anticipate every word you think you know, on every trial.

Record A was then played until the subject learned it to the criterion of one successive correct anticipation of the last fourteen words of the fifteen word list. Notes were kept of any notable reactions of the subject and detailed scoring was kept on each word presentation for each trial.

Scoring was done under the word to be anticipated rather than the cue word for the anticipation. If a word was said clearly before the record began to say it, it was counted correct; any other type of response was counted incorrect.

After the learning period the subject was told that he would be contacted later about the time he was to come to the EEG laboratory to sleep.

The importance of his cooperation in not talking about his learning experience was made clear to the subject and he was asked to say nothing about it to anyone.

Sleep Procedure: Each subject was contacted in person within a day or two of the first night he was to come to the EEG laboratory. He was instructed to come at his regular bed-time for the night he was scheduled.

Upon arrival at the EEG laboratory the subject was prepared for the night by the placing of the silver disc-electrodes, fastened to the scalp with collodion.

The subjects were staggered, the first night they slept in a folding bed of the type also used for the other sleeping place. The first night was to get the person used to the apparatus and the procedure. Usually they were restless. The second night they were so tired they usually were eager to sleep. After the first night they were asked not to take any nap before coming again that night.

The subjects came for two consecutive nights on a staggered schedule so that the first night they could sleep in a bed in the laboratory workshop and the second night sleep in the actual shielded EEG subject-room.

Procedure was the same both nights. The beds were identical, the sleeping rooms similar, the environment of both sleeping situations similar.

The chief purpose of the double night of sleeping was to provide for the first night producing fatigue and ensuring deep sleep the second night. Also it helped to get the subject acquainted with a rather complex and strange sleeping situation.

The first night of sleep all subjects were left undisturbed. Also, on the second night, the control subjects were left alone after going to bed.

After putting the experimental subject to bed the experimenter would check the situation by having the subject open and close his eyes, to see if he had a clearly seen alpha rhythm. This procedure was usually carried out on all subjects, during their second night, as an EEG record of some sort was due each subject, and short trials were made on all prior to going to sleep.

After closing the experimental subject in the shielded room, the experimenter would quietly set up the record-player for use later in the night. It was set up near the window in the room at which the speaker was placed.

When the experimenter returned to the laboratory to play Record B he would run the EEG for a time until satisfied that the subject was asleep.

The EEG would be running when Record B was first presented, and the sampling of the sleep would run until there was ample opportunity for lightening in sleep which would have shown consistent alpha runs. If the sleep level remained deep enough the EEG pen-recording unit was held ready until the start of the next record. Most recording was concentrated towards the introducing of each new play of the record as most disturbance was noted then.

If a subject showed clear alpha patterns so that wakefulness was definite the record playing was suspended.

The record has six repetitions of the list for each play, and it was played five times to each subject making a total of thirty times the list was presented during sleep to the experimental group.

The subjects were awakened in the morning at their request. The first morning, removal of the lead wires with acetone was the only procedure. The subject was asked not to talk over his visit with anyone and was asked not to take a nap during the day.

The morning after the second night the procedure included the answering of a questionnaire concerning the previous night, the details of this questionnaire are given in the section on MATERIALS. Soon after answering the questionnaire, the subject was taken down the hall two doors to where the gramophone had been set up (after its use during the night) and the subject was presented with the learning of Record B.

Presentation of Record B: All subjects were presented with the task of Record B the morning following their second night's sleep.

The subject was given the same statement of the learning task as given him with Record A. The directions were prefaced with the remark that he might remember the rules but they would be given again for his convenience.

Recording and scoring was done exactly as it was done with Record A.

After the subject had learned list B to a criterion of one successful anticipation he was dismissed with a final note of appreciation for his cooperation, an admonition about not talking about the experiment, and the statement that when the experiment was over he would be told what it was all about.

For purposes of clarity the overall procedure has been arranged in tabular form in Table II.

Table II

General Outline of Procedure

Step	*Experimental Group*	*Control Group*
1.	Learn Record A	Learn Record A
2.	Sleep first night	Sleep first night
3.	Sleep second night	Sleep second night
4.	Hear record B 30x while sleeping	Hear no record
5.	Answer questionnaire in a.m.	Answer questionnaire in a.m.
6.	Learn Record B	Learn Record B

RESULTS

Because this is an exploratory study, we will be less interested in the qualitative differences shown among the subjects than we will be in a comparison of the group results. Also our interest will settle on the group results on Record B. Concerning Record A, we will confine ourselves to inquiring if there was any significant difference in learning between the experimental and control groups.

Table III presents the number of trials required by each subject to learn the list on Record A and on Record B. The first column gives the number which identifies the subject, the second column gives the number of trials required by each subject to learn the list of words on Record A, the third column gives the number of trials required to learn the list on Record B.

Table IV compares the difference between the mean number of trials for each group in learning Record A. Column 1 lists the group, column 2 the number of subjects in each group, column 3 the means, column 4 the standard deviation of the means, and column 5 the critical ratio of the difference between the means. The critical ratio in Table IV is —1·01 which means that there is no significant difference between the means of the groups in learning Record A.

Table III

Number of Trials Required to learn Record A and Record B.

Subject No.	*Record A*	*Record B*
	(Experimental Group)	
65	35	20
52	35	18
4	34	18
39	34	15
47	33	19
48	32	26
71	32	21
40	30	16
53	29	10
55	29	16
49	28	11
67	28	19
7	26	13
57	25	16
9	24	10
72	23	17
14	22	18
56	19	16
26	17	14
74	16	8
	(Control Group)	
3	43	33
18	41	34
46	37	23
15	36	32
59	35	19
43	35	14
38	33	19
8	25	15
27	25	17
20	25	21
12	24	26
22	24	14
21	24	18
10	23	15
11	20	16
44	19	12
68	16	14
37	16	9
70	16	18
73	12	9

Table IV

Comparison of Means of Numbers of Trials Required to learn Record A

Group	*Number*	*Mean*	*Standard Deviation*	*Critical Ratio*
Experimental	20	27·55	8·79	−1·01*
Control	20	26·45	6·32	

* A negative difference here is a difference in favour of the Control Group.

Table V gives a comparison of the difference between the standard deviation of each group in learning Record A. In this table, column 1 gives the group, column 2 states the number in each group, column 3 gives the standard deviation of each group, and column 4 gives the critical ratio of the difference between the standard deviations. The critical ratio is 1·40 which means that there was no significant difference between the groups in respect of the variance, or distribution of scores within each group, on Record A.

Table V

Comparison of Variability in Learning Record A

Group	*Number*	*Standard Deviation*	*Critical Ratio*
Experimental	20	8·79	1·40
Control	20	6·32	

A comparison of the difference between the group means of the trials required to learn Record B is given in Table VI. Column 1 gives the group, column 2 the number, column 3 the mean number of trials required by each group in learning Record B, column 4 the standard deviation of these means, and column 5 the critical ratio of the difference between the means. The critical ratio is 1·50, which means that there is no significant difference between the mean number of trials required for each group to learn the list of words from Record B.

Table VI

Comparison of Means of Numbers of Trials required to learn Record B

Group	*Number*	*Mean*	*Standard Deviation*	*Critical Ratio*
Experimental	20	16·05	8·79	1·50
Control	20	18·90	6·32	

The record of total error per trial and the cumulative total error made by each group in learning Record B is given in Table VII.

Table VII

Errors in Learning Record B

	(Experimental Group)		(Control Group)	
Trial Number	*Total Error Per Trial*	*Total Cumulative Error Per Trial*	*Total Error Per Trial*	*Total Cumulative Error Per Trial*
2	250	250	266	266
3	217	467	256	522
4	194	661	232	754
5	180	841	213	967
6	186	1,027	193	1,160
7	144	1,171	187	1,347
8	135	1,306	174	1,521
9	130	1,436	135	1,656
10	121	1,557	131	1,787
1	89	1,646	108	1,895
2	88	1,734	104	1,999
3	72	1,806	112	2,111
4	71	1,877	94	2,205
5	57	1,934	78	2,283
6	44	1,978	62	2,345
7	32	2,010	57	2,402
8	32	2,042	31	2,433
9	17	2,059	36	2,469
20	5	2,064	32	2,501
1	2	2,066	39	2,540
2	2	2,068	20	2,560
3	7	2,075	26	2,586
4	8	2,083	24	2,610
5	1	2,084	29	2,639
6	0		10	2,649
7			8	2,657
8			7	2,664
9			9	2,673
30			9	2,682
1			10	2,692
2			4	2,696
3			1	2,697

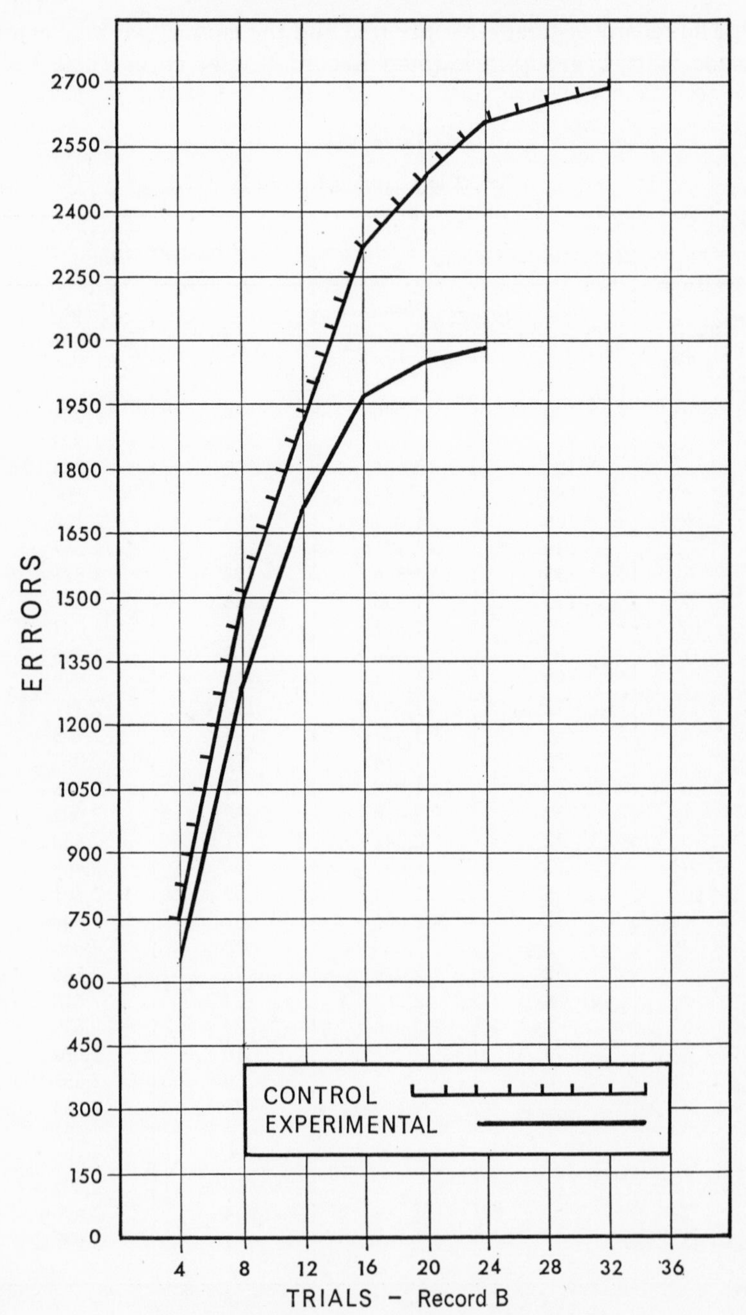

Fig. 2.1. Graph showing cumulative errors per trial

The number of the trial is listed in column 1; the error per trial of the experimental group is given in column 2; the cumulative total error per trial for the experimental group is listed in column 3; the total error per trial of the control group is listed in column 4; and the cumulative total error per trial of the control group is listed in column 5. The data of the cumulative total error per each group are made graphic by presentation in Fig. 2.1.

We have a further interest in the results on Record B. It is important to know the percentage of savings obtained in learning the second record. This 'savings' is determined by dividing the score of a subject on Record B by that obtained on Record A. The resulting figure is the percentage of time 'saved' in learning the second record.

Table VIII gives the information on the percentage savings by subject, according to rank and the cumulative percentage of savings as each subject is added to the group. Column 1 in Table VIII gives

Table VIII
Percentage Savings in Learning on Record B

(Experimental Group)				(Control Group)			
Rank	*Subject*	*Savings*	*Cumulative Savings*	*Rank*	*Subject*	*Savings*	*Cumulative Savings*
1	53	65·6	65·6	1	43	60·0	60·0
2	49	60·8	126·4	2	59	45·8	105·8
3	9	58·4	184·8	3	37	43·8	149·6
4	39	55·9	240·7	4	38	42·8	192·4
5·5	74	50·0	290·7	5	22	41·7	234·1
5·5	7	50·0	340·7	6	8	40·0	274·1
7	52	48·6	389·3	7	46	37·9	312·0
8	4	47·1	436·4	8	44	36·9	348·9
9	40	46·7	483·1	9	10	34·8	383·7
10	55	44·9	528·0	10	27	32·0	415·7
11	65	42·9	570·9	11·5	73	25·0	440·7
12	47	42·5	613·4	11·5	21	25·0	465·7
13	57	36·0	649·4	13	3	23·3	489·0
14	71	34·4	682·8	14	11	20·0	509·0
15	67	32·2	715·0	18	18	17·1	526·1
16	72	26·1	741·1	16	20	16·0	542·1
17	48	18·8	759·9	17	68	12·5	554·6
18	14	18·2	778·1	18	15	11·2	565·8
19	26	17·7	795·8	19	12	−8·3	557·5
20	56	15·8	811·5	20	70	−12·5	545·0

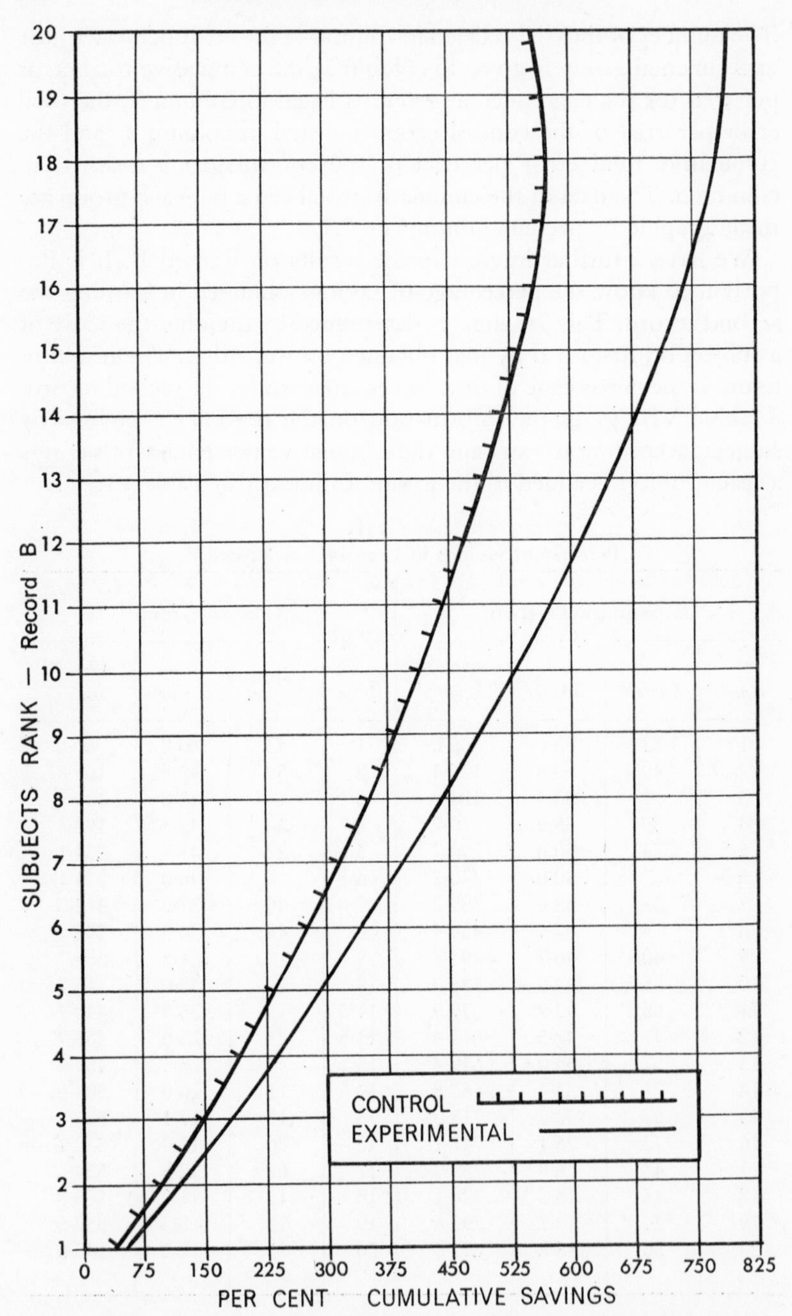

Fig. 2.2. Graph of percentage cumulative savings according to rank

the rank of the subject in respect of his percentage savings in learning on Record B. Column 2 lists the number of the subject; column 3 gives the percentage savings for each subject, in the experimental group; column 4 gives the total of cumulative savings; column 5 the rank of subjects in the control group; column 6 the subject's number; column 7 his percentage savings; and column 8 the total of cumulative savings for the control group. Fig. 2.2 presents the cumulative savings in graphic form.

We are interested in knowing if there is any significant difference in the means of the percentage of savings scores on Record B. This question is answered in Table IX. Column 1 lists the group; column 2 the number in each group; column 3 the mean percentage of savings of each group; column 4 gives the standard deviation of these means; and column 5 gives the critical ratio of the difference between the means. The critical ratio of the difference between the means of savings in learning Record B is 2·54. This is significant at the 1·1 per cent level and means that there is only eleven chances in a thousand that if there was no real difference between the groups in learning Record B would we obtain these results.

Table IX

Comparison of Means of Savings Scores on Record B

Group	*Number*	*Mean*	*Deviation of Means*	*Critical Ratio*
Experimental	20	40·6%	0·148	2·54
Control	20	27·2%	0·176	

Two other tables and two final figures are given to complete the information on what happened to the subjects.

Table X presents the percentage of time during which the record was played to the sleeping experimental subjects that the EEG was run. Column 1 lists the subject by number, and column 2 gives the percentage of time during the record playing that the EEG was running.

Table X

Per cent of Total Playing Time of Record B to Experimental Group—During which Sampling of Sleep was Recorded by EEG

Subject	% *time*
4	26·7
26	23·8
9	40·1
53	30·5
39	53·9
57	13·3
14	29·5
56	100·0
7	40·1
40	21·0
48	100·0
71	93·3
52	22·0
65	18·1
55	30·5
67	18·1
47	100·0
49	26·7
74	42·9
72	100·0
Mean %	46·5

Fig. 2.3 graphically presents the record of when the subjects of this experiment got their auditory stimulation, in relation to time of retiring. All of this is super-imposed on a figure from a study by Blake giving the relative presence of major EEG wave patterns during a night's sleep. This figure shows that our subjects were given their auditory stimulation during that period at night when the *alpha waves* are at their *minimum*.

Table XI gives the pertinent information on those subjects who were disqualified during their final part of the procedure. Column 1 identifies the subject by his number, column 2 states the cause of disqualification, column 3 gives his score on Record A, and column 4 gives his score on Record B.

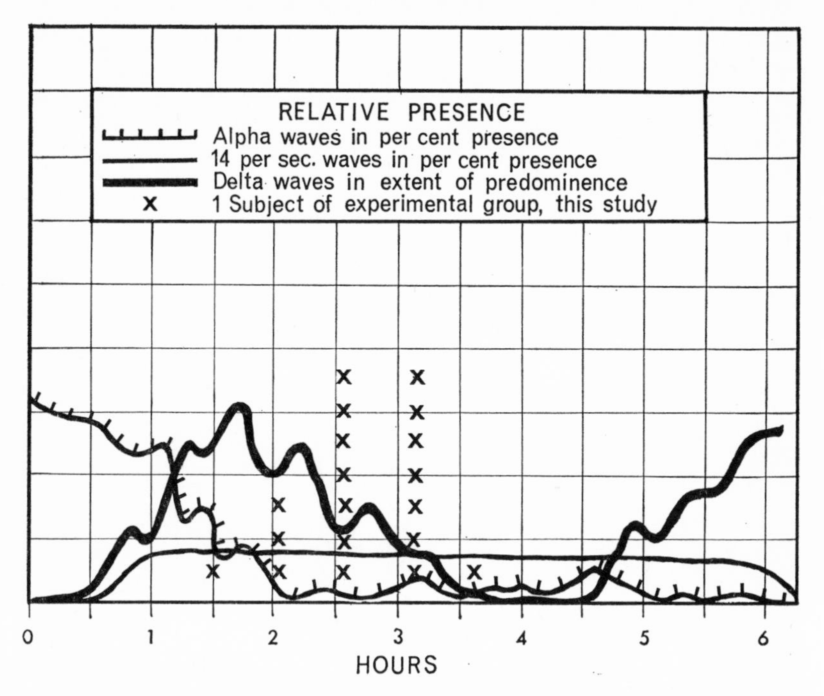

Fig. 2.3. Graph showing subjects of experimental group of this study, superimposed on 'Schema of Potentials during a Night's Sleep' (after Blake), according to duration of time between retiring and playing of record B during sleep

Table XI

Subjects Disqualified

Subject No.	*Cause of Disqualification*	*Score Record A*	*Score Record B*
2	Awoke during night	27	12
19	Flat EEG, might have awakened	47	16
31	Awoke during night	38	6
34	Awoke during night	11	8
35	Awoke during night	25	18
45	Awoke during night	25	6
75	Awoke during night	33	12

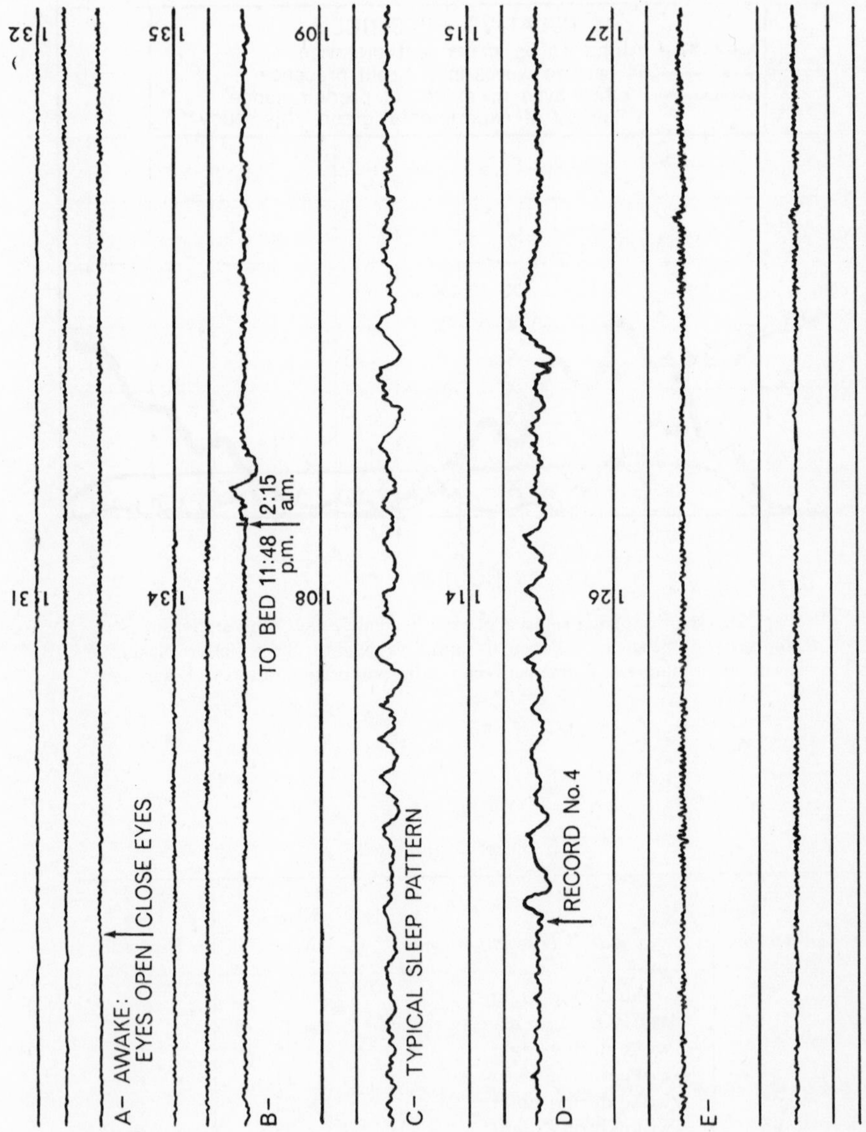

A– AWAKE:
EYES OPEN | CLOSE EYES
1 31
1 32

B–
TO BED 11:48 p.m. | 2:15 a.m.
1 34
1 35

C– TYPICAL SLEEP PATTERN
1 08
1 09

D– RECORD No. 4
1 14
1 15

E–
1 26
1 27

F–

Fig. 2.4 Electroencephalograms for a subject hearing a recording of words while he was asleep

Fig. 2.4 shows a series of EEG recordings taken from subject No. 34 who was disqualified for waking up while Record B was playing, the readings show many typical patterns met in this study. The top section, A, shows to the left the patient just after he has retired. He is awake and his eyes are open. The arrow points to the place on the EEG at which he was told 'close your eyes'. The resulting alpha rhythm shows the kind of evidence used in determining if the subject awakened. The line B shows at the left the alpha rhythm still present as the person is awake when left at 11.48 p.m. The arrow indicates when the EEG was turned on at 2.15 a.m., the low amplitude, medium frequency waves showing the subject in a medium sleep.

The line at C shows the high amplitude, low frequency, random waves typical of a deep sleep. At line D the subject is in a light sleep due to the record having been played three times already. At the start of the fourth play of the record the subject gives a response to the auditory stimulation typical of the 'K Complex' described by Loomis and his colleagues. On the right side of D is a hump in the record. This is an artifact showing sweating, after which the presence of the alpha waves indicate the subject is wakening.

Line E shows the subject a few moments later. The continuous presence of alpha rhythm here shows the subject to be definitely awake and thus disqualified.

The numbers on the lines in the figure refer to ten-second intervals and finer lines, not seen, but on the original EEG, give time divisions by fifths of a second. The lines at E simply indicate ink lines of EEG pens that had been turned off, and a duplication of the alpha pattern on another channel of the EEG machine.

This completes the statement of the results of this experiment. The significance and interpretation of these results will be dealt with in the following section.

DISCUSSION

In terms of the problem taken for investigation in this study, four essential questions are to be answered. First, were the experimental and control groups similar enough to begin with to allow for a comparison later? Second, can we be sure that the experimental subjects received the experimental variable during the prescribed situation of being asleep? Third, was there any evidence of a significant difference between the results of the experimental and control group after the introduction of the experimental variable? Fourth, if significant differences were found, can they be adequately explained on the basis of the introduced experimental variable?

That the control and experimental groups were not significantly different in respect to learning Record A is clearly demonstrated. The critical ratio of the difference between the means of the groups was −1·01. The critical ratio of the difference between the standard deviation of the group scores was 1·40.

We can answer our first question in the affirmative. It is likely that the experimental groups were similar enough in the beginning to permit later comparisons.

The question as to whether or not the experimental subjects were asleep while Record B was played to them can be answered with relative but not absolute certainty. The ever-shifting potential patterns of the EEG may show some alpha occasionally at any stage during a night's sleep. Reference to Blake's graph (Fig. 2.4) shows that none of the waves completely disappear for any length of time. However, one is able to read the EEG with some certainty. A subject does not jump from sleep to waking without some intervening stimulus.

Whenever the EEG indicated that a subject was lightening his sleep pattern a more continuous record was taken than when the record showed a continuous deep level of sleep.

The mean percentage EEG sampling time was 46·5 of the total time the record played to the subjects. Blake considered five-minute samplings throughout the night adequate to compile her data. She discarded wave runs of less than two minutes as being unserviceable for concluding as to the definite presence of a wave pattern.

Dr. Hans Lowenbach, head of the EEG laboratory at Duke Hospital, reviewed every page of the EEG records taken. Only those were kept in which he felt that sleep was present throughout the record.

The EEG records give us a reasonable amount of evidence that our experimental subjects were *asleep* during the time that Record B was played to them during the night of their second sleep, previous to the morning when they learned it while awake.

The question as to whether or not there was a significant difference between the groups in learning Record B hinges on the significance of the raw score versus the savings score. In Table VI the critical ratio of the difference between the means number of trials required to learn Record B is 1·50. This means that there was no significant difference between the mean raw scores of the groups.

The critical ratio of the difference between the means of the savings score on Record B, however, is 2·54 and this is significant at the 1·1 per cent level. This indicates that the groups are clearly different in respect of their savings scores. This difference is in the favour of the experimental group, indicating that they did significantly better on the second record, relative to their performance on the first, than did the control group.

A significant critical ratio on the raw scores is much to be desired in establishing conclusively that the groups differed in their learning of Record B. However, the mean of the raw scores would represent a more crude measure than the mean of the savings scores, and as such the latter gives us some indication that there was a real difference in the learning performance of the two groups on Record B.

Whether or not the differences can be accounted for on the basis of the experimental variable introduced is dependent on our analysis of other possible contributing factors. An analysis was done on all measurable factors of procedure. Such factors were: number of days between the learning of Record A and Record B, amount of sleep obtained by each subject, time interval between awakening and the learning of Record B, time of day when Record A was learned. No significant differences were found. Details of all these data were not placed in this report simply as an economy of the reader's time and effective presentation. The material is filed with the original data at the Psychology Department of the University of North Carolina.

The failure to use equated lists was due to the limited number of words to choose from after the eliminations of the preliminary trials. This might conceivably operate as an important factor. It was noticed that some subjects seemed to connect the words on Record B more readily than on Record A. A comparison of the lists will show that in some ways the list on Record B was more grammatically structured.

It is doubtful if any of the subjects had previous knowledge of the list on Record B. Care was taken to make clear to each subject the importance of not sharing his experience with other students. No objective measure of this variable was taken and so its effect is unknown. However, if it operated it did so at random and perhaps offers no systematc variable in one particular group.

So far as measured variables are concerned then, no significant difference was noted. This leaves us with the likelihood that the major factor operating in the development of a significant difference in the savings scores of the two groups was the experimental variable. This was the playing of Record B to the experimental group while they slept.

Our results confirm those of LeShan and Thurstone. An attempt here was made to control the entire procedure closely. Special effort was given to obtaining objective evidence that the subjects were asleep while they received the stimulus material. This was done at a level exceeding previous studies. Lack of equated learning lists and sampling only with the EEG, however, leaves much to be desired.

Little note has been taken in this discussion of the significance of our results in terms of learning theory. Likewise, no attempt has been made to explain why there might be retention of auditory material presented during sleep.

The author has limited himself in this study to finding the answer to the one simple question: can people retain auditory stimulation given to them while asleep? The evidence of this study strongly suggests that they can.

Obviously there are a host of questions raised by the answer given above. What are the effects of intensity of stimulus, type of material, time of night given, massed versus spaced representation, type of sleeper, post-sleep waking interval, number of presentations, etc.?

It is the author's hope that further work will be done under more rigid controls, larger numbers of subjects and one hundred per cent coverage of the experimental sleep period by the EEG. Perhaps such work will furnish us information from which we can define the function of the phenomena of retention of auditory material presented during sleep.

SUMMARY

To investigate the retention of auditory material presented during sleep, a list of fifteen meaningful one-syllable words was played off a record thirty time to twenty college students while they were asleep. A control group of twenty subjects did not have the list played to them while they slept.

Both groups had previously learned a similar list off a record, making similar scores, while awake. Both groups learned the second list while awake the morning following the night's sleep.

Objective evidence that the experimental group was asleep while hearing the record was obtained through sampling the presentation period with the EEG.

A comparison of the savings scores of both groups on the second record showed a significant difference in favour of the experimental group.

The evidence obtained strongly suggests that there is retention of auditory material presented during sleep.

3

THE RETENTION OF MATERIAL PRESENTED DURING SLEEP

Bernard H. Fox *and* Joseph S. Robbin

Editor's note: The conclusiveness of this study suffers somewhat from the failure to *observe* the subjects during sleep. Nevertheless, the importance of the problem and the persuasiveness of the findings have dictated acceptance and publication.

There is occasion for great surprise on discovering the exceedingly small number of experiments involving the possibility of learning during sleep. This possibility follows as a corollary to the induction of particular dream states by external stimuli during sleep. Schmidhofer (11) and others (2, 9, 10) are among those who have demonstrated this phenomenon, although the effects shown by Schmidhofer, relating to reduction of terror dreams by suggestion during sleep, are difficult to evaluate since waking suggestion was also carried on. The possibility also follows as a direction of study from the work of Jenkins and Dallenbach (5), Van Ormer (13), and others. Attention should also be drawn to the hypnopaedia described in Huxley's *Brave New World* (4).

LeShan's attempt to cure nailbiting in children did utilize sleep suggestion alone (8). A record with fifty repetitions of the sentence, 'My fingernails taste terribly bitter,' was played six times a night on fifty-four successive nights to a group of twenty experimental children. None of the children was informed of the experiment. Of the twenty controls, 100 per cent still bit their nails after this period. Of the experimentals, 40 per cent no longer continued the practice. The personalities of the children were not investigated thoroughly.

Elliott (1) reports an unpublished study by Thurstone, who attempted to teach Morse code by presenting stimuli during sleep to a group of sixteen naval students. He is supposed to have got very promising results. [See Chapter 2.]

Although no highly positive findings were obtained, Elliott's results seem to indicate that learning may take place during sleep, and that more experimentation is necessary. In view of the difference between his findings and the present results, it is suggested that the classical excess of savings in the learning of more meaningful words over that in learning less meaningful be scrutinized more closely in the sleep-learning situation.

In the present experiment a more sensitive technique is used: together with the control group and the experimental group and the experimental group (facilitating of learning) an additional group is utilized, in which interfering material is given during sleep.

METHOD

Subjects: An initial group of sixty-two subjects (*S*s) located in the Washington area were given the preliminary testing and questioning in this experiment. The final group consisted of thirty adults ranging in age from twenty-one to forty (mostly in the early twenties) who were selected on the basis of convenience, voluntary cooperation, and scores on the pre-test. Eight of the *S*s worked during the day, the remainder being full-time students. There were eighteen men and twelve women in the final group. All *S*s in the final group said they were in good health, free from hearing impairments, and unfamiliar with Chinese. An additional group of ten out of the original sixty-two *S*s were put through the procedure but were disqualified at some stage due to a violation of some control.

Apparatus: A Revere tape recorder with microphone was used. Volume and tone were held constant with tone at treble and amplitude at about one-third capacity. The sound could be heard distinctly but not loudly through a miniature Telex pillow speaker. An automatic clock, not visible to *S*, set the playback in operation at 2.30 a.m. and shut it off at 3.00 a.m.

Experimental design:

1. Pre-test
   a. Learning by 62 *S*s of English equivalents of 15 Chinese words.
   b. Equating of three groups of 10 *S*s each on the basis of above results.

2. Sleep procedure
   a. Sleep presentation of different material to each of the groups.
      (1) Facilitation group (A)—25 Chinese words (different from the 15 words in pre-test) with true English equivalents, for total of *ca*. 29 min.
      (2) Interference group (B)—same Chinese words as in facilitation group and in same order, but with randomly mismatched English equivalents, for *ca*. 29 min.
      (3) Control group (C)—music during sleep for a like period of *ca*. 29 min.
3. Post-test
   a. Learning the next morning by all groups of list learned by the facilitation group during sleep. This learning was to a criterion of one correct repetition.

Pre-test procedure: The *S*s were all pre-tested at their homes between 8.00 a.m. and 11.30 a.m. The *S* could not see the tape recorder or the operator during the test. The following instructions were read before the trials began:

'There has been recorded on this machine a list of Chinese words with their English equivalents. You are to listen very carefully as they are being played and try to remember the English translation of each of the Chinese words. After the list has been presented once, you will receive a rest period of several seconds followed by the Chinese words without their English equivalents. You are to try to recall the correct translation of each of these words as they are presented and say them out loud as soon as possible. After this, we will play the original record again and continue the same procedure until you have learned the entire list correctly once.

'Are there any questions?'

'Remember, you are to listen carefully during this first record and respond with the correct English translation on the second.'

The following words were used in the pre-test with Mandarin intonations indicated by the superscripts: bai^{2}-clear; jien^{4}-see; ba^{1}-eight; shang^{4}-on; nan^{2}-male; gu^{3}-old; yang^{2}-sheep; kuo^{3}-mouth; shu^{1}-book; jin^{1}-gold; di^{4}-earth; da^{3}-strike; nien^{4}-year; an^{1}-peace; dzo^{4}-sit. These words, and the later list, were taken from a booklet on the Chinese language (12) and were pronounced with the indicated number intonations in a moderate voice.

In the pre-test list, the time between Chinese and English was about 1 s, and between pairs of words, about 2 s. The same Chinese words without equivalents followed after a pause of 10 s. An interval of 7 s was allowed between Chinese words to give *S* time to recite the equivalent English word. A period of 15 s for tape rewinding separated successive trials. Total time per trial (Chinese-English plus Chinese plus intervals) was 197 s.

If *S* recalled a word between trials, he was given credit providing he could name the correct Chinese equivalent. This happened infrequently for about one-half the *S*s.

After the criterion of one perfect trial was reached, *S* was informed that he would be notified for the second portion of the experiment and was requested not to discuss the pre-test with anyone.

The *S*s were then divided into three matched groups. In each group there were three *S*s who took four trials to reach the criterion, three *S*s who took five trials, and four *S*s who took six trials. Later in the experiment some of the above were disqualified because they had to break off the experiment, because they woke up during the sleep presentation, or because they reported bad sleep habits. These were replaced by *S*s who had pre-test scores identical with those of the disqualified *S*s.

Sleep procedure: Contact for the sleep procedure was usually made within three or four days of the pre-test. At this time the *S*s were instructed to abstain from coffee, alcohol, and any unusual excitement on the day preceding this night. All *S*s used reported that they were usually asleep an hour after retiring.

The *E* arrived at the *S*'s home between 8.00 and 10.30 p.m. to set up the machine. At first, this was placed close to the bed; later, this position was changed to a more distant one when it was discovered that many *S*s awoke because of the noise and vibrations (they said) of the machine during the playback, even though to the listener in daytime such noise was inaudible.

Gibbs and Gibbs (3) suggest that maximum depth of sleep is attained at about 2.30 to 3.00 a.m. if *S* retires at 11.30 p.m. However, it has been pointed out (6) that this is not true for all sleepers. Kleitman's work (7) indicates a series of fluctuations of depth of sleep during the night. In any case, the machine was set to run for the half-hour between 2.30 and 3.00 a.m.

The *S*s were reminded to be in bed by 11.30 and to refrain

from all forms of reading, writing, and conversation upon awakening.

Each group was given only one night's exposure to the apparatus for the test run. The facilitation and interference groups both were presented during sleep with fifteen repetitions of the appropriate list of Chinese words. The list with correct translations, used with the facilitation group, was as follows: tien^{2}-field; mu^{4}-eye; li^{1}-strength; ta^{4}-great; ming^{2}-bright; shao^{3}-few; lin^{2}-grove; siao^{3}-small; jia^{1}-home; sheng^{1}-life; tu^{4}-ground; ko^{3}-may; dao^{4}-road; fen^{1}-knife; lo^{4}-fall; rih^{4}-day; jun^{1}-sir; dung^{1}-east; hao^{3}-good; yen^{2}-talk; ru^{2}-like; süe^{3}-snow; wu^{3}-five; lai^{2}-come; je^{4}-this. The control group heard Stauss waltzes for a like period. Recorded time of each tape presentation was a little over 29 min.

The interference group heard the Chinese in proper order but with mismatched English 'equivalents'. The list was as follows: tien^{2}-five; mu^{4}-cast; li^{1}-road; ta^{4}-may; ming^{2}-come; shao^{3}-life; lin^{2}-this; siao^{3}-talk; jia^{1}-great; sheng^{1}-few; tu^{4}-bright; ko^{3}-strength; dao^{4}-field; fen^{1}-eye; lo^{4}-grove; rih^{4}-snow; jun^{1}-fall; dung^{1}-knife; hao^{3}-ground; yen^{2}-day; ru^{2}-sir; süe^{3}-good; wu^{3}-small; lai^{2}-home; je^{4}-like.

Post-test procedure: The following morning *E* arrived at *S*'s home between 8.00 and 10.30 a.m. depending on *S*'s convenience. An attempt was made to come as close as possible to the normal waking hour to prevent the effects of retroactive inhibition from becoming too active. Each *S* was asked if he had heard the machine go on during the night, if he had had any dreams, and if he felt more fatigued than on most other mornings. The post-test record was placed on the machine and *S* was given the same instructions that were given him during the pre-test situation. Recording and scoring were done in a similar manner. After the criterion of one perfect trial had been reached, *S* was requested to describe the method he used in learning the list. After this, he was thanked for his co-operation and given an admonition about not discussing the experiment with anyone.

An effort was made at the beginning of the experiment to mislead the *S*s as to the purpose of the experiment by telling them that their spontaneous vocalizations during sleep would be recorded. Most refused to be misled, however, and it was necessary to inform the *S*s as to the nature of the experiment.

RESULTS AND DISCUSSION

The three groups chosen from scores on the pre-test all had means of 5·1 trials and *SD*'s of 0·83 trials to learn the list to one correct repetition. The results for each *S* in the post-test, followed sleep stimulation, are shown in the accompanying table.

Trials to Learn Post-test Material after Exposure to Sleep Stimuli

Subject	*Pre-test Trials**	*Post-test Trials*		
		Control Group	*Facilitation Group*	*Interference Group*
1	4	8	6	12
2	4	8	7	10
3	4	6	5	11
4	5	7	6	9
5	5	9	4	12
6	5	9	5	11
7	6	8	8	10
8	6	7	5	11
9	6	7	5	12
10	6	8	5	13
Mean	5·1	7·7	5·6	11·1
σ_m	0·28	0·30	0·37	0·38

* These trials were used as the basis for matching the ten *S*s in each group. The correlations between the pre-test trials and post-test trials are 0·04–0·06, and 0·20 for the control, facilitation, and interference groups respectively.

The mean difference between each of the groups and each of the others was significant at better than the 1 per cent level of confidence whether difference were taken as correlated or uncorrelated ($df = 18$, t for Control vs. Facilitation Groups is 4·37, t for Control vs. Interference Groups is 7·08, and t for Facilitation vs. Interference Groups is 10·37). Furthermore, it is clear from the scores of the individual *S*s that these group differences are the result of factors which almost without exception affect each individual in the same direction.

The experimental situation did not allow verification by *E* of the condition of actual sleep during the night, as was the case in Elliott's study (1). However, the *S*s were questioned about this, and all those who reported hearing the machine or waking up were eliminated as *S*s. These numbered ten. If any *S*s in the group of thirty actually did wake up without reporting it, then the number was probably distributed about equally throughout the groups. Moreover, since all *S*s (with the exeption of matched *S*s No. 7 in the Control and Facilitation Groups) show effects in the expected directions, it is clear that the results cannot be explained on the basis of a few *S*s in each group who awakened but failed to report doing so.

It is of interest that all *S*s reported learning the list by associating the Chinese word with the English, rather than by learning the English words in sequence, a possibility in this type of learning situation when the order of presentation of pairs is not varied from trial to trial.

An interesting addendum, supporting the demonstration of influence of Chinese syllable presentation during sleep, is that dreams relating to the stimuli appeared. One *S* dreamed of a street scene in China; another of the pre-testing situation; and a third that her instructor stood over her reading a long list of Chinese syllables. (The instructor was the one who actually did read to the tape recorder.) This phenomenon has been amply demonstrated (2). The further implications of these findings are enormous and obvious.

SUMMARY AND CONCLUSIONS

Out of sixty-two *S*s given a pre-test on learning the English equivalents of fifteen Chinese words, thirty *S*s were selected on the basis of equivalent scores and perfectly matched into three groups. A facilitation group (A) heard a different list of twenty-five words and correct equivalents repeated fifteen times during sleep; a control group (C) heard music for an equal period during sleep; and an interference group (B) heard the twenty-five words and incorrect equivalents made up by mismatching the correct ones. The next morning the average number of trials taken to learn the list presented to the A group was as follows: facilitation group, 5·6; control group, 7·7; and interference group, 11·1. These differed significantly from one another.

It can be concluded that learning can occur during sleep and can be detected by the saving method.

REFERENCES

1. C. R. Elliott, An experimental study of the retention of auditory material presented during sleep. Unpublished Master's thesis, Univ. N. Carolina, 1947.
2. A. H. Fontanier and B. Stokvis, Psychologie und Psychophysiologie des Wecktraumes. *Acta Psychiat. Kbh.,* 1940, **15**, 69–99.
3. F. A. Gibbs and E. L. Gibbs, *Atlas of electroencephalography.* Cambridge, Mass.: Addison-Wesley Press, 1941.
4. A. L. Huxley, *Brave new world.* New York: Doubleday Doran, 1932.
5. J. G. Jenkins and K. M. Dallenbach, Oblivescence during sleep and waking. *Amer. J. Psychol.,* 1924, **35**, 605–612.
6. H. M. Johnson, T. H. Swann and C. E. Weigand, In what position do healthy people sleep? *J. Amer. med. Ass.,* 1930, **94**, 2058–2068.
7. N. Kleitman, *Sleep and wakefulness.* Chicago: Univ. Chicago Press, 1939.
8. L. LeShan, The breaking of habit by suggestion during sleep. *J. abnorm. soc. Psychol.,* 1942, **37**, 406–408.
9. M. Levin, Reconstruction dreams. *Amer. J. Psychiat.,* 1939, **96**, 705–710.
10. M. M. Makhdum, On the stimulus-response relationship in dreams. *Indian J. Psychol.,* 1939, **14**, 87–90.
11. E. Schmidhofer, Suggestion therapy during sleep. (Report delivered to Amer. Psychiat. Assn., Cincinnati, 1951.)
12. F. E. Sommer, *Reading Chinese.* New York: Frederick Ungar, 1943.
13. E. B. Van Ormer, Retention after intervals of sleep and of waking. *Arch. Psychol., N.Y.,* 1932, **21**, No. 137.

mar

4

LEARNING DURING SLEEP?

Charles W. Simon *and* William H. Emmons

Approximately twenty-two years of the average man's life is lost in sleeping. Economically minded persons and harassed students have long searched for some means to use this time to further advantage. For nearly a third of a century, now, there has been a growing interest in the possibility of trying to learn while one sleeps.

The science fiction writers were among the first to propose sleep-learning as an educational technique. In 1911 a magazine called *Modern Electrics* published a fiction story by Hugo Gernsback (4) in which the hero learned during sleep. The process was simple. Upon retiring, the student placed the material to be learned on a machine which played it automatically while he slept. In 1932 Aldous Huxey (9), in his *Brave New World,* scoffed at the possibility of improving the *S*'s intellect while he slept, but described the world of the future as one which utilized the sleep period to train the lifelong attitudes of its populations. Other science fiction writers have continued to use the idea of sleep-training in their stories.

Popular news and picture magazines, citing experimental evidence, constantly reinforce the public's interest and misinformation about this osmotic form of education. From time to time a national news service will release a story telling of some individual who works for a living by day and studies chemistry, operatic arias, or other lessons while sleeping at night. On 'People Are Funny,' a popular radio stunt show, an audience participant learned a few short sentences and a girl's name while he was apparently asleep on the stage before the audience.

Following closely on the heels of public interest have come the entrepreneurs. Commercial firms have sprung up throughout the country selling recording devices which automatically turn on and off to permit the individual to learn while he sleeps. Impressive publications have been distributed by many of these firms propagandizing their products and extolling the validity and value of sleep-training (19, 21). On the whole, their claims of success for sleep-training have been extrapolations beyond the available supporting data. The majority of claims have been based on distorted facts, statements by unqualified authorities, and armchair hypotheses. Non-critical use of the information, anecdotal evidence, and the citing of inadequate research, much of which will be reviewed in the present paper, have made these commercial publications poor criteria for the support of the validity of the sleep-learning process.

In its constant search for new methods to speed training during national emergencies, the military, too, has tried to sleep-train its personnel. In both the first and second world wars, exploratory efforts were made to teach service men Morse code during their sleep. [Comdr. R. R. Humes, USN. Personal communication, January 25, 1954; L. L. Thurstone. Personal communication, October 19, 1953.] A VA Hospital doctor reported the successful use of sleep-training as a supplement to waking-training in a mental health program (20). Unfortunately, most of these incidents have been too inadequately controlled to judge their effectiveness during sleep, and in general their results have not been sufficiently striking to justify the extra energy and expense required to carry them out.

It is the scientist who has been slow in investigating these claims for successful sleep-learning. Although psychologists have been concerned with problems of learning from their formalized beginning, there has been relatively little interest in the psychological processes which take place during sleep and a rather sceptical—although untested—attitude toward the value of studying sleep-learning. One of Pavlov's students, Krasnogorski (11), did attempt without success to condition the salivary reflex in a young child during sleep. Recently, however, a resurgence of interest in the problem has occurred. In the present paper the available research on the sleep-learning phenomenon has been collected and subjected to a critical evaluation.

Ten such studies were found. Of these only three have been published (3, 12, 13). Five were academic theses at the Master's or Bachelor's level (1, 2, 5, 8, 23) of which one was read at an APA meeting (23). The remaining two were described in private communications from the authors. [L. L. Thurstone. Personal communication, October 19, 1953, and L. LeShan. Personal communication, October 27, 1953.] Although a number of other references were found, insufficient details were available for an adequate review or else they could not be classified as research under even the broadest definition.

The criticisms in this paper are not for the purpose of belittling these pioneer studies. These criticisms are believed necessary since these studies—many of which are unpublished—are being cited and their conclusions accepted both by the general public and some scientists. Because of the unusual methodological problems in this area of research, a review may help future workers to avoid similar mistakes.

DESCRIPTION OF THE SLEEP-LEARNING STUDIES

The experiments reviewed in this paper are described briefly below. In some of the studies, *S*s were eliminated for various reasons. Only the number of *S*s actually completing the experiment is reported.

Thurstone, in 1916, supplemented the waking training of sixteen Navy men in a Morse code course with material presented during sleep. The criteria of sleep used in this study are unknown. The *S*s finished the course three weeks earlier than had been expected. Thurstone concluded that the results 'indicated some gain' for the sleep-trained group in their ability to send and receive Morse code.

LeShan (12), in 1942, tried to break the fingernail-biting habit of twenty boy campers, ages eight to fourteen, by playing the phrase, 'My fingernails taste terribly bitter,' through a loudspeaker 300 times a night for fifty-four nights. The *S*s were asked if they were awake before turning on the input; if the *S*s appeared restless, the input was turned off. The nails of the *S*s in the experimental group and an equal number of *S*s in a control group were checked every two weeks for eight weeks for signs that the nail-biting had stopped. Since forty per cent of the experimental group and none of the control group stopped biting their nails. LeShan felt this indicated 'the possible therapeutic use of suggestion during sleep'.

LeShan in 1943, taught a single *S* a different list of nonsense syllables each morning for twelve days. On the fifth and eighth nights, the list to be learned the next day was repeated fifty times while *S* slept. The criteria of sleep used in this study are unknown. Fifty per cent fewer trials were required to learn the two sleep-trained lists than to learn the ten nonsleep-trained lists. LeShan concluded that the sleep-training facilitated learning.

Elliott (2), in 1947, studied the effects of thirty repetitions of a list of fifteen common three-letter words during sleep on the per cent saved in learning the list by the anticipation method the following day. Two groups of twenty male college students of equal learning ability spent one night adapting to the laboratory environment. The word list was repeated serially to one group of *S*s while they slept. An EEG record was used as a criterion of sleep. No material was played when the *S* showed 'clear alpha patterns' although the EEG was turned off when *E* believed *S* would stay asleep. On awakening the next morning, the two groups learned the sleep-trained list by the anticipation method and were asked if they awoke during the night. The group receiving the sleep-training showed a significantly greater percentage of savings than the control group (p = 0·05). [The p values representing the results of tests of significance are all reported as if they were based on a two-tailed t test, irrespective of what the author used. The p levels greater than 0·15 were not reported.] No significant differences between groups were found on the basis of errors or absolute number of trials to learn. Elliot concluded that there is some retention of auditory material during sleep.

Hedges (5), in 1950, tried to improve the speech of three mentally retarded and aphasic children (ages eleven, 7½, and six) by sleep-learning. Short sentences, paragraphs, and simple consonant sounds were played to the children between 433 and 1501 times distributed over seven to thirteen nights. The machine was not turned off if an *S* awoke. The third child required fewer waking lessons to learn the sleep-trained consonant than it had required previously to learn a nonsleep-trained consonant. The babbling of the first child increased. The second child showed no effects. Hedges interpreted this as showing 'the possibility of perhaps speeding' the training of the third *S*.

Fox and Robbins (3), in 1952, taught thirty college males and females a list of twenty-five pairs of English-Chinese vocabulary. The *S*s were divided into three groups, matched on a pre-test. Two vocabulary lists were prepared; in the first list, word pairs were matched as they were to be learned on the post-test (the facilitation list), while in the second, they were mismatched (the interference list). These lists were played fifteen times to two of the *S* groups approximately three hours after they had retired to go to sleep. The third group—a control—heard only music while they slept. Although *E*s did not observe *S*s during the input period, they disqualified all *S*s who said they had awakened during the night. The facilitation group required fewer trials and the interference group required more trials to learn the post-training list than did the control ($p <$ 0·001). The *E*s concluded that learning could occur during sleep and could be detected by the savings method.

Leuba and Bateman (13), in 1952, believed that they had taught the words of three songs, eight to twenty-seven lines long, to a lightly sleeping *S*. Each song, unknown to *S* beforehand was, played to her five times a night for three successive nights as she slept. During the input period, *S* was not observed by *E*, although for three brief periods, *S*'s husband observed no restlessness on the part of the *S*. The *S* claimed she did not awaken during the night. Given only the song title the next day, *S* was able to write the lyrics of two out of the three songs with no errors and of one with only minor errors. The *E*s believed the sleep-trained was successful. No learning occurred in a later study during and following the use of sedatives.

Hoyt (8), in 1953, taught ten pairs of English-Chinese vocabulary to his *S*s. Twenty *S*s were matched on a pre-test and given one night to acclimatise to sleeping in the laboratory. On the experimental night, one group of eight *S*s received twelve repetitions of a list paired in the same manner as that to be learned the next morning (facilitation list). A second group of eight *S*s received a list of comparable words, but with the pairs mismatched (interference list). The remaining four *S*s acted as a control group and received no sleep-training. During the input period, *S*s were observed by *E*. If they awoke or heard the stimulus material, they were to turn on a light. If this occurred, or if they stirred, the recording was turned off until *S* lay quiet for a suitable length of time. The next morning *S*s were asked if they had awakened during the night. Those that had not were given the paired vocabulary list to learn to two correct anticipations. Statistically insignificant differences were found to favour greater savings for the interference group rather than the facilitation group in both the mean number of trials required to learn the list as well as the number of correct responses occurring before the criterion was reached. No comparisons were made with the control group. Hoyt felt that under the conditions of this study, learning during sleep could not be detected.

Stampfl (23), in 1953, had six college males learn lists of ten nonsense syllables while acting as their own controls. Different lists were repeated four, eight, sixteen and thirty-two times on different nights while *S*s slept, and were learned to one correct anticipation on the morning following the repetition of a particular list. At other times, the same *S*s were tested on other lists after no sleep-training. Before presenting the stimulus material, *S*s were asked if they were awake. During the input period they were watched, and if movements occurred, the input was stopped. Since no significant differences were found for savings in either trials or errors between learning sleep-trained and non-sleep-trained lists, no comparisons were made among performances after different numbers of training repetitions. Stampfl felt that the sleep-learning hypothesis was uncertain and improbable.

Coyne (1), in 1953, carried out a series of exploratory studies on a variety of psychological problems using from four to six male college students as *S*s. He believed the results to be generally favourable for sleep-learning. Unfortunately, a statistical error was discovered in Coyne's thesis after he had written his discussion and conclusions which led to a more favourable interpretation of the results than was justified. Although *E* could observe *S* as he slept, he primarily depended on *S* to press a buzzer as soon as he awakened during the night. The problems Coyne studied are described below:

1. An interference list of adjectives was presented twenty-five times to the sleeping *S*. A similar list was learned to one perfect anticipation the next morning. A control group had no sleep-training. The sleep-trained group did poorer than the control group ($p = 0{\cdot}07$).

2. When the first problem was repeated using *S* as his own control, more errors were made on the list which had received the interfering sleep-training ($p = 0{\cdot}15$). No difference in savings (trials to learn the post-training list) was observed.

3. Twenty pairs of numbers and words were presented twenty-four times during a single 45-minute period to the sleeping *S*s. These same *S*s also received another list for the same number of repetitions distributed over a four-hour period. On subsequent mornings, *S*s were required to answer the appropriate word when

given the number found on the list on which they were trained during the night, after that list had been mixed with ten additional new number-word pairs. A greater percentage of sleep-trained words were associated with the correct numbers than those words not trained during sleep ($p = 0{\cdot}15$). Distributed sleep-learning resulted in fewer recall errors than did massed sleep-learning ($p = 0{\cdot}05$).

4. While the *S*s slept, one list of adjectives was repeated 100 times; on a different night, another list was repeated twenty-five times. On the morning following the sleep-training, the list was learned to one perfect repetition. No significant differences were found in performance between the two amounts of training.

5. The *S*s were required to solve a number of problems by finding *E*'s solution of a concept composed of the correct combination of letters, colours, and their relative positions. The solution to one problem had been repeated 180 times while *S* slept the night before. Insignificant differences were found favouring the performance on the sleep-trained problem.

6. While *S*s slept, one list of nonsense syllables was presented thirty times beginning at two o'clock and, on a different night, another list was presented thirty times beginning at five o'clock. Since it was discovered that the two lists were of unequal difficulty, comparisons between performance at different times of presentation were not made.

7. During sleep, the contents of a particular picture were described to *S*s ninety times. The following morning, a number of out-of-focus pictures were shown, including the one described during sleep. The degree of focusing required before *S* could identify the pictures was the measure of learning. No significant differences in the case of identifying sleep-trained and nonsleep-trained pictures were found either when *S*s were asked to give unaided responses or when multiple-choice solutions were provided.

Rather than examine each of the ten sleep-learning studies independently, this paper has been organized to discuss them all on the basis of the following categories: experimental design, statistical considerations, methodological considerations, and sleep criteria.

EXPERIMENTAL DESIGN

The use of a control group or of using *S* as his own control is recognized as a necessary procedure in order to know whether a certain experimental effect is real or not. In a number of the sleep-learning studies, however, both of these techniques were conspicuously absent or inadequately handled.

Thurstone recognized the inadequacy of his *uncontrolled experiment* teaching Navy men Morse code and attempted to run a second study in order to compare the performance of one group which received sleep-training with another which did not. This study was discontinued, he reported, when it was discovered that ambitious Navy instructors of the control group had been giving extra day-time instruction in order not to be out-taught.

Hedges (5) used *no controls* with two of the three speech-defective children he attempted to sleep-train. Since improvement in speech is a maturational problem, even for retarded children, the need for a control was paramount. The increased babbling of the first child may have been independent of the sleep-training and due solely to an additional month or two of growth, although Hedges believed that it took place immediately after the introduction of the sleep-training. Since *S* also received waking-training on the same material, it is impossible to know to what extent one can attribute the increase in babbling to sleep-training. No apparent learning took place with the second *S*. Although Hedges' third *S* acted as his own control by learning to pronounce one consonant with sleep-training added to his waking-training and another consonant without the sleep-training, this was an inadequate control measure since the experimental design was such that the sleep-trained consonant followed the nonsleep-trained consonant. Any improvement in the latter could be attributed to practice as well as to maturation.

Nor was a control used in the work of Leuba and Bateman (13). In this study, *S* presumably had no previous knowledge of the songs played to her during sleep, yet was able to write the lyrics without further training on awakening. If this were the case, any learning which took place during sleep would be a significant improvement, although materials such as songs and poetry probably have some internal predictability. This form of experimental design represents an *implied control*. It is implied that *S* acted as her own control for had she been tested previously, no appropriate responses could have been made, nor could one suspect that maturational factors were operating to produce positive results.

A number of *E*s actually used their *S*s *as their own control*. In LeShan's second study, he compared the number of trials an *S* required to learn a list with and without sleep-training over a period of days. By having the nontrained periods before and after the sleep-trained periods, the superiority of the sleep-trained lists could not be attributed simply to practice or maturation. On many of his studies, Coyne (1) gave sleep-training to his *S*s one night and no sleep-training on the next, counterbalancing the order for these procedures between two groups of *S*s. However, when the *S* acts as his own control, either the study material which is used under the varying conditions must be carefully equated, or additional counterbalancing must be introduced into the experimental design to correct for the inequalities. No *E* used this counterbalanced design; some made use of the published tables on which similarities and associability of the stimulus material had been previously calculated for the items. Several of Coyne's (1) studies were unanalyzable after he discovered the study material had not been equated.

Four of the experiments were designed to use *separate control groups*. In Elliott's (2), Fox and Robbins' (3), and Hoyt's (8) studies pre-testing took place in order to equate the mean performance of the control and experimental groups. LeShan (12) used unmatched groups in his study with fingernail-biting children. The median age of his twenty experimental nailbiters was slightly less than ten years. His control was divided into two groups consisting of eight nailbiters with a median age of nine years, and twelve more nailbiters with a median age of twelve. Some question might be raised concerning LeShan's failure to equate better the experimental and control groups on age, for there is reason to suspect a relation between nail biting and age. Wechsler (25) found a sharp rise in nail biting for boys around the age of twelve; if this is so, there would be a lower probability for the older control group to stop biting its nails than the younger experimental group, thus reducing the effectiveness of the older group as a control.

Two of the experimenters added a *second experimental group* to their design. Fox and Robbins (3) and Hoyt (8) used both a facilitation and an inhibition group in order to obtain a more sensitive indication of the value of sleep-training. Of all of the studies, only that of Fox and Robbins (3) provided the control group with a neutral stimulus —music—for the same amount of time as that in which the experimental group received the verbal test material. If there are any disturbances during sleep due to the stimulus and if these in turn affect recall, such a procedure is a wise one.

Although none of the *E*s was directly concerned with the problem, the use of an *additional control group* to compare results from sleep-training with the equivalent amount of waking-training would have been quite illuminating.

STATISTICAL CONSIDERATIONS

Only five of the *E*s (1, 2, 3, 8, 23) treated their data statistically to see if the sleep-training improved performance significantly. The remaining *E*s used clinical criteria to evaluate the effects of sleep-training.

Although Elliott's (2) results favoured the performance of the sleep-trained group over the nonsleep-trained group, he failed to find a significant difference at the 5 per cent level in the number of trials it took to relearn the training list. Elliott had equated his groups on a pre-test, but did not attempt to match the individual *S*s for the analysis. Since equating tends to decrease differences between means, failure to remove the variance due to *S*s inflates the error variance and decreases the probability of getting significant differences. When the present authors (22) did an analysis of covariance with pre- and post-test scores from Elliott's data, the differences between the mean number of trials to learn a new list by sleep-trained and nonsleep-trained *S*s were significant below the 0·05 probability level.

Coyne (1) used the *one-tailed t test* to evaluate his data. The wisdom of this treatment is questionable. In order to avoid abuses and controversy, exploratory work should be as cautious in its interpretations of results as it should be daring in attempting new ideas. Using the one-tailed *t* test does not allow for the possibility that differences might be in the direction opposite to that hypothesized (6). This is serious in any exploratory work; it is particularly dangerous in sleep-learning studies where one could seriously suspect that the intervening training during sleep might actually hinder normal waking recall.

Half of the *E*s (2, 3, 8, 12; Thurstone) used a reasonably large *number of S*s as compared to the number used in most psychological studies; in the remaining cases, the number was smaller. When the number of *S*s is small, one might be more critical of accepting the null hypothesis merely because the level of significance was not below the traditional 5 per cent level. For studies as exploratory as these, significance levels of 15 per cent could be arbitrarily considered encouraging. Since the expense in time and money is relatively small, preliminary work in sleep-training should favour fewer Type II errors in order not to reject valuable experimental leads by accepting a false null hypothesis.

METHODOLOGICAL CONSIDERATIONS

A number of *E*s believed that differences in methodology might have been responsible for the divergent successes and failures found in the sleep-learning studies. These and other considerations are discussed below.

Subjects: The majority of the studies employed the traditional college student—male and female—as *S*s. Thurstone used Navy men and LeShan used young boy campers. Hedges (5) bravely attempted to provide sleep-training as a supplement to the waking-training of children who had speech deficiencies and who were suspected of being mentally retarded. None of the *E*s attempted to study the effects of either age or sex on sleep-learning.

The selection of *S*s may have an effect on whether successful sleep-training results are attained or not. Underwood, while reviewing Fox and Robbins' paper in the 1953 *Annual Review of Psychology,* commented that 'such low variability [on performance scores] among *S*s on the test list is rarely found in normal transfer experiments with such material, but this may again only reflect the presence of a highly select and homogeneous sample'. Low within-group variability was certainly in part responsible for the high degree of significance of the differences between the sleep-trained groups and the control.

Whatever the variability of the group, it would appear wiser to choose individuals who have shown the capacity to learn while awake. Perhaps the effects of sleep-training are so subtle that its benefits will be found only when it is applied to individuals with very high IQ's.

Number of Repetitions: The experiments can be divided into two groups on the basis of this variable—those who gave an exceptionally large number of repetitions of the material during sleep (5, 12) and those that gave significantly fewer repetitions (1, 2, 3, 8, 13, 23;

LeShan). The large number of repetitions were actually spread over a number of nights and ranged from a total of 433 times over a period of eight nights to 16,200 times over a period of fifty-four nights. The smaller number of repetitions ranged from eight to 180 times, with one study (13) playing the material five times per night for three successive nights. More repetitions were characteristic of the field as opposed to the laboratory studies. Both groups obtained both positive and negative results, although the tasks were varied sufficiently so that direct comparisons could not be made. LeShan's (12) study, in which 40 per cent of the experimental group stopped biting its nails, represented a successful example where a great deal of repetitious training seemed to have affected a semi-involuntary behaviour.

Stampfl (23) and Coyne (1) found no differences when they tried to study the effects of different amounts of repetitions on sleep-learning. Actually since neither *E* used a nonsleep-trained group as a control, neither could conclude that any sleep-learning took place at all in this phase of their study. Coyne (1) suggested that in his study there may have been no greater differences in savings after one hour of repetitions than after four hours because the material was simple enough to be learned in one hour and additional practice could not improve it. This is a reasonable hypothesis, as is its antithesis—that during sleep, learning is sufficiently slow so that little is learned even after four hours of repetitions. Sleep-learning, if it is to occur at all, may require that an extremely large number of stimulus repetitions take place. It will be important to evaluate sleep- versus waking-training from the standpoint of economy of both time and effort.

Presentation: The manner in which the study material is presented to the sleeping *S* has been considered by some *E*s as critical to the success or failure of the training. Two dimensions of this variable are the time of presentation and the order of presentation.

The problem of *presentation time* is an important one since during the sleeping period, time is related to some extent to the depth of sleep, which in turn may be related to trainability. Deeper sleep tends to be more prevalent in the early period of sleep, while lighter sleep tends to occur later (18). Of course, the levels vary considerably throughout a normal night's sleep.

Coyne (1), studying the effects of presenting the material at different times during the sleep period, failed to equate his lists beforehand and could draw no conclusions from his results. He recognized that presentation time might be inversely related to the amount retained. He suggested, however, that this was due to the recency of the presentation to the recall period. It is interesting to speculate whether or not the Jenkins-Dallenbach interference effect (10) occurs within the sleep period for materials presented during sleep.

The differences Coyne found between massed and distributed learning might also be accounted for on the basis of presentation time. Although he concluded that distributed sleep-learning was superior to massed sleep-learning, there is no way to determine whether this was so because of the spacing of the training or because some of the distributed inputs occurred during the period just before waking—often a light drowsy state—while the massed inputs occurred only during the deeper and possibly less receptive period.

The *order* in which the material was presented during sleep may also affect the results of sleep-training. In a waking state, serial learning has been shown to be easier than learning material presented in a varying order (7). Thus, if any learning takes place in sleep, a serial presentation would more probably increase any positive effects which might occur. Also, if the sleep state is one in which no mental organization takes place, this would favour the learning of only the more organized serial presentation.

Hoyt (8) and Stampfl (23) varied the order in which their material was presented and failed to find that any sleep-learning took place. Fox (3), LeShan (12), Elliott (2), and Leuba (13) believed they found evidence of successful sleep-learning. Thurstone probably varied the order of his material, but his *S*s were practised over a period of months so that the effects of presenting the material in a varying or an unvarying order may have been minimized.

The varying presentation order in Hoyt's study was methodologically different in one major respect from that used in Stampfl's study. Since the former study used paired-associate material, varying the order in which the pairs were presented would have less effect than it had in the latter study where the order of words in a list was varied during sleep-training, even though they had to be recalled serially during the waking period. Any positive effects of sleep-training in the latter case may have been neutralized by the negative effects built up through non-serial learning.

Training Problems, Materials, and Mode of Input: The types of psychological problems studied by the majority of sleep-training investigators have been quite limited. With the exception of Coyne's (1) work on concept formation and perceptual sets and LeShan's (12) and Hedges' (5) therapeutic studies, the remainder of the research has been involved with training problems which require the memorization of word lists. It is unlikely that all types of problems are suitable for sleep-training, although exploratory studies should examine many rather than a few possibilities.

Of the material used in the studies requiring verbatim recall, the degree of meaningfulness ranged from lists of nonsense syllables through short words to foreign language vocabulary. We know that the more meaningful the material, the easier it is to learn in the waking state (7). Stampfl (23) suggested that this might explain why his results with nonsense syllables were poorer than Elliott's (2) who used a list of adjectives, and why Fox (3), using a Chinese-English vocabulary, got even more striking results. This does not seem to be a critical variable, however, for Hoyt (8), using the same Chinese-English vocabulary as Fox (3), got negative results, while LeShan and Coyne (1), using nonsense syllables, got positive results.

All of the *E*s used an auditory input. This is certainly the most obvious technique and would appear to be the most economical; however, other sensory channels need not be ignored. It may be necessary to flash lights on closed eyelids or to apply tactual stimuli to the fingertips in code in order to 'reach' the sleeping *S*.

Techniques and Measures of Retention: The techniques used to measure the retention of training material can have considerable influence on the amount of material recalled. However, in the present studies, there did not appear to be a pattern of successes or failures consistent with the technique used.

A number of *E*s did not require the verbatim recall of the verbal material presented during sleep. Instead, they evaluated retention on *S*'s ability to *use the material* in post-training tasks or on an *observed change* in *S*'s behaviour after the training. LeShan (12) examined his *S*s' fingernails every two weeks to see if the children had stopped biting their nails. This technique might have been slightly more objective had the examiner not known which children were and were not receiving the sleep-training. Hedges' (5) clinical evaluations of his children's speech improvement required even more subjective judgments. Because of the very complexity of his measure. Hedges wondered whether it was sensitive enough to detect improvement. Coyne (1), in several studies, had his *S*s describe an out-of-focus picture, the identity of which had been given to them during sleep, and to determine *E*'s solution of concepts composed of the correct combination of certain stimulus variables, the answer to which had also been provided during sleep. Thurstone's *S*s were evaluated on their ability to send and receive Morse code. Both Coyne's and Thurstone's results could be quantified.

Leuba (13) gave his *S*s the titles of songs played during sleep and required them to *recall unaided* the lyrics. Positive results were claimed for sleep-training in this study.

The *savings method* has been used by a majority of *E*s (1, 3, 8, 23; LeShan), for they believed it to be a more sensitive measure of retention. Stampfl (23) believed that although material could not be consciously recalled at any moment, its presentation during sleep may have still modified the nervous system sufficiently to make learning easier and a savings effected. However, use of the savings technique may confuse the measure of retention with a measure of the ability to learn since both are confounded within the same performance score. None of the *E*s using the savings measure compared the time to relearn a list with the time it took the same *S* to learn an equivalent list presented after sleep. Comparisons with the original list presented before sleep are not sufficient. The positive transfer which occurs from the pre-test to the post-test—the phenomenon of 'learning how to learn'—may account for some of the apparent savings which several researchers believed they found. However, Stampfl (23) gave three practice lists to be learned before the experiment in order to bring *S*s' learning curve closer to its asymptote and thus reduce the 'learning to learn' effect.

A still more sensitive technique for measuring retention is that of *recognition;* at least in Luh's (16) classical study this was so after a two-day interval between training and the post-training test. Coyne (1) used this technique in the form of a multiple-choice test for one of his exploratory studies on perceptual set, but still failed to get positive results. Hoyt (8) told of an exploratory study in which he presented a single number-word pair to a sleeping *S* who was under constant observation for a total of 11 hours on three successive nights. On awakening after the third night, *S* was given the number and asked to pick the correct word from a group of ten. He was unable to do this correctly. A major difficulty with the recognition method is that it must be corrected for chance guessing. With words, however, this correction for chance is difficult since all words do not have an equal probability of being recognized (17).

Variations in the score used to measure retention have failed to consistently differentiate success and failure in sleep-learning. Many of the *E*s (1, 2, 8, 23; Thurstone, LeShan) used the *number of trials* to learn post-training material to one perfect repetition as a measure of retention. Hoyt (8) required that the lists be learned to two perfect anticipations; this may tend to make his results slightly more reliable. Some *E*s (1, 2, 8, 23) also used as measures of retention the *number of errors* or correct responses made on the first trial or later trials, or on cumulative trials. Where the *S*'s performance was used to measure retention, the measure was characteristic of the task, e.g., Coyne used the extent of focus of the projector as the measure of performance in his perceptual set study. The measure that is used may determine in part the results which are found. For example, Coyne (1) noted that the measure by trials often favoured the opposite results than those favoured by the measure by errors. Error measures generally lead to less conclusive results than those measured by trials. This situation does occur in waking-research and need not be contradictory, although it certainly affects the conclusions drawn as well as the practical applications of the results.

Before final conclusions can be drawn concerning the feasibility of sleep-learning, more recall techniques should be tried. Simon and Emmons (22) discuss this while considering the possibility of secondary cerebral storage mechanisms for material introduced during sleep. [Dr. Bernard Fox, in a private communication (June 26, 1954), described his attempt to use hypnosis as a means of facilitating the recall of sleep-trained material. A 55-year-old man was brought to a point where deep hypnosis was possible. In his normal sleep he was presented with a list of ten words repeated for a half-hour. During this period, *S* was observed and the input turned off whenever he moved. The next morning, he was unable to recall any words unaided. When he was hypnotized, he made only one association which *might* have been related to one of the words. Still under hypnosis, he recognized fewer words than would be expected by chance when the ten were interspersed randomly in a group of thirty. Neither reading the words aloud nor making him choose by a forced-choice method produced any more positive results.]

SLEEP CRITERIA

Perhaps the most damaging criticisms of the sleep-learning studies to date have been the inadequate control of sleep and the criteria used for defining sleep. So elusive is the process of sleep from the psychological standpoint and so little is known about the actual physiological mechanisms which cause sleep that the problem of determining whether *S* is asleep is to a great extent a semantic one. Although both direct observation and *S*'s subjective report are reasonably reliable for deciding if *S* has been asleep over a block of time, neither can be considered sufficient to know if *S is* asleep at any moment in time. Therefore, the care with which *E* determines the sleep condition of his *S* at the time of the input is highly important and determines the degree of confidence which one may place in the conclusion that learning during real sleep is or is not possible. Some *E*s (1, 2, 3) eliminated *S* from the experiment if he awoke or said he heard the stimulus. Other *E*s (12, 23) shut off the stimulus until *S* went back to sleep.

In four of the studies (2, 3, 8, 13), *E*s *asked S*s *after the training if they had awakened.* This is an unsatisfactory criterion of sleep for experimental studies since it is a common experience to awaken during the night, perform a number of rational acts before retiring again and remember nothing the next day (8, 18). Hoyt stated that one *S* was observed to awaken during the night, leave the laboratory to go to the bathroom, and later return to bed. The next morning *S* remembered nothing about it. In two of these studies (3; 13) *E*s were not even present to *observe S*s as an added check. [Fox stated 'if any *S*s in the group of 30 actually did wake up without reporting it, then the number was probably distributed about equally throughout the groups. Moreover, since all *S*s with one exception show effects in the expected directions, it is clear that the results cannot be explained on the basis of a few *S*s in each group who awakened but failed to report doing so' (3, p. 78). It may be on the basis of many.]

In one experiment (3) the *time of night* was considered a partial criterion of sleep; training was applied during the period when studies have shown sleep to be at its deepest. However, published sleep curves are based on statistical averages and cannot be used to predict accurately the sleep characteristics of the single individual. Individual sleep curves vary considerably from time to time during the night (15).

Two of the *E*s (12, 23), *before presenting the stimulus material, asked Ss if they were asleep*. Since LeShan's (12) *S*s were adolescent boys in camp, naive as to the purpose of such questioning, one may wonder if asking them if they were asleep would be a sufficient check. It has been observed that even willing *S*s often fail to respond to such questions, although they admit hearing them later. Another major difficulty with this technique is that *S* may actually have been asleep when the test question was asked, but later would awaken sufficiently to hear the subsequent input. In these studies, no systematic check was made to be sure that *S*s did not awaken *after* the initial test, except to note if they moved.

Coyne (1) and Hoyt (8) had their *S*s *press a button whenever they awoke* in order to stop the input of training material. This method alone is not sufficient since it has been found that often the desire as well as the ability to do this is not present although *S*s are able consciously to hear and understand the material. Since much of the material used in these studies was short and specific, even a few seconds of waking presentation would have been sufficient to allow *S*s to hear and learn much of the stimulus while awake.

Stampfl (23), LeShan (12), and Hoyt (8), in addition to asking their *S*s if they were or had been awake, also *noted whenever they moved,* and turned off the machine at that time. This criterion of sleep is not completely satisfactory since EEG records indicate that sleep may lighten to almost a wakening state before movement occurs, as well as afterwards, or when there has been no movement at all (15). Hoyt (8) found that two of his *S*s said they had awakened but showed no observable movements, while three subjects said they had not awakened but showed from two to six movements each. This suggests that the criteria of asking and noting movements did not correlate very well. In Hedges' (5) study, the parents occasionally observed the children to see whether or not they awoke during the sleep-training; two children awoke. In the first case the number of training repetitions were not counted for the time *S* was awake. However, without a waking control, this correction is meaningless. The other *S* awoke while the recording was playing and began drowsily to follow the instructions given on the record. Hedges felt this aided the progress observed in that case.

Elliott (2) used the electroencephalogram to determine the *S*'s sleep level. Independent workers using a variety of techniques have established a significant correlation between the brain wave patterns and the depth of sleep (14). Because the writers believe that properly evaluated electroencephalograms represent the most objective, continuous, and practical on-the-spot indicator of sleep depth available, Elliott's (2) positive results—often quoted by the commercial firms in support of their claims for sleep-learning—are quite noteworthy. An examination of his sleep criterion revealed one major flaw, i.e., Elliott did not keep the EEG running during the entire training period. Therefore, no continuous check was made of the *S*'s sleep level while the stimulus was being played. The EEG was turned on at the beginning of the training and kept on until *E* believed that sleep would remain deep enough; then he would shut it off for the remainder of the half-hour stimulus period. With Elliott's data, a correlation of −0·39 was found between the amount learned and the amount of monitoring. This was not significant at the 5 per cent level but in a direction which suggested that more savings occurred with less monitoring. The writers (22) also compared the amount of savings made by a group of Elliott's five *S*s who were monitored nearly all of the training time with the savings of the remaining fifteen *S*s who were monitored on an average slightly more than a fourth of the time, and never more than 54 per cent of the time. For the first group, the average savings in trials to learn was 27·5 per cent; for the second group, the average savings was 45·0 per cent. The difference of 17·5 per cent was highly significant below the 2 per cent level of significance and we can conclude that when a thorough check of the sleep condition was made with the EEG during training, considerably less savings took place.

That any savings occurred for the groups monitored nearly 100 per cent of the time might be accounted for in two ways without assuming that learning actually occurred during sleep. First, the apparent savings may be simply an effect of the 'learning how to learn' phenomenon discussed earlier in the section on 'Methodological Considerations.' Second, Elliott stated that whenever an alpha pattern was 'clearly' present he concluded *S* was awake and turned off the input machine. In so doing, he quite likely permitted many of his *S*s to listen while they were already awake since movement, tenseness, or the opening of the eyes may sometimes block a clearly established alpha.

The expense of the EEG equipment negates its widespread use. This does not mean that without it, however, adequate sleep-learning studies cannot be done. The use of a combination of the criteria and continuous monitoring may be sufficient to insure some rough but adequate control of *S*'s sleeping condition. It is interesting to note that Hoyt (8) and Stampfl (23), finding negative results, were the two *E*s using the greatest number of multiple and continuous criteria.

The continuity of monitoring cannot be over-emphasized; for in spite of wishful thinking to the contrary, *S*s do awaken while the input is being presented. Two out of three of Hedges' (5) *S*s awoke. As many as half of Coyne's (1) *S*s awoke in some of his studies. Elliott (2) reported that six of his *S*s awoke. Only two out of sixteen of Hoyt's (8) *S*s in the experimental group failed to awaken during an input period. LeShan (12) also stated his *S*s awoke, but did not specify how many. One-fourth of Fox's (3) *S*s awoke, and were eliminated from the study.

The conditions under which *S*s sleep can influence to some extent the soundness of their sleep. Elliott (2) and Hoyt (8) required *S*s to sleep in the laboratory one night previous to the experiment. Any sleeplessness occurring on this first night probably induced a deeper sleep on the second. Hedges (5), Fox (3), and Leuba (13) used *S*s while they slept in their own homes, while Thurstone, LeShan (12), and Stampfl (23) used *S*s who had been sleeping in familiar 'homes away from home' for some time.

Although most of this discussion has centred around the problem, 'Was the sleep state deep enough?' Stampfl (23) and Leuba (13) suggested that there is an intermediate point between waking and deep sleep that is optimal for sleep-learning. Some negative results, they believed, may have been obtained because *S* was too *deeply* asleep. Whether this is true or not is an experimental question for future *E*s to answer.

SUMMARY AND CONCLUSIONS

Ten sleep-learning studies were reviewed. Many of these have been cited uncritically by commercial firms or in popular magazine and news articles as evidence in support of the feasibility of learning during sleep. A critical analysis was made of their experimental design, statistics, methodology, and criteria of sleep. All of the studies had weaknesses in one or more of these areas.

It is highly speculative whether or not the studies reviewed in this paper have presented any acceptable evidence that learning during *sleep* is possible. The inadequate control of a number of experimental variables makes the validity of the conclusions drawn by many of the *E*s unwarranted. The conditions under which the results were found tend more to support the contention that some learning takes place in a special kind of waking state wherein *S*s apparently do not remember later on if they had been awake. This may be of great practical importance from the standpoint of economy in study time, but it cannot be construed as *sleep-learning*. More carefully controlled experiments in the future may provide us with a clearer answer to the question, 'Can one learn during sleep?' as well as to provide comparative data between waking and resting learning from the standpoint of economy of time and effort. The problem is partially confounded by an inadequate definition of sleep.

REFERENCES

1. M. L. Coyne, Some problems and parameters of sleep learning. Unpublished Honours thesis, Wesleyan Coll., Conn., 1953.
2. C. R. Elliott, An experimental study of the retention of auditory material presented during sleep. Unpublished Master's thesis, Univer. of N. Carolina, 1947.
3. B. H. Fox and J. S. Robbins, The retention of material presented during sleep. *J. exp. Psychol.,* 1952, **43**, 75–79.
4. H. Gernsback, Ralph 124C 41+. *Modern Electrics,* 1911, **4**, 165–168.
5. T. A. Hedges, The effect of auditory stimuli presented during the sleep of children with delayed speech. Unpublished Master's thesis, Univer. of Wichita, 1950.
6. W. E. Hick, A note on one-tailed and two-tailed tests. *Psychol. Rev.,* 1952, **59**, 316–318.
7. E. R. Hilgard, Methods and procedures in the study of learning. In S. S. Stevens (Ed.), *Handbook of experimental psychology*. New York: Wiley, 1951. Pp. 517–567.
8. W. G. Hoyt, The effect on learning of auditory material presented during sleep. Unpublished Master's thesis, George Washington Univer., 1953.
9. A. L. Huxley, *Brave new world.* New York: Doubleday Doran, 1932.
10. J. G. Jenkins and K. M. Dallenbach, Obliviscence during sleep. *Amer. J. Psychol.,* 1924, **35**, 605–612.
11. N. I. Krasnogorski, Bedingte und Unbedingte im Kindesalter und ihre Bedeutung für die Klinik. *Ergeb. d. Inner Mediz. und Kinderhk.,* 1931, **39**, 613–730.
12. L. LeShan, The breaking of habit by suggestion during sleep. *J. abnorm. soc. Psychol.,* 1942, **37**, 406–408.
13. C. Leuba and D. Bateman, Learning during sleep. *Amer. J. Psychol.,* 1952, **65**, 301–302.

14. D. B. Lindsley, Electroencephalography. In J. McV. Hunt (Ed.), *Personality and behavior disorders*. New York: Ronald, 1944, Pp. 1033–1103.
15. A. L. Loomis, E. N. Harvey and G. A. Hobart. Cerebral states during sleep, as studied by human brain potentials. *J. exp. Psychol.,* 1937, **21**, 127–144.
16. C. W. Luh, The conditions of retention. *Psychol. Monogr.,* 1922, **31**, No. 3.
17. G. A. Miller, Speech and language. In S. S. Stevens (Ed.), *Handbook of experimental psychology*. New York: Wiley, 1951. Pp. 789–810.
18. F. J. Mullin, N. Kleitman and N. R. Cooperman, Studies on the physiology of sleep changes in irritability to auditory stimuli during sleep. *J. exp. Psychol.,* 1937, **21**, 88–96.
19. M. Powers, *Mental power through sleep-suggestion*. Los Angeles: Wilshire Book Co., 1949.
20. E. Schmidhofer, Mechanical group therapy. *Science,* 1952, **115**, 120–123.
21. M. Sherover, Learning during sleep: is it possible? New York: Modernophone, Inc., 1954.
22. C. W. Simon and W. H. Emmons, Considerations for research in a sleep-learning program. Santa Monica, California: Rand Corp. Paper No. 565, 1954.
23. T. Stampfl, The effect of frequency of repetition on the rention of auditory material presented during sleep. Unpublished Master's thesis, Loyola Univer., Chicago, 1953.
24. B. J. Underwood, Learning. *Annu. Rev. Psychol.,* 1953, **4**, 31–57.
25. D. Wechsler, The incidence and significance of fingernail biting in children. *Psychoanalytic Rev.,* 1931, **18**, 201–209.

5

RESPONSES TO MATERIAL PRESENTED DURING VARIOUS LEVELS OF SLEEP

Charles W. Simon *and* William H. Emmons

The authors wish to acknowledge the valuable assistance of Louie W. Mason, Jr. and James L. Barnes in the analysis of the data in this study. Appreciation is expressed to the faculty and students of Santa Monica City College, to the Santa Monica Police Department, and to the volunteer *S*s within The RAND Corporation for their cooperation throughout the project.

Recently, there has been an increased interest in the possibility of learning during sleep. A critical review of the few scientific studies in this field to date lead to the conclusion that the evidence supporting claims of learning during actual sleep is inconclusive. The chief criticism against the existing studies is their failure to continuously determine the sleep state of *S*s during the stimulus input period (16).

After considerable exploratory work (15), the present experiment was designed to study the effect of presenting material at different levels between wakefulness and deep sleep on the ability of *S*s (*a*) to respond to it immediately, and (*b*) to recall it later upon awakening. It was hypothesized that learning during sleep was improbable.

METHOD

Subjects: Twenty-one male experimental *S*s were used. In order to facilitate the detection of gradual changes which occur in the EEG between wakefulness and light sleep, it was necessary to use only *S*s having a persistent occipital alpha rhythm when awake and relaxed with their eyes closed. Ten *S*s were junior college students, nine were scientists, and two were policemen. Results from students and policemen were combined since they were similar on critical variables. Means and *SD*'s of descriptive variables for the experimental subgroups were determined. For the scientist group, these values were: age, 30·6 yr. ±5·0; IQ, 122·6 ± 6·0; items correct on pre-test, 11·7 ± 3·4. For the college men and policemen combined, these values were: age, 23·2 yr. ±6·3; IQ, 108·6 ± 4·7; items correct on pre-test, 6·8 ± 3·0.

Forty junior college males and 24 male scientists acted as a control group without regard for their alpha rhythm. These *S*s were used to obtain an estimate of the probability of correct answers being chosen on a multiple-choice test, since it seemed unlikely that educated *S*s would select their answers to unknown questions solely by chance. This control group was first given a pre-test to determine the number of test questions known without training and before seeing the multiple-choice alternatives. With no intervening training and after items correct on the pre-test were removed, the pre-test significantly predicted scores on the multiple-choice test. This prediction was not significantly improved when IQ or age was added in a multiple-regression equation.

Control and experimental subgroups were matched on means and variances of their IQ, age, and pre-test scores. Only the variances of the age and IQ of the college subgroups were unmatched. [Supporting and additional statistics along with data by *S* have been deposited with the American Documentation Institute.]

Apparatus: The *S*s slept in clean comfortable beds in three separate soundproof, air-conditioned, electrically-shielded booths. EEG electrodes were applied to the right occipital area, the vertex, and the left mastoid process. The electrode wires were arranged to allow relatively free movement and comfort during sleep. Two monopolar EEG recordings (right occipital and vertex) were made from each *S* using a six-channel Offner electroencephalograph and Dynograph inkwriter. A marker pen mounted on the inkwriter automatically marked the exact time an auditory stimulus was presented to *S*. The learning material was recorded on magnetic tape and played through loud-speakers placed inside the booths. A two-way intercommunication system allowed *E*s to communicate with *S*s.

Procedure pre-testing period: Several hours before retiring, *S*s were pre-tested to discover what information they knew in order to have a base from which to evaluate how much had been learned following 'sleep-training' on the same material. They were encouraged to guess answers to as many questions as they could, since a chance guess might be the correct one. No time limit was imposed.

Ninety-six general information questions were culled from various books on the basis of the following criteria: (*a*) the information was not generally known; (*b*) the answers required were not outside the verbal experience of the *S*s; (*c*) questions could be answered in short phrases or single words. These same ninety-six questions and their answers were recorded on tape at five minute intervals for presentation during the sleep period. The answer was presented as a restatement of the question with the critical information near the end. For example, Question: 'In what kind of store did Ulysses S. Grant work before the war?' Answer: 'Before the war, Ulysses S. Grant worked in a hardware store.'

Preliminary period: Following the pre-test *S*s prepared for bed and the EEG electrodes were applied. Three *S*s were run simultaneously. Since it was not possible to adjust the auditory intensity of the stimulus material in each booth individually, it was necessary to find a level satisfactory to all three. 'Satisfactory' was defined as the point at which the training material could be heard clearly by the waking *S*, yet not be loud enough to materially disturb him once he was asleep. As *S*s lay in their booths, practice verbal material was played at approximately the same loudness as the experimental stimulus material was to be played. This loudness level was adjusted after a number of tests so that the *S* with the highest threshold was able to hear the words clearly.

Before turning out the lights and allowing *S*s to go to sleep, the following instructions were given: (*a*) if they awakened during the night at any time, they were to call out their name and booth number as soon as possible and to say that they were awake; (*b*) if they heard the answer to any of the question-answer combinations during the night, they were to wait until the answer was completed, and then call out their name and booth number. In order to impress these instructions on *S*, each was asked to repeat them back to *E*.

Training period: Within five minutes after *S* retired, the tape recorder was turned on and the question-answer combinations were played into the booths at approximately five minute intervals. A pen automatically marked the EEG record whenever a question or answer was played. The *E*s marked on the record whether or not *S* stated he heard the answer. Records of any other pertinent information were kept, e.g., if *S* awoke, his remarks, and so forth.

Post-test period: Shortly after the last question and answer was played, *S*s were awakened (if they were not already so), permitted to dress, and wash their face and hands. The same questions which they received on the pre-test and during the training were again presented for them to answer; as before, *S*s were encouraged to guess. This unaided recall was followed by a multiple-choice test in which five alternative answers (including the correct one) were provided with the questions.

Control group testing: All members of the control groups were given the ninety-six questions and asked to answer them by guessing whenever they were not certain. Following a brief rest and no training, they were given the questions along with the multiple-choice answers and re-tested.

Intelligence testing: Following the completion of the experiment, both experimental and control groups were given the thirty-minute Otis Self-Administering Test of Mental Ability, Form D.

RESULTS

The basic data available for analysis were: (*a*) the levels of sleep during the training period as indicated by EEG records, (*b*) the frequencies with which *S*s immediately reported they had heard an answer, and (*c*) the frequencies with which *S*s correctly recalled an answer, both unaided and by recognizing the correct multiple-choice alternative.

Sleep levels: Those portions of the EEG record occurring simultaneously with the presentation of the answers were categorized into twenty-two distinguishable patterns. These twenty-two EEG patterns were divided into eight groups, or sleep levels, which were ordered on their proportion of visually observable cyclical activity within the alpha frequency range (8–13 c/s) and on their amplitude, frequency, and the effects of stimulation when alpha frequencies were no longer present. This order corresponds to *S*'s state of consciousness between wakefulness and deep sleep and is described in Table 1.

The categories were based on *S*s having continuous or nearly continuous waking alpha and read primarily from the monopolar occipital record. The letter symbols and the descriptions of the sleep levels in Table 1 approximate those of other experimenters in the field. Most investigators believe that an individual is asleep when

Table I

EEG and Psychological Conditions along the Sleep-Wakefulness Continuum

Level	% *Items*	% *S*s	*Electroencephalogram*	*Psychological Condition*
O	8	90	Continuous or nearly continuous alpha of maximum amplitude and frequency of not more than 1 c/s slower than the *S*'s normal alpha frequency. Frequency and amplitude are slightly less after sleeping than before.	Awake. Relaxed with eyes closed. Responsive to external stimulation.
A+	9	100	More than 50% of the scoring period contains alpha. Also low level, random activity characteristic of an alpha block may be present with alpha disappearing at the onset of stimulation and returning shortly after its cessation.	Drowsy.
A	12	95	Less than 50% alpha but scoring period contains at least three cycles of activity having the same frequency as the O level. The alpha amplitude may be of the same or considerably lower amplitude than before.	Attention wanders; reverie. Increased reaction time.
A−	14	100	Contains cyclical activity having a frequency more than 1 c/s slower than the Level O record. May include waves of mixed duration with periods between 0·12 and 0·08 s with no one period being dominant. Also includes records showing no alpha rhythm during stimulation, but with alpha occurring within 30 s prior to stimulation or following but not both.	Partial awareness.

Table I—*continued*

Level	% *Items*	% *Ss*	*Electroencephalogram*	*Psychological Condition*
B	22	100	Absence of alpha during the stimulus period and the adjacent 30 s of record. Stimulus effects may occur consisting of low level fast activity or an increase in activity containing both high and low frequency components, with some waves having periods within the alpha range. Low-level delta activity is present in the absence of stimulus effects.	Transition. Dreamlike state. Infrequent responses to external stimulation. Onset of sleep. Easily awakened.
C	18	100	Absence of alpha with an increase of delta and the appearance of sleep spindles (14 cps). This state is characterized by stimulus effects such as increases in amplitude of delta waves with the onset of the stimulus. Type of effects vary with individuals.	Light sleep. No behavioural responses to external stimulation (unless stimulus awakens). Dreams sometimes remembered.
D	7	90	A further increase in delta amplitude with a reduction in frequency and diminution of stimulus effects and sleep spindles. Amplitude of delta almost at maximum.	Deep sleep. No memory for dreams. Difficult to awaken.
E	3	57	Absence of sleep spindles and stimulus effects. Very large, delta activity with smooth waves of 0·5- to 1·5 s duration.	Very deep sleep.

Level C is reached, although some believe the onset of sleep occurs toward the end of Level B (3, 5, 9, 11, 12).

The EEG records were analyzed independently by two *E*s, after first agreeing on a few major classification principles. Their independent readings of the eight levels correlated 0·877 (corrected contingency coefficient) with $\sigma_c = \pm 0{\cdot}024$ when the true correlation is zero. Following this first reading, the two *E*s worked together to agree on the categories for all 2,016 items, elaborating on the principles for such categorization and compromising in a few cases where it was necessary. The breakdown of EEG levels during the drowsy stages before sleep is finer in this paper than has been reported previously. In the final analysis of the 2,016 sections of record, 7 per cent were unclassifiable due to artifacts which obscured the EEG pattern.

Levels O through A will be designated as 'alpha levels' and B through E as 'non-alpha levels.' Cyclical activity within the alpha frequency range (8–13 c/s) is found in the first four levels and is absent in the second four, with the exception of highly questionable alpha frequencies appearing during stimulation at the borderline between waking and sleeping. Sleep levels always refer to the levels at the time of stimulus presentation and never at the time of the immediate response or of later recall. All scoring of the EEG records was completed prior to the scoring of the information tests. When there was doubt as to the presence of alpha due to its low amplitude, very small quantity, or masking by other activity, it was the policy to place these patterns into the deepest alternative level.

Immediate response and unaided recall: The 'immediate response' or 'reported heard' analysis was based on 1,827 items; items were removed when the EEG was obscured by artifacts and when it was impossible to determine which of the three *S*s running simultaneously had responded. The 'unaided recall' analysis was based on 1,690 items; items were removed when the EEG was obscured by artifacts and when the items were known on the pretraining test.

The percentage of items reported heard at time of presentation and the percentage correctly recalled unaided, upon awakening, are shown in Fig. 5.1. These percentages in Fig. 5.1, based on the combined data for all *S*s and items occurring at each level, decrease as the amount of alpha decreases and delta appears, that is, as the sleep level deepens.

Of the items recalled correctly on the entire test, the following percentages were reported heard: Level O, 90 per cent; Level A+, 85 per cent; Level A, 79 per cent; Level A−, 69 per cent; Level B, 49 per cent. Below Level B no items were reported heard and only eight out of 508 items were answered correctly. Four *S*s indicated that after an extended period of wakefulness, they heard answers but deliberately failed to report since they wanted to go to sleep.

The percentage correct at each level when based on the combined data did not differ significantly from the percentage correct computed as the mean of all *S*s' individual percentage correct ($t = 1{\cdot}82$, 7 *df*). All individual *S*s showed the same tendency to reduce the percentage heard and recalled as alpha disappeared.

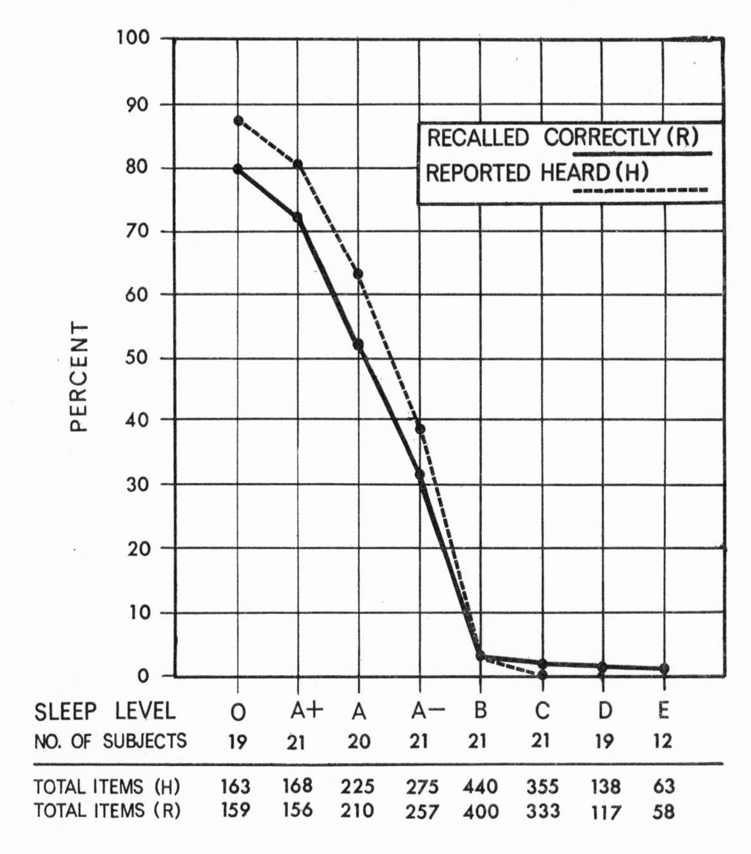

Fig. 5.1. The percentage of items reported heard during the stimulation at varying levels along the wake-sleep continuum and the percentage subsequently recalled correctly unaided.
The number of *S*s contributing to each level and the number of items from which each percentage was computed are shown

Some items, however, were immediately responded to and recalled later in Levels B through E. The breakdown of these items by level, type of response, and number of *S*s contributing are shown in Table 2. Twelve of the 19 correctly recalled items presented in Level

B appear to be the effect of bona fide learning. These were cases when the Level B EEG patterns were of specific types occurring during stimulation and were related to arousal from sleep. These patterns were characterized by low level, fast random activity quite similar to the 'activation pattern' found in animals (10, 14), as well as by an increase in random activity containing both high and low frequency components. In the latter pattern, mixed alpha frequencies

Table 2

Number of Items Reported Heard (H—), Answered Correctly (R—), or Both (HR) in the Non-Alpha Levels

Level	*Items Possible*	HR	H—	R—	*No. of Ss Contributing*
B	400	8	18*	11†	15
C	333	0	0	5	4
D	117	0	0	2	2
E	58	0	0	1	1
All	908	8	18	19	

* Five of these were answered correctly on the pre-test.

† Two of these may or may not have been heard; answers were too indistinct to determine which of three *S*s reported.

occurred simultaneously with significant quantities of delta activity. Both patterns appeared to be different aspects of a stimulus effect at the borderline between sleep and wakefulness. Since both alpha and delta appeared, the pattern was assigned to Level B, the transition state, rather than Level A— in accordance with the policy stated earlier. When these patterns are observed, arousal is imminent if stimulation continues. All of the items reported heard and recalled correctly (HR), half of the items reported heard only (H—), and four of the items recalled correctly (R—) in Level B could be accounted for by these patterns associated with arousal.

Eight items in Table 2 were heard only without any arousal patterns being observed. It cannot be determined from this study whether the answers which were reported heard were also understood; at least, they were not recalled.

Were the remaining items recalled correctly in Levels B through E (after removing items occurring during the arousal patterns) really learned during sleep-training? Since the range of reasonable answers to many of the questions in this experiment was restricted, the likelihood of a correct guess on the post-test increased if an *S* habitually changed his answer from first to second trial. Although it can never be proven that these fifteen out of 508 items were answered correctly by guessing, the hypothesis was tested as follows: An index of changeability was determined for each *S* by examining only those items which he answered incorrectly on both pre- and post-tests; this was done in order to avoid changes brought about by obvious learning. When the number of items recalled correctly without being reported heard and not associated with arousal EEG patterns was correlated with the percentage of incorrect answers changed between pre- and post-test by the twenty-one *S*s, the relationship was positive ($r = 0{\cdot}68$). This correlation, significant below the 0·01 probability level, supports the hypothesis that those persons changing their answers the most increased the number of correct guesses that they made. In other words, the fifteen correct items could be the result of guessing.

Examination of individual *S*'s data revealed that they all followed the same trend as shown by the curves in Fig. 5.1. The few cases of apparent recall that are shown in Table 2, accounting for roughly 1·5 per cent of all the items below Level B, are attributable to only a few *S*s. No *S* contributed more than two items and their occurrence in any sleep level was haphazard.

Recognition test: Fig. 5.2 shows the percentage of items recalled correctly for all *S*s when multiple-choice answers were provided, along with the standard error of these percentages. As in Fig. 5.1, with a decrease in alpha frequencies at the time of presentation, there was a corresponding decrease in the number of items recalled later. Unlike the others, however, the recall curve from this recognition test leveled off around 23 per cent instead of dropping to zero.

Since it was possible for *S*s to answer correctly solely by chance on the multiple-choice test, it was necessary to compare the percentages obtained by the experimental groups with an empirical estimate of what the theoretical percentage would be. Although 20 per cent was chance expectancy for this test, the difficulty of making a perfect multiple-choice test with answers equal in selectivity caused the *E*s to use scores of a control group as the basis for estimating the expected value.

It was found that the scientist control subgroup answered 26 per cent correctly without training and the college control subgroup answered 22 per cent correctly. The expected percentages shown in Fig. 5.2 were based on empirical values from the control groups

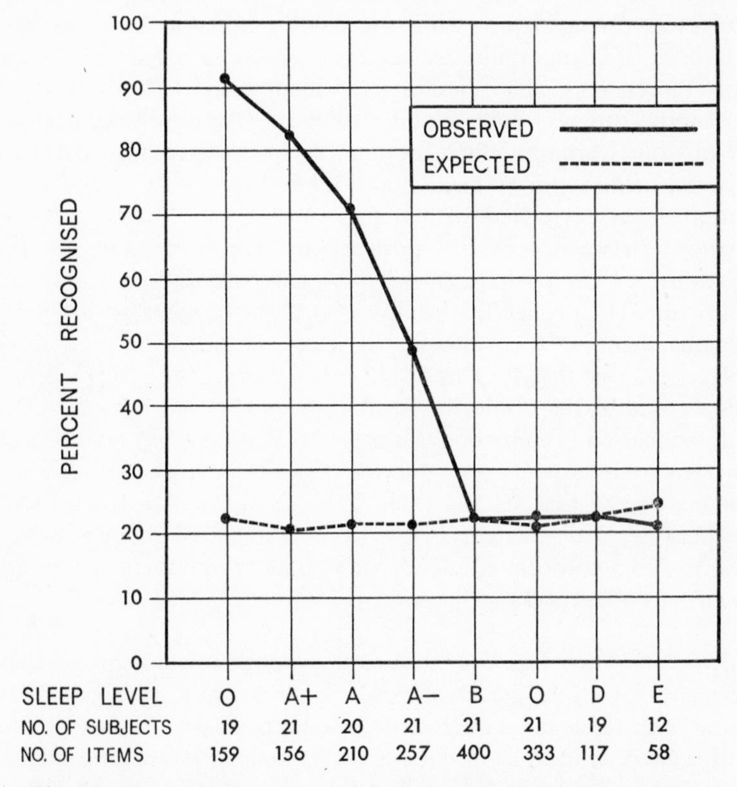

Fig. 5.2. The percentage of answers recognised on the multiple-choice test after being presented at varying levels along the continuum between awaking and deep sleep state.
The shaded portion represents plus and minus one standard error of the percentage. The expected value was that obtained from an untrained control group of comparable ability answering the same items

weighted according to the items contributed by the scientist and college-police experimental groups in each sleep level.

Thus, from Fig. 5.2, it can be seen that the expected values remain essentially the same for all sleep levels, while the values observed from the experimental group changed. In Levels O through A−, the experimental *S*s showed a considerably higher percentage correct, while in Levels B through E, the percentage correct for the experimental group was essentially equal to (within $\pm 0{\cdot}5$ per cent) and in most cases less than the mean expected value.

Table 3

χ^2's of Individual *S*s Showing the Significance * of Differences between Observed and Expected Values of Learnings in Alpha and Non-Alpha Levels

S	*Levels* O *through* A–	*Levels* B *through* E	*S*	*Levels* O *through* A–	*Levels* B *through* E
1	10·38	0·14	12	110·89	0·55
2	33·12	0·40	13	37·27	0·67
3	46·39	3·97†	14	37·51	0·08
4	151·30	0·39	15	80·58	2·65
5	7·31	0·54	16	38·68	0·20
6	32·43	2·00	17	32·00	3·57
7	55·69	0·15	18	109·24	0·84
8	5·41	0·05	19	113·78	1·08
9	47·35	0·01	20	78·57	0·31
10	43·10	1·65	21	6·24	1·9
11	0·47	0·03			

* χ^2 values higher than 3·84 (1 *df*) indicate that *S* answered significantly more items correct on the multiple-choice test than would be expected from the mean of his control subgroup ($P = 0{\cdot}05$).

† This *S* answered 5 out of 49 correctly. This was significantly *less* than the 10·8 expected correct when based on scores of his appropriate control subgroup.

Since the values in Fig. 5.2 were based on combined data for all *S*s, hiding possible individual learning, the data were analyzed by *S*. In order to have a sufficiently large expected value for computing χ^2 for each *S*, level O through A– (alpha levels) were combined as were Levels B through E (non-alpha levels). These were compared with the mean percentage correct for the appropriate control subgroup. The χ^2s from these analyses are shown in Table 3. No experimental *S* recalled correctly significantly more multiple-choice items than would be expected from the estimated percentages obtained from the untrained control group.

In order to determine whether any learning had occurred in the lightest sleep level but had been masked by combining those data with the deeper sleep levels, individual χ^2's were computed whenever possible for the results in Level B. Twelve of the *S*s had scores equal to or less than the expected value. Three *S*s scored insignificantly higher than the expected value (χ^2s = 0·34, 0·21, and 0·01; 1 *df*). For five cases, expected values were so small that χ^2 could not be computed. Two of these, with a 22 per cent expected value, had 5 out of 14 and 4 out of 16 answered correctly while three *S*s, with a 26 per cent expected value, had 4 out of 7, 2 out 4, and 3 out of 10 answered correctly. Only one *S* showed a significant χ^2 of 5·9, with 1 *df*. for Level B. For this *S*, 11 out of 24 items were answered correctly. Of these 24, 8 occurred when EEG patterns associated with arousal occurred; when these items were removed, 5 out of 16 were correct where 4 correct were expected.

DISCUSSION

The results support the hypothesis that learning during sleep is unlikely. Although a few items were answered correctly unaided, with the easier recognition test (13) no more items were answered in Levels B through E by the experimental group than would be expected from the performance of the untrained control group. Since it is generally conceded that sleep occurs somewhere during Level B, then it appears that learning was slight, if any, at this point or below. There appears some basis for assuming that many of these atypical cases were artifacts and not true sleep-learning.

What had been done in this sleep-learning study that had not been done adequately in any previous studies (16) was the careful monitoring of *S*s during the presentation period so that their levels of sleep during training were always known. The use of the EEG for this purpose proved most adequate.

The experiment was designed to get a continuous function rather than a dichotomous relation between responsiveness and consciousness along the wake-sleep continuum. Preliminary exploration (15) suggested the present design to be an appropriate one, although it involved certain calculated limitations related to the selection of *S*s, the conditions under which experimental and control groups were tested, and the number of stimulus repetitions.

Research on alpha dominant *S*s cannot justifiably be generalized to the general population, although there is no conclusive evidence that alpha dominant and rare alpha individuals differ on factors contributing to learning—certainly not on intelligence (11). The *S*s were chosen with above average IQ's to maximize the probability of learning. In the preliminary work, *S*s with considerably less dominant alpha rhythms were sometimes used. Although the borderline between drowsiness and sleep was more difficult to detect from the EEG with these *S*s, material presented when delta activity was present was never recalled later.

Experimental and control groups were tested under slightly different conditions. The control group in the present study was given one unaided pre-test followed by the multiple-choice post-test with no intervening training. The experimental group received an unaided pre-test followed by training and then a second unaided post-test before taking the multiple-choice post-test. To what extent the additional unaided post-test effects the comparison between groups is unknown. However, it has generally been shown that additional practice such as this second test provided enhances learning (6). This again would increase the probability that the experimental group would show even more learning on the multiple-choice test than the control. This was not found to be the case in the Levels B through E associated with sleep.

Experimental *S*s were given each item only once during training. [Prior to the publication of this paper a second study (4) was completed in which material was presented to *S*s between sixteen and eighty-two times. No learning occurred so long as the material was presented in non-alpha levels.] This was necessary to correlate an answer with a sleep level, for sleep levels varied throughout the night and had items been repeated, there would have been no assurance that they would have occurred in the same levels each time. Neither Stampfl (17), Hoyt (7), nor Coyne (2) found that varying the number of repetitions had any effect in their sleep-learning studies. None of these investigators found evidence of sleep-learning. The meaningfulness and simplicity of the test items tend to favour retention (6); tests showed that approximately 86 per cent of previously unknown items could be retained by awake and alert *S*s with a single repetition.

The above three limitations were accepted by the *E*s since in most cases they should tend to enhance any sleep-learning potential that might exist and thus disfavour the hypothesis which was tested. In spite of this, the evidence for learning was inconsequential as long as a rigid control on the measure of the depth of sleep was maintained.

Although it appears that learning during real sleep is not feasible, the practical utilization of the drowsy state for training is still open to speculation. The results in this study show that approximately 30 per cent of the simple and highly organized material presented in the period just prior to sleep was recalled. Just how efficient learning in this state is has not been sufficiently evaluated experimentally. Anderson (1) found that the amount of recall decreases when training follows sleep closely. One must weigh the advantages of limited learning against the possible harmful effects from loss of sleep as well as against the time demanded to learn in the subnormal receptive state. It may be that in the drowsy state preceding sleep, the individual is more susceptible to suggestion; perhaps one's attitudes or habits can be modified during this pre-sleep period when criticalness is minimized (8). Perhaps the future development of new and unknown techniques* will permit someone to learn complex material while he sleeps, but for the present, sleep-learning is not the simple matter that some *E*s and commercial firms, which sell equipment for this purpose, would lead us to believe.

* Editor's note: The presumptive prediction of the authors concerning the future development of new and unknown techniques, achieved by the Russians, came true. The Rand report, produced in 1956, though considerable in size, EEG efficiency and voluminous in text, seemed to be, as evidenced by the testing procedures followed, an unpractical undertaking. The studies were carried out with 21 subjects of average intelligence. The subjects had, at all times, EEG electrodes attached to determine the activity of the alpha waves before sleep, during the various periods or stages of sleep, and during the sleep-learning periods.

Experiments lasted only for one night, contrary to the Russian experiments. The basic psychological requirements for any sort of successful learning, such as motivation, the repetition of texts specially recorded from a psycho-acoustic angle for achieving optimal perception during the stages of sleep, were completely ignored. The Simon and Emmons report stresses that, in the instance where learning did take place during sleep, they were unable to determine if the subject was asleep.

It is quite surprising that American scientists indulged themselves in a rather reserved attitude concerning hypnopaedia, which was probably due to their prejudice against Pavlovian concepts mentioned already in the works of Dr. W. Sargant and Professor H. J. Eysenck. In the analysis of the more concrete activities of the central nervous system by means of the methods of experimental behaviour and by electrophysiological techniques, the investigator faces only one aspect of the phenomena leading to the differences in the interpretation of the EEG and behavioural arousal which create confusion in the conception of sleep, as it is understood by the experimental psychologist, the Pavlovian and the electrophysiologist. A co-ordination and interpretation on a common basis of the results obtained from different angles should be the task of researchers in the future.

SUMMARY

Twenty-one *S*s were selected on the basis of IQ (average or above) and an EEG showing a continuous alpha rhythm when they were awake and resting with their eyes closed. They were given a pre-information test of the sleep-training material and then permitted to sleep for 8 hr. No attempt was made to control the depth of sleep although EEG's were taken continuously from the occipital region. Ninety-six questions and answers were played to *S*s once each at five minute intervals throughout the sleep period. The *S*s were instructed to indicate immediately if they heard an answer. On awakening the next morning, *S*s were given the questions and asked to write the answers. Following this they were given five alternative answers and asked to check the correct one.

EEG patterns occurring during stimulation were assigned to one of eight sleep levels. Both the percentage of immediate responses and the percentage of items recalled correctly decreased as the percentage of alpha frequencies decreased. Shortly after occipital alpha frequencies disappeared from the EEG, immediate responses and item recall also stopped. This was more evident when tested by recognition than by unaided recall. Approximately 5 per cent of the items presented during non-alpha levels were responded to immediately, recalled later, or both. A majority of these items occurred when particular EEG patterns associated with arousal occurred; alternative explanations other than sleep-learning are offered for the few remaining items. Learning during real sleep is concluded to be impractical and probably impossible. The possibility of utilizing the drowsy state where material is retained is discussed.

REFERENCES

1. D. V. Anderson, The effect of relaxation on the recall of nonsense syllables words, and poetry. Unpublished Doctor's dissertation, Univ. of California, Los Angles, 1953.
2. M. L. Coyne, Some problems and parameters of sleep learning. Unpublished Honours thesis, Wesleyan Univ., 1953.
3. H. Davis, P. A. Davis, A. L. Loomis, E. N. Harvey and G. Hobart, Human brain potential during the onset of sleep. *J. Neurophysiol.,* 1938, **1**, 24–38.
4. W. H. Emmons and C. W. Simon, The non-recall of material presented during sleep. Santa Monica, Calif.: The RAND Corp., Paper No. 619, 1955.
5. F. A. Gibbs and E. L. Gibbs, *Atlas of electroencephalography*. Cambridge, Mass.: Lew. A. Cummings Co., 1941.

6. C. I. Hovland, Human learning and retention. In S. S. Stevens (Ed.), *Handbook of experimental psychology*. New York: Wiley, 1951. Pp. 613–689.
7. W. G. Hoyt, The effect of learning of auditory material presented during sleep. Unpublished Master's thesis. George Washington Univ., 1953.
8. L. LeShan, The breaking of a habit by suggestion during sleep. *J. abnorm. soc. Psychol.,* 1942, **37**, 406–408.
9. D. B. Lindsley, Electroencephalography. In. J. McV. Hunt (Ed.), *Personality and behavior disorders,* Vol. II. New York: Ronald, 1944. Pp. 1033–1103.
10. D. B. Lindsley, Emotion. In S. S. Stevens (Ed.), *Handbook of experimental psychology*. New York: Wiley, 1951. Pp. 473–516.
11. D. B. Lindsley, Psychological phenomena and the electroencephalogram. *EEG clin. Neurophysiol.,* 1952, **4**, 443–456.
12. A. L. Loomis, E. N. Harvey and G. A. Hobart, Cerebral states during sleep, as studied by human brain potentials. *J. exp. Psychol.,* 1937, **21**, 127–144.
13. C. W. Luh, The conditions of retention. *Psychol. Monogr.,* 1922, **31**, No. 3 (Whole No. 142).
14. G. Moruzzi and H. W. Magoun, Brain stem reticular formation and activation of the EEG. *EEG clin. Neurophysiol.,* 1949, **1**, 455–473.
15. C. W. Simon and W. H. Emmons, Considerations for research in a sleep-learning program. Santa Monica, Calif.: The RAND Corp., Paper No. 565, 1954.
16. C. W. Simon and W. H. Emmons, Learning during sleep? *Psychol. Bull.,* 1955, **52**, 328–342.
17. T. Stampfl, The effect of frequency of repetition on the retention of auditory material presented during sleep. Unpublished Master's thesis, Loyola Univ., Chicago, 1953.

6

THE HYPNOPAEDIC NIGHT

Jacques Genevay

This new method of education, 'hypnopaedia', is new only in certain respects. We can trace its precedents in history, even in legend.

How has the idea of hypnopaedia been adopted, when specialists in education have at their disposal a whole arsenal of already proven material and methods? The day-to-day examination of children and adults by means of psychological tests at the Leone Bourdel Laboratory of Applied Psychology in Paris has resulted in our researching into efficacious means of bringing out individual aptitudes. Indeed, we often noticed that numerous difficulties were involved in this bringing-out process. A child will be shown to be, from the tests, intelligent, with a good memory, easily taught, with a good character basis, well formed, and school reports will be brilliant up to the fourth form, for instance, but from a certain time onwards this child will go backwards—unable any longer to keep up with the class. The parents then usually make a great effort for him to have special coaching with private teachers, but to no avail. The school year has to be repeated, with the risks attendant on such a venture (failure complex, inhibitions, definite debarment from certain educational courses and university entrance).

In explanation of these troubles at school (the same troubles exist, of course, at adult level) an affective traumatism is sometimes found to be blocking the attention. The psychologist then brings the parents to a new understanding of the problem and gets them to create a new emotional environment, but these changes do not always bring with them the expected scholastic spurt.

The doctor, for his part, can reduce or treat causes of physical handicap, but these efforts do not always result in better performance in school again.

Various writers have sought the origins of these sometimes chronic failures in children who are otherwise quite normal, well integrated or well re-integrated emotionally and physically. These educationists and psychologists arrive at one very clear conclusion: on the one hand, the children suffer from a greater or lesser insufficiency of automatisms of memory and intelligence and, on the other, they have never learned to utilise this intelligence, to use it to bring into play the cultural automatisms which they ought to have acquired from school curricula. This is the action indicated by the psychologist when he speaks of acquired knowledge being put 'under tension'. It is, of course, necessary for acquired knowledge to exist.

In effect, to resolve a problem, to understand a text, to assimilate a fact means grasping an actual situation in the light of what one already knows, i.e., seeking the significance of a whole interpreted with the aid of the decoding grids which exist in oneself (or do not exist) and which one has assimilated in the course of previous experiences and situations. This is, therefore, perception through a memory content and organisation available for reference. 'Understanding,' says the authority Delacroix, 'is preceding perception with mnemic content,' in other words, by means of references from memory and experience stored somewhere in the subconscious and brought to the surface.

We find ourselves faced with three kinds of facts forming the basis of intellectual success for the child at school and the adult in life.

1. Need for mnemic-intellectual automatisms, i.e., knowledge of the general working type: multiplication tables, square tables from 1 to 100, administrative 'departments', historical dates, theorems, formulae, etc.

2. Need for an engagement of intellectual aptitudes conducive to exploiting this working knowledge.

3. Need for a quality of intelligence which leads one towards the conceptual, the abstract, and the generalisation process.

The first two points belong especially in the field of education, and hypnopaedia complements traditional teaching usefully and efficiently, in that it is particularly apt at *enriching the memory* and at *getting it to be organised*. The third point refers more to the capacity with which nature has endowed us of being or of not being intelligent, for there is in intellectual performance an unequal division about which we can do nothing. We can encourage inborn talents to their point of maximum efficiency, but we cannot create anything where there is nothing. During our experiments in hypnopaedia, either with individuals or groups, we have never been able to change dunces into geniuses, but it has been possible to make out of reputed dunces average pupils, and even quite good ones in certain cases, that is, it has been possible to develop their personal potential to its maximum.

If the mnemic-intellectual automatisms (which, according to Le Gall, are this general working knowledge) are in a satisfactory condition, if structures are firmly established, if the intelligence is trained by a variety of exercises (this being the school teacher's role) to make the most of all its resources and to exploit them when necessary, one can be sure of having created conditions favourable to good intellectual success.

In a collective hypnopaedic experiment, carried out in a school, the relation has been calculated between the level of aptitudes in general and scholastic success with a group of experimental pupils and a group of control pupils. A correlation was arrived at which was twice as high between aptitudes and scholastic success, after a series of hypnopaedic exercises with the 'automatophonised' group, by comparison with the control group. This means that, thanks to hypnopaedia, pupils were given a chance to exploit twice as many aptitudes as they would have exploited under normal conditions.

HYPNOPAEDIA—HISTORY

Hypnopaedia, both as a teaching method and as a scientific method, has been formulated only quite recently. But the underlying spirit has been rediscovered and can be said to be quite familiar to us. One of my correspondents, an orientalist, informs me that certain priests, whose duty it was to give instruction in the sacred books, used to whisper verses of scripture into the ears of trainee-priests just as the latter were falling asleep. The 'night/nocturnal whisperer' had already been discovered.

One chronicler, the writer of a humorous article on hypnopaedia, states that good King Numa already had a nocturnal micro-speaker in the person of the nymph Egeria.

Much more recently, Richepin, in his book *Miarka, the Girl With the Bear,* has recalled that the little girl who was to succeed the gipsy king was taught by her grandmother, who, every night when she was falling asleep, whispered into her ear something from the old traditions.

Easier to verify are those experiments which have been done since the end of the war, particularly in certain countries. The Americans use hypnopaedia to teach foreign languages and military codes, also probably to train their special agents. [Editor's note: The Americans have *not* produced any language courses specially recorded for hypnopaedic teaching techniques. The application of pharmacologically aided hypnopaedia in the technique of memorising codes or other information for intelligence personnel is open due to the possibility of retaining information presented during anaesthesia, and the recall may be triggered off by the use of special stimuli.] At present, there are in America records which make it possible, by nightly repetition and under special conditions, for mathematics, history, etc., to be learned.

The actual suggestion, the hypnopaedic suggestion which takes place on the edge of sleep, at the edge of the pillow, has also been known about for a long time, and psychosomatic medicine shows that children who are bed wetters can be cured and that certain forms of re-education are possible, where conditions are favourable. Claparede says that enuretic children have been cured by suggestion during the first few minutes after falling asleep.

If hypnopaedia has not so far become more widespread, it is because it made it necessary for an operator to remain at the subject's bed for several hours during the night, to intervene at suitable moments—the key-moments—and it will be seen how inconvenient this can be both for the monitor and for the sleeper. Before describing quickly the automatophone, which is the automatic tool used in this method, and which replaces the monitor, we should like to outline the scientific fundamentals of hypnopaedia.

SCIENTIFIC FUNDAMENTALS

(*a*) *Activity during waking and sleeping:* The hypnopaedic method has its origin and justification in the knowledge of the mechanisms of perception, memory and learning and in the terms of those psychophysiological data on sleep, which are now better known since the Second World War.

The state of sleep is particularly interesting, in that it affords the experimenter a subject who is relaxed and receptive, but at the same time vigilant and intelligent with regard to certain points which preoccupy him and which remain the 'points illuminated,' as Lhermitte says.

While activity during waking hours—i.e., the normal activity which takes place during the day, when we are active—is controlled by the law of effort and tension, the night is given over to relaxation.

The effort of fixation during the active period can induce opposite effects to those being sought, effects of blocking and inhibition. This is well known and is described by the term: law of converted effort. When one wishes to learn too much, everything becomes muddled. And these inhibitions sometimes have a retrograde effect, i.e. not only does nothing 'go in', but the ideas just recently painfully acquired are progressively lost. This inhibition can, in certain cases of intellectual excess tension, account for everything learned during the day. One recalls the work of Pavlov and Beaudouin on these problems.

By contrast with the waking state, sleep responds particularly well to the concept of focusing, centring and polarising vigilance, apart from any voluntary effort at attention. Since the ear is the only organ needed at night, when we sleep we do not entirely sever our links with the outside world, but continuously keep a watchful antenna, as it were, on the world around us.

Someone has aptly said that our eyes have eyelids but that our ears have no 'ear lids'. This is probably because they must never be allowed to rest. In fact, one always notes electrical activity during the night when one undertakes electro-encephalographic analyses in the zones of audition.

By day, we pay attention at one and the same time to smells, to heat, to a variety of elements which disperse our effort to concentrate and which force us into a state of quite considerable spontaneous tension of a parasitic nature, in order to exclude everything which might disturb us. It is when this attention is relaxed that we can centre our interest on a precise point and—work. But what a loss of output!

During sleep, in certain conditions, processes of elimination and defence no longer exist: the attention is concentrated entirely *on what it hears and expects,* given that the magnetic tape on the automatophone only produces what one has oneself recorded on the previous day, with one's own complete consent and participation.

The classic example is quoted of the mother of a family, worn out with fatigue, who is sleeping 'like a log', and does not hear a military convoy passing down the street (although this is most unusual). Yet she reacts immediately to the scarcely audible whimpers of the new baby in the next room. The example is also known of willing oneself to awaken, etc. Biographies of famous men, research scholars and scientists, contain examples of problems having been solved during sleep.

This shows to what extent sleep is an intelligent, living state and to what extent it is part of the process of adaptation. Sleep is a psycho-physiological state which is part of a life of communication. It is not a state of complete break—the best proof of this being that, if sleep were such a state of total alienation from the outside world, it would be impossible ever to waken someone who had fallen asleep.

(*b*) *The sleep curve:* In actual fact, deep sleep, which is the real restorer as fas as the organism is concerned, and which should not be disturbed, only lasts a few hours (three or four hours, according to the type of sleeper). The remainder of the time is devoted to falling asleep and preparing to awaken. The latter is, incidentally, a much longer process than falling asleep, which can often be virtually instantaneous.

When one is falling asleep, the functions of muscular reactivity are the first to fade out, but we have seen that the receptive auditory functions are never entirely eliminated. Bergson has said: 'To sleep is to disengage oneself.' But this formula should be completed by adding: it is not to cease to perceive, it is actually to perceive electively. This perception is selective and conforms in every aspect of its activity to the interests of the sleeper. Only those externally originated sensory messages *which are of interest to the sleeping subject* acquire significance and are understood and assimilated by the intelligence at night.

Exact electro-encephalographic studies show the structure of sleep. In the accompanying chart (Fig. 6.1) we take a typical night: at ten o'clock, go to bed, begin to fall asleep a few moments later; at seven o'clock, wake up. A dotted line shows the curve of weakening consciousness, which affects first the muscular functions, then the visual ones (these cease suddenly), and the other sensory functions, apart from the ear. Starting from a normal level of activity when the child lies down, the curve descends rapidly in thirty to sixty minutes

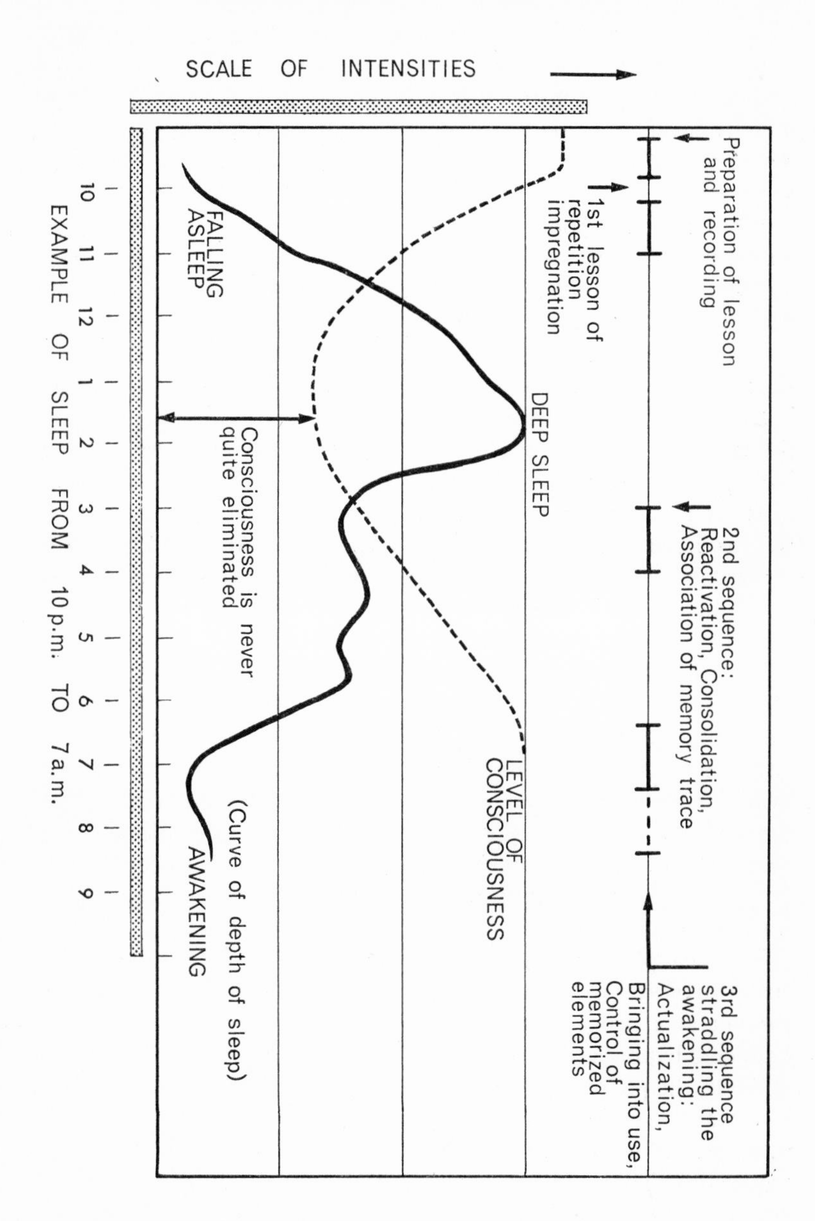

Fig. 6.1. Favourable moments of sleep for hypnopaedic periods

after the eyes are closed. It reaches its nadir three or four hours after falling asleep has taken place, then ascends again gently but often with a few breaks, until awakening occurs. It resumes its normal activity level more or less within half an hour of the awakening. There are, of course, individual fluctuations, but this curve can be vouched for statistically.

What happens to the depth of the sleep during the general weakening of consciousness: the depth of the sleep increases during the first three or four hours and reaches a maximum. From 2.30 to 3 a.m. the sleep grows progressively lighter, but this in an often irregular way. Finally, in many subjects, after this phase of light sleep a last deepening is noted, slightly before awakening occurs.

In sleep, the first phase is still favourable for audio-perception, the more so since the attention is spontaneously engaged, the ears having taken over from the eyes. The second phase, that of deep sleep, is no longer favourable for perception, as certain American writers have shown. It must be respected in its entirety, for it represents that restorative sleep which is indispensable. Nevertheless, it can be shown that an audio relationship with the outside world remains in certain respects.

Then comes the very interesting phase, during which the psycho-physiologists show that all the regions of the cerebral cortex tend to communicate with each other in a way in which they never do at any other moment of diurnal or nocturnal activity. The teacher has available there a zone particularly favourable for memorisation and for audio and visual associations. The audio stimulation at that moment seeks and commits to memory the visual processes fixed during the diurnal activity with regard to the message recorded on the magnetic tape.

The last phase of sleep involves progressive transition from a state of rest to the life of consciousness awaiting the sleeper. We are present at a progressive awakening and, just before this actually happens, hypnopaedia can step in for a last time.

Thus, the phases of deep sleep and real restorative sleep appear in two waves, according to the age and habits of the sleepers. All the intermediate phases produce a partial sleep which has been called hypnoidal. The subject is not entirely asleep although he is in complete repose. It is during these hypnoidal phases that he has electrical activity which can lead to dreaming, but also to memorising, to working out solutions to certain problems, etc.

(*c*) *Affective censorship and principles of action:* It will be noted that the effect of focusing auditory vigilance, the absence of disturbances which have to be countered, and also the connection between the various regions of the cortex increase the efficiency of intellectual effort and in some way sharpen and reinforce perception. Exact experiments have actually shown that the sleeper can appreciate the affective quality of stimulation while sleeping. This leads to the consideration that during the night there exists a sort of automatic affective censorship which could easily block the way to excitations dangerous to the subject from a general biological point of view. We have, in fact, shown this to be the case, and that every message which is of no concern to the subject or which could traumatically affect his balance caused awakening or elimination of the sound distributing apparatus. Since the whole organism will spontaneously defend itself, *moral guarantees* arise in relation to possible improper uses which could be made of hypnopaedia. Naturally, these defensive reactions normally only occur with subjects in good health. In cases of physical breakdown or overwork it is probable that the censorship processes are considerably disturbed or weakened. These censorship reactions are also known in electro-encephalography and have been designated 'K-complexes'. When a sleeper is subjected to a disagreeable excitation which can disturb his sleep or be harmful to him, he does not react to the first excitation, nor, generally, to the second. But, with the fifth or sixth excitation, if he does not awaken, a kind of electrical shunting action operates in him, a discharge which is translated into a sudden muscle movement, a change of position. This does not harm the sleep, being rather like the action of someone taking a siesta and who, annoyed by a fly buzzing round him, knocks it away with his hand without actually waking up. Recorded graphically, this appears as a sudden wave of great intensity, which seems to correspond to the instantaneous integration of all the values of the foregoing excitations.

Thus, hypnopaedia relies on the particularly favourable circumstances offered by certain sleep phases and on the mechanisms controlling this psycho-physiological activity. But, on the other hand, hypnopaedia also relies on certain very important facts derived from the psychology of learning: in order that material should be memorised, the appropriate sensory message should be repeated a certain number of times. It is thus recognised that repetition opens up elective ways for the subsequent passage of the nervous influx.

It is also known that repetition is correlated with the depth of the trace, but these repetitions or groups of repetitions must also have a certain time relationship with each other; this is Jost's law of spacing.

It is also necessary that the material to be memorised should be assembled in a simple, representative way to make up a unity of knowledge which contains potentially a principle of action (comparable to certain groups of cells of an organism in process of formation which the embryologists call 'organiser tissues'). This material must be referred to former acquisitions of the same type, which 'ring a bell'. It amounts to integration of the new material with earlier acquired structures.

Between the moment of learning and that of the first effective exploitation of the knowledge it is necessary that there should be a means of possible dispersion and temporisation.

It is extremely important that more than one sensory centre should be employed in perceiving and apprehending directly the material to be memorised, and also in the extensions of such perception which occur in the cerebral cortex at certain times during the night, as we have already seen.

Finally, the affective interest of the subject who is learning must be awakened to the utmost extent and invariably in a positive manner. The mechanism by which the memory is lost normally or in certain mental disorders is very instructive for the practice of hypnopaedia. The laws regarding dissolution of the memory are known (Jackson's law, Delay's law): what gets forgotten can range from the most recent to the most distant, the most complicated to the most simple, the most intellectual to the most automatic. One has forgotten a great deal which has been acquired with effort but one remembers what has been acquired mechanically and 'by heart'.

Now let us examine how a 'hypnopaedic night' is organised:

THE HYPNOPAEDIC NIGHT

Referring to the sleep table (cf. *Revue du Son*, No. 69, Jan. 1959), the text to be memorised is recorded on the automatophone, shortly before going to bed. This is the preparatory phase. This recording should be done in a level voice, without, for example, in poetry making any tonal stress, but merely reproducing the mechanical rhythm. When the light is extinguished the automatophone switches itself on automatically or by remote control to reproduce, in a low-tone speaker under the sleeper's pillow, the text recorded previously. This text, which must always be very short (never to last more than five minutes), is repeated, according to the subject, from ten to twenty times.

The low-tone speaker located under the pillow and having a regulator accessible to the user must be adjusted to a very fine level of perception. It must not be forgotten that during the night the threshold of hearing is lowered quite considerably.

At the end of the first repetition sequence the automatophone, which has been appropriately programmed, stops automatically and ceases to run, all the machinery cutting out.

The deep sleep phase then proceeds normally and the subject rests under the usual conditions. At about 2.30 or 3 a.m. a second sequence of repetition starts up automatically, lasting no longer than one hour, according to the length of the text recorded. It is during this phase that the memory trace is not only consolidated but also organised and that associations between the different sensory areas take place.

Then, when we are quite near to awakening, about one hour before the intended time, e.g., at about 6.30 a.m., the apparatus switches on for the last series of repetitions. This is stopped voluntarily by the subject when he finally awakens to get up. At the moment of awakening, the subject can, in the majority of cases, recite what he has heard. If this repetition is not entirely by heart it is at least quite closely related to the text transmitted. It is remarkable how the phonetic accent and music of a language can be acquired easily under these conditions, if one passes from hypnopaedic sessions to reciting in a loud voice, using at the same time as a guide the apparatus now adjusted higher.

The total number of repetitions for the three phases together can, according to the texts to be learned and the type of sleep of the sleepers, amount to thirty, to fifty and even to sixty.

Method of Director Schemes: In certain other cases, where it is no longer a question of learning by heart but of becoming steeped in a given subject (e.g. in preparing for a conference or for examinations), the director schemes method is applied, whereby the text is reduced to basic essentials and becomes the structure for a piece of knowledge without being the knowledge itself.

To explain this director schemes method, reference can be made to an experiment recently conducted by us in a school. We decided to prepare a history class by hypnopaedic methods. The pupils had not been warned at all of the details of the operation. The history lesson for the next day dealt with the beginnings of Rome. This lesson had been reduced to its basic essentials, to a skeleton structure, consisting of a summary of date references, some proper names, and mention of some elements linking together this period of history, the entire text lasting some seventy-five seconds.

The presence of the low-tone speakers under the pupils' pillows had been accounted for by transmitting a little music while the children were going to sleep. Thus, the first repetition phase had been suppressed, so that the children should not hear the text before they were entirely asleep. The first sequence thus took place one hour after the children had fallen asleep.

On the following day the history teacher conducted his lesson in the normal way. He made the following observations: the children subjected to the experiment, who remembered nothing of what had happened during their sleep and who were not even conscious of having heard anything particular, were immediately particularly attentive to the teacher and his lesson, as if the knowledge being passed on to them from his desk *awakened an echo in them.* Attention and class participation were quite abnormal. By contrast, the pupils of the control group behaved in an essentially traditional way. Some of the pupils from the experiment said to the teacher at the end of the lesson: 'Sir, it's very funny, but it's as if we had already heard that somewhere.' And for a very good reason!

From the very precise questioning carried out after this lesson it was noted that the experimental group gave 63% more good answers than the control group.

Some time later another test was made to see to what extent this memory prepared by the director scheme might have weakened. And from the experimental group there was a gain of 42% over the control group.

What is important here is the fact that the children approached the history lesson with a lively intelligence already rendered receptive and having a synthetic idea (unconscious, but real) of the 'beginnings of Rome'. Therefore, they did much more than accumulate facts during the lesson: they understood them and at the same time fixed them in their memory.

Hypnopaedia does not only fit the memory with general working knowledge, but develops that faculty of memory which becomes increasingly organised and which makes for increasing suppression of useless effort, which can better be used to solve problems. Hypnopaedia, to a certain degree, therefore, encourages the exercise of intelligence.

In a general way, in classes, if one balances the children's aptitudes and compares the level of these aptitudes with scholastic success, one sees that the children's potential is only very partially engaged. In particular, lessons tend to proceed as if the audio memory had never been involved, almost the entire effort being related to visual processes. The hypnopaedic technique restores to significance verbal and auditory processes, thereby making for much more effective 'returns.'

The Automatophone: We come now to the automatophone. Without going into too much technical detail, this apparatus consists of two distinct stages.

1. The magnetophone proper, of normal construction, but furnished with those refinements usually found in good international apparatuses (head-set connection, direct-radio and electrophone connection, stop pedal with back spacing for several syllables, two tape running speeds, etc.);

2. The assembly of automatic equipment installed in the cover, whose function is to replace an operator. The latter would, simultaneously, control the running of the tape or follow by ear the text being transmitted, in order to know when it stops and starts; he/she would manipulate the various magnetophone keys to activate the cycle 'read, stop, rapid rewinding'; would stop the rapid rewinding at the precise moment at which the beginning of the text would again pass the reading head, would remember certain orders for switching-on and cutting the repetition sequences according to an eight-hour or even a twelve-hour programme, and would, finally, attend to general security and satisfactory progress of the operations.

The automatic devices which replace the operator have basically three functions: control of magnetic tape running, manipulation of keys 'listen', 'stop', 'rapid rewinding', 'stop', according to a predetermined circuit, i.e., fixed circuit, and, finally, time programming extended over twelve hours. With regard to the control of the tape running, the movement of the reel when unwinding is transformed into a linear development which forces an indicator to move between two micro-breakers, one controlling the start for reading and the other, a mobile one, corresponding to the end of the text reading.

The information gathered by the system of mobile indicator and micro-contacts is transmitted to the manipulator. When the mobile indicator activates the micro-contact for 'end of reading', a motor is excited by means of a relay and sets up a cyclic movement of cams which act successively on the 'stop' key and the key for rapid reverse movement on the magnetophone keyboard. When the latter key is engaged the tape is taken back at high speed to the beginning of the reading and the mobile indicator controlling the movement of this tape comes into contact with the micro-breaker for 'beginning of reading'. The information gathered at this moment is transmitted to the manipulator motor, which causes the 'stop' key to be depressed in such a way as to render the apparatus inert and then the 'read' key on the keyboard to be depressed. The cycle thus begins again and is continued indefinitely.

The 'programming' function for operating repetition sequences is catered for by a time programme which issues orders to cut or to set in motion, thus either cutting the repetition cycle or starting it up. This time programme consists basically of a revolving cylinder, driven by a motor which makes one revolution per hour. This cylinder has on its outer surface a helicoidal groove pierced by holes at two-minute intervals. Riders are fixed in the holes, so that a programme with a maximum duration of twelve hours can be compiled. A 'search head', whose movement is precisely synchronised with that of the grooved cylinder, explores continuously the turns, being lowered or raised according to when it encounters 'shut-off' riders or 'start-up' ones. Time adjustment devices make it possible to work precisely to the minute. When the entire cylinder has been explored by the search head, the driving motor automatically cuts out and the time programme stops. It has been necessary to envisage a particular system to postpone the order to cut, which can come during the reading of a text, until the moment the text ends. It is, in fact, essential in hypnopaedia to transmit uninterrupted texts, so as not to disturb the structures built up by the repetition. This 'memory' system cuts the repetition sequence at the exact moment when the cycle begins again at 'read'. When an order to start is read on the time programme by the search head the text is ready to be transmitted immediately.

Finally, remote control systems allow repetitions or single readings of recorded texts to be switched on by external means, according to whatever is available (opening of a door, interruption of a photo-electric beam etc.).

Once the programme is fixed to the time-breaker and the micro-contact for 'end of reading' suitably adjusted, one only needs to close the cover so that the automatic equipment can contact the magnetophone and the automatophone be ready to operate. [Editor's note: The technical specification of the 'automatophone' is already out-dated by the introduction of an endless tape cartridge for uninterrupted repetitions, used in conjunction with a suitable time switch to control the tape recorder.]

The preparation and control of a hypnopaedic programme are very simple, and we have examples of children eight to ten years old who can carry out the various operations alone without difficulty.

Possibilities of Hypnopaedia: The possibilities of hypnopaedia (and, in general, of repetition techniques) are many and varied. I have stressed its contribution in schools for children who have difficulty in keeping up and who have, for various reasons, to repeat classes. But in the sphere of psychological and even psychiatric re-education there are some very interesting and original applications: Dr. Bernard Granier for example, has applied the hypnopaedic method to the re-education of sufferers from aphasia and also of children with enuresis. Other experiments are being conducted, notably with regard to directed dreams.*

CONCLUSION

It is probably premature to draw definite conclusions with regard to hypnopaedia, a science only in its youth and still in its very first experimental years. The concrete results already obtained in various fields permit one to entertain quite well-founded hopes.

Hypnopaedia has sometimes been reproached for encouraging laziness and as appealing to the less desirable psychological mechanism of the individual. I believe that this reproach is essentially

* Editor's note: Hypnopaedic experiments conducted by the Russians and by R. J. Berger (1963) confirm the author's views on the possibility of modifying dream contents by meaningful verbal stimuli.

undeserved. On the contrary, one can regard the hypnopaedic method as a significant contribution to the ennobling of the human effort—in so far as it allows man to devote his intelligence more to constructive and research tasks by freeing him from the shackles of an apprenticeship to elementary automatism—an apprenticeship which, in itself, produces nothing that is educative or forward looking.

Intelligence is, in itself, made up by that wonderful mechanism which the psychologists call 'the function of synthesis of the organism' and which is the capacity to formulate, to organise and to classify the diffuse information derived from the outside world. It is an instrument ever ready to exploit acquired experience, when some definite action is to be taken on a problem needing solution. Thus, intelligence must be supplied with the material that it needs to carry out its plan, just as a builder's foreman can draw on a well-stocked and well-arranged supply yard to build his house. 'For let us make no mistake: we are automata as well as minds,' as Pascal has already pointed out.

May hypnopaedia also play its part in enhancing that finest gift bestowed on us by the Creator.

7

THE ASSIMILATION AND MEMORISATION OF SPEECH DURING NATURAL SLEEP

A. M. Svyadoshch

Is it possible that, *during natural sleep and without awakening,* a person can hear speech uttered in that period and remember its content the next day? Is it possible for a person sleeping naturally without awakening to assimilate and to master a story or a lesson read by someone? In other words, is it possible not only to assimilate but also to master speech during natural sleep?

This question is of interest not only for the study of the possibilities of acquiring knowledge during sleep but also for studying the physiology of sleep, assimilation and memory, the psychology of the creative process and of unconscious forms of complex psyhological activity, for the analysis of certain autochthonous and delirious ideas and in the search for methods of psychotherapeutic influence during sleep. It has been little studied hitherto. Special work devoted to it consists only of our own (1940; 1947) (12, 13); a note on the work of Charles R. Elliott (1948) (22); and two articles by Emmons and Simon (1956) (23, 29), to which we shall return later.

The possibility of assimilating speech during *natural sleep* has long been noted. Authors who have devoted attention to the psychology of dreams, for example I. E. Stepanov (17), Maury (26), Leroy (25) and S. Freud (19) among others, have observed that a sleeper may sometimes assimilate isolated words. These words, however, are visualised, i.e., converted into visual images in dreams, and have the character of plays upon words and puns so that the meaning of the word is distorted. Thus, for example, the name 'Rosa' may be changed into a bed with a canopy of roses; the surname 'Belotserkovskiy' ('Whitechurch') may be assimilated by the speaker in the form of a white church, a white snow-covered field, a Ukrainian village with white cottages, and so on. In this case the fact that he is taking in words is not realised by the sleeper.

There is no doubt that a sleeper can also assimilate speech without distorting it. This is attested by the observations of doctors treating children by 're-education during sleep' (Burdon (21) and N. V. Vyazemskiy (5) and others). On awakening, the children did not know that they had assimilated speech during sleep; however, the remedial effect which had taken place was evidence of the fact that the speech had been mastered by them.

The occasion of our own study of the assimilation of speech during natural sleep was a report by a patient aged fifty-four, to the effect that at the age of eighteen, when in good health, she was waiting one day for the arrival of some visitors, one of whom was to be a man who was a good singer. The guests were late and she fell asleep. On awakening the next morning she felt that she knew a song which she had never before heard. It turned out that the song had been sung in an adjoining room by the delayed visitor. She remembered the tune and the words of the song, but not the fact of having assimilated it. This so impressed her that she often used to tell of it within the family circle. We asked a further 100 healthy persons whether there had ever been an occasion in their lives when, having fallen into a natural sleep as usual, they had heard through their sleep without waking up the conversation of people around them, a story read while they were asleep, a broadcast programme, etc., and had remembered what had been said when they woke up.

We received a positive answer in two cases. In one, a woman neuropathologist, aged thirty-five, reported that at the age of nineteen, when she was a student on the primary course of a medical institute and was studying anatomy with some friends, she fell asleep while one of them continued to read aloud. On waking up after a while she remembered everything that had been read while she was asleep. Incidentally, a similar phenomenon was observed in his own case by one of the patients described by K. I. Platonov (1957) (11). In our other case, a girl, aged ten, had noticed that not infrequently, after falling asleep naturally and waking up in the morning, she remembered what her parents had said while she was asleep. This possibility has evidently not passed unnoticed, for J. Johnson warns adults against loud conversations in the rooms of sleeping children; the latter, she says, are not incapable of assimilating them during sleep.

We then carried out the following experiment. During the natural sleep at night of 100 healthy subjects of different sexes and ages, who had not been warned of the prospective experiment, we twice read a short story, telling them to remember what they heard. It was found that during the reading of the story they either slept on and next morning remembered nothing that had happened, or else woke up. The same result was later given by the experiments of Emmons and Simon (23, 29). In their experiments the sleeping subjects either failed to master speech during sleep or were awakened as a result of the speech.

In another of our experiments, one of twenty subjects, a boy aged twelve, after twenty readings of a poem while he was asleep, although he remembered nothing the next morning of what had happened, was able to learn the poem by heart unusually quickly—eight times more quickly than a control poem. The remaining nineteen subjects in similar experiments did not show quicker mastery of the poem, or of words of a foreign language, as compared to control material.

> Note: Eight years after our experiments a note appeared that in the U.S.A. a professor of psychology at the University of North Carolina, Charles R. Elliott (22) apparently succeeded in every case in obtaining learning of speech by similar methods. He recorded on a gramophone record fifteen words of three letters each. These words were played over thirty times during the sleep of twenty students possessed of good hearing (the occurrence of sleep was confirmed by electroencephalographic data). On awakening, all twenty students who had been learning during sleep learned these words unusually quickly, noticeably more quickly than twenty control subjects who had not learned during sleep. We have not ourselves come across the author's own account of these experiments, so that the data mentioned in the note cannot be regarded as trustworthy. *Komsomolskaya Pravda* No. 43/10983 reported on similar experiments in hypnopaedia, i.e., learning during sleep, in an article—'The Tape Recorder Whispers to the Sleeper.'

The experiments we conducted point to the fact that the spontaneous appearance of the capability of assimilating speech during sleep is rarely met with. This is supported by the evidence of everyday experience, which shows that people who fall asleep during a radio programme do not usually remember next morning what was transmitted while they were asleep.

Once convinced that the spontaneous appearance of the faculty of assimilating speech during natural speech is rarely met with, we tried to develop that faculty experimentally. Experiments were carried out from 1936 onwards, under clinical conditions, upon the group of experimental subjects of Professor S. L. Levin in the Laboratory of the Higher Nervous System of the Leningrad Scientific Research Institute for Safeguarding the Health of Children and Adolescents, and also in the First Leningrad 'I. P. Pavlov' Medical Institute, the pediatric clinic of Professor N. I. Krasnogorskiy, the psychiatric clinic of Professor N. I. Ozeretskiy, the orthopaedic clinic of Professor M. I. Kuslik in the S. M. Kirov Academy of Military Medicine, and the psychiatric clinic of Professor V. P. Osipov. Under laboratory conditions they were carried out in the laboratory of physiology and pathology of sleep of the I. P. Pavlov Institute of Physiology. The data obtained were presented by us in essentials in 1940 in the form of a dissertation on the theme 'The assimilation of speech during natural sleep'.

CHARACTERISTICS OF THE SUBJECTS AND PROCEDURE

The experiments were carried out on twenty-five psychically healthy subjects of both sexes, specially chosen for the purpose out of about 400 subjects according to signs of high suggestibility,* interest in the experiments and indications that they were capable of falling asleep at a given time or at a given signal. All the subjects chosen had good hearing. Their sleep at night was fairly deep (they did not wake up at the control reading of a text), calm and without frequent awakening.

The ages of the subjects ranged from ten to sixty. There were eight aged ten to sixteen, thirteen aged seventeen to twenty-seven and four older than twenty-seven. Four had received higher education, six were students at institutes, nine had received complete or partial intermediate education and six were attending classes III to VI at a middle school.

* Methods of determining suggestibility are given in A. M. Svyadoshch's book *Neuroses and Their Treatment,* Medgiz, 1959, 247–8.

The experiments were carried out in the following order:

1. During natural sleep at night texts were read to the subjects; then next morning on awakening, in the waking state and, in some cases, under hypnosis, the subjects were questioned about the previous night (first control experiment).

2. The subjects, sleeping naturally, were awakened at night and stories were read to them. On awakening the next morning, and again repeatedly after a number of time intervals, the subjects were questioned about the previous night (second control experiment).

3. The faculty of assimilating speech during natural sleep was developed in the subjects.

4. During natural sleep at night texts were read to the subjects which were similar to the texts for the control experiments. On awakening and after the same time intervals as in the control experiments, the subjects were questioned about the previous night (fundamental experiment).

5. In the daytime, in the waking state, a text was read to the subjects similar to that of the fundamental experiment, and after the same time intervals the reproduction of the text was determined (third control experiment).

In the evening the subjects went to bed and fell asleep as usual. One to five hours after they had fallen asleep, at a distance of about two metres from the head of the bed of the sleeper, a text was read quietly. The subjects meanwhile continued to sleep and did not wake. A number of precautions were taken to exclude supplementary stimuli: light, the sound of footsteps, the creaking of doors, etc. The texts were read by us or by other persons, or were reproduced from recordings.

In the second control experiment the subjects were awakened by a call or a touch. When they opened their eyes and replied logically to questions, they were asked to listen to a text and to try to memorise it so as to be able to give it word for word the next morning. The text was then read, a similar one to that of the fundamental experiment. After a final request that they should remember and be able to give everthing word for word the next day, the subjects resumed their interrupted sleep.

All the texts began with introductory words: a count from one to twelve, and the sentences: 'Listen and remember the story (or the title of the text). Tomorrow you will remember it all word for word and will be able to tell it.' The text of the story was then repeated twice, after which there followed the concluding words: 'Sleep more deeply; do not wake up. Tomorrow you will remember it all and will be able to tell it word for word.'

For convenience in calculation, the texts were conventionally divided into a series of short paragraphs consisting of one or two sentences representing a subject-unit. The texts were chosen as being unknown to the subject and corresponding to the level of his development; a number of texts were composed by ourselves. The texts that were read were of a literary nature (fairy-tales, narratives, stories, retold versions from novels by Claude Farrère, S. Galler and others), chapters from courses of theoretical mechanics, theoretical acoustics and also philosophical works and words of a foreign language.

Questioning was carried out in some cases in the morning on awakening from sleep, and in other cases twelve or forty-eight hours after awakening. To allow appraisal of the retention of what was assimilated, some subjects were questioned again after sixty hours and thirty days about what had taken place in the night.

Eight of the subjects, after questioning in the waking state, were again questioned in a state of deep hypnotic sleep. Measures were taken to avoid direct or indirect suggestion during questioning.

In order to characterise reproduction as regards quantity and quality, percentage reproduction was determined: the ratio between the number of subject-units (paragraphs) correctly reproduced and the number of those read, and the percentage of confabulation (erroneous reproduction): the ratio between the amount of confabulation (in sentence-units) and the number of sentence-units.

In laboratory conditions the experiments carried out were monitored by actography and pneumography.

The faculty of assimilating speech during natural sleep was previously developed by means of suggestion. Suggestion was carried out with twelve subjects in a state of deep hypnotic sleep (Forel's stage III), with seven subjects in a shallow hypnotic sleep (Forel's stage II) and with six subjects, not previously hypnotised, in the waking state.

The suggestion was: 'Tonight you will sleep peacefully without waking. While you are asleep you will hear counting up to twelve and you will then hear a story. You will sleep the whole time without waking, but through your sleep you will hear, take in and remember the story. Tomorrow you will remember it all and be able to tell it word for word.' (The suggestion that a count of twelve would be heard, and its execution at night during the sleep of the subjects, was introduced by us on the supposition that the counting would serve as a conventional signal thanks to which the 'point of alertness' would be more easily developed in the cortex; its introduction is not essential.)

In conducting the first experiments with three subjects, we gave them the suggestion to sleep not 'peacefully' but very soundly and deeply. It was found that, on awakening, the subjects remembered neither the texts read to them during sleep nor the fact that they had been read, whereas on changing the formula of suggestion all three could reproduce the speech assimilated by them during natural sleep. It is possible that the suggestion to sleep 'very soundly' exerted an inhibiting effect on the whole cortex, including the 'point of alertness', responsible for the assimilation of speech. It is less probable that as a result of the depth of sleep (on awakening the subjects said they had slept very soundly, had heard nothing while asleep and had had no dreams) amnesia for the texts assimilated during sleep had set in, as is supposed to occur in connection with certain dreams.

Probably, if it were suggested to the subjects that they should sleep 'particularly lightly', the point of alertness would be developed even more easily than after the suggestion to sleep 'peacefully'.

The subjects to whom suggestion was given in a state of shallow hypnotic sleep, or in the waking state, were further recommended to make use of autosuggestion* (to repeat mentally, with concentration, ten to fifteen times before sleep, words to the effect that they would sleep, hear and remember speech while they were asleep), and also to summon up in themselves by an effort of will an appropriate state of mind for assimilating speech during sleep.†

* Concerning the techique of suggestion and autosuggestion, including autogenous training for medical purposes, see A. M. Svyadoshch: *Neuroses and Their Treatment*, Medgiz, 1959.

† We later became convinced that when these methods do not give results the following procedure may be used. Approach the sleeper, touch his finger and hold it lightly so as not to awaken him (the entire depth of the inhibiting effect of sleep on the sleeper is thereby diminished). Then repeat in a gentle whisper for two or three minutes, following the rhythm of the breathing, the words: 'Sleep deep-er, sleep deep-er.' The rhythm of pronouncing the words is then slightly slowed or quickened. The rhythm of the sleeper's breathing often slows or quickens correspondingly. This is an indication of the establishment of contact with him (though, if the rhythm of breathing does not change according to the rhythm of the words, this does not rule out the establishment of contact). Then the following phrases are repeated two or three times: 'Listen to the story and remember it! Tomorrow you will remember it all!' The reading of the story is then proceeded with.

Recently we were recommended to have recourse to autogenous training in order to develop the faculty of assimilating speech during natural sleep.

Autogenous training is a method of auto-suggestion in a state of relaxation (muscular slackness). It was proposed about forty years ago by J. Schultz (30) for the treatment of neuroses, stenocardia, bronchial asthma and other ailments, but has only become widely used as a method of psychotherapy during recent years (A. M. Svyadoshch (14), Müller-Hegemann (28) and others).

It is explained to the subject that he is to be taught the fundamental technique of auto-suggestion in a state of complete repose and muscular relaxation. Once he has mastered it, he will be able to develop in himself the faculty of assimilating speech during sleep. Then the actual training is proceeded with. For this purpose, the subject is instructed to adopt a comfortable position three times a day daily, lying down, or sitting in the 'coachman's position'—the head hanging forward, the hands and forearms placed on the upper surface of the thighs and knees, the legs arranged comfortably and the eyes closed. In this position, summoning up a state of mental relaxation and calm, he must think with mental concentration: 'My right hand (or, for left-handed persons, left hand) has become quite heavy!' This formula is to be repeated six times. He then mentally repeats once: 'I am perfectly calm.' From time to time, as a test, he may try to lift his hand the merest trifle to convince himself that a feeling of heaviness has appeared.

This exercise is repeated for ten to fourteen days. After the first four to six days of the exercise the feeling of heaviness in the hand becomes more and more distinct. It then spreads to both hands, the legs and finally the whole body. The subjects must correspondingly suggest to themselves: 'both hands', 'both legs', 'the whole body has become heavy'.

After the subject has learned to summon up in himself the feeling of heaviness, he is told to summon up a feeling of heat.

For this purpose, after the appearance of the feeling of heaviness, he repeats mentally five or six times: 'My right hand has become hot' and, after a few days of training, 'both hands have become hot.' New formulas of auto-suggestion are then added: 'My heart is beating calmly and firmly' (at first, the hand is placed over the region of the heart so that the heart-beat can be felt); 'I am breathing easily, my breathing is even and calm,' 'My forehead is pleasantly cool.'

During each session all the auto-suggestion formulas of the previous sessions are repeated in as shortened a form as possible. For example, for 'I am calm', 'calm!' For 'My hands and legs are heavy,' 'heaviness!'; for 'my hands are hot,' 'heat!' and so on. To master each of these formulas of auto-suggestion, exercise for two to three weeks is required. A new formula of auto-suggestion is added only after the previous one has been mastered. In this way the whole course takes about 2½ to 3½ months. The duration of each session is one or two minutes.

To bring oneself out of the state of repose and muscular relaxation, sharp mental commands are given: (1) 'Bend the arms', whereupon two or three sharp movements of bending and unbending are performed at the elbow; (2) 'breathe deeply', 'open the eyes.'

The subject is warned beforehand that he must not suggest to himself (unless it is prescribed by a doctor as a remedial measure) that his head is hot, since this may bring about an undesirable flow of blood to the head; nor must he suggest to himself a slowing of the heart's action.

The investigations which I carried out jointly with O. P. Baranovskaya and A. S. Romen showed that, in the state of calm and muscular relaxation induced by autogenous training, the electroencephalogram shows a diminution of electrical activity and the periodic appearance of slow waves (two or three per second) of fairly large amplitude. This is regarded as characteristic of shallow sleep. Evidently the state of calm and muscular relaxation in autogenous training is a state of autohypnosis, i.e., incomplete, partial sleep with a 'point of alertness' into which the subject plunges himself. In this state it is possible to provoke by means of auto-suggestion everything that can be provoked by suggestion during deep hypnotic sleep, for example catalepsy and even the cataleptic bridge (A. S. Romen), hallucinations and hypermnesia. On evoking the idea 'my hand is hot', in most subjects there is a rise in skin temperature of two or three degrees (A. M. Svyadoshch and A. S. Romen).

After the subject has mastered auto-suggestion thanks to autogenous training, he is instructed to proceed to develop in himself the faculty of taking in speech during natural sleep. To this end, he is advised, during the session of autogenous training, to suggest to himself before sleep: 'Tonight I shall sleep without waking. Through my sleep I shall hear and remember a story (or: I shall hear a count up to twelve, after which I shall hear and remember a story). I shall sleep and hear, sleep and hear without waking up. Tomorrow I shall remember everything.' If single acts of auto-suggestion prove insufficient, they may be repeated three times a day for three weeks.

Note: In 1936, jointly with S. G. Faynberg (14), (15, p. 256) we demonstrated the possibility of hypnotism by means of sound recordings. On the tape was recorded the text of a session of hypnosis. On playing it back, the subjects fell into a hypnotic sleep, carried out what was suggested to them and awoke in the same way as when a hypnotic session is carried out by a doctor. In connection with this I performed experiments in which a text was played over, which first slightly stimulated the sleeper and then plunged him into hypnotic sleep. During this sleep, stories were reproduced by the recording, after which, by means of the same recording, the hypnotic sleep was changed to natural nocturnal sleep. Success was achieved in securing mastery of speech in the case of fourteen out of twenty subjects. Since assimilation of speech took place not during natural sleep but during hypnotic sleep, we shall not dwell upon these experiments, although they do point to a further way of achieving the mastery of speech during the period of nocturnal sleep.

RESULTS OF EXPERIMENTS

The control experiments in which texts were read to the subjects during sleep *before* the faculty of assimilating speech had been developed in them showed that the verbal stimulus we used did *not* cause awakening, and that they lacked the spontaneous faculty of taking in and mastering speech. Out of seventeen subjects, twelve showed no noticeable reaction to the reading of texts as far as their breathing was concerned; in five of the subjects, a brief reaction which did not interrupt the general rhythm of breathing was noticed.

The control experiments in which the subjects were awoken at night, had a text read to them and then went to sleep again showed that, out of twenty-two subjects, five did not remember the next morning that they had woken up at night, answered questions, heard a story and tried to remember it. They declared that they had slept all night without waking up, and were quite unable to remember the text that had been read. Four remembered that they had been roused and had woken up during the night, but had no recollection whatever of the text read to them. Eight remembered that they had been roused and had woken up during the night. Out of these eight, three had an imperfect recollection of the content of the text read to them (on an average they reproduced 32·8 of the content of the text, with a good deal of pseudo-reminiscence and confabulation amounting to as much as 50% of the text reproduced), and five reproduced the text well (on the average, 82·4% of the text, and that without significant distortions.) All eight of the subjects remembered that they had woken up during the night and heard a story.

> Note: The rousing of some of the subjects at night was gradual in character; during the reading of the text the subjects were in a state of pronounced drowsiness. In the case of others, the rousing was sudden and complete. Total or partial amnesia for what had taken place was observed, as a rule, with gradual rousing, and a high degree of reproduction with sudden rousing.

It is important to mention that, in the assimilation of texts during a period of brief awakening from sleep, what the subjects remembered best of all the next morning was the fact of having been awakened; then, their experiences during the period; the worst remembered was what had been said to them, and in particular the text of the story read to them. On the other hand, what was most quickly subject to amnesia was the assimilated experimental speech, then the thoughts and feelings of the person awakened and, last of all, the fact of having been awakened. In not a single case did it happen that a subject who had been woken up and had heard a story remembered the content of the story while failing to remember that he had been woken up and that the story had been read to him. On the actograms and pneumograms, during the assimilation of speech in the period of brief rousing from sleep, there was recorded a sharp interruption of the sleep rhythm of breathing and the appearance of motor activity.

As was shown by the experiments carried out, in the case of twenty out of twenty-five of the subjects chosen by us it was possible to develop the faculty of assimilating speech during natural sleep.

In all cases the process of assimilation of texts itself was not realised by the subjects; that is to say that they slept without being aware that they were meanwhile hearing and remembering speech. *The content of the speech assimilated during sleep was in some cases experienced as thoughts which had somehow or other come into their heads, arising spontaneously, and in other cases as events resulting from a logical train of action proceeding in a dream.* In isolated cases the content of the text was converted to a greater or lesser extent into the visual images of dreams. However, in the majority of cases the perception lacked any visual character.

For psychological analysis, particular interest is presented by observations in which the faculty of assimilating speech was developed during deep hypnotic sleep, and in which the subjects when in the waking state did not remember anything about the prospective experiment. In this respect the following experiment is typical:

In the Laboratory for the Higher Nervous System of the Leningrad Scientific Research Institute for safeguarding the health of children and adolescents, directed by Professor N. I. Krasnogorskiy, the faculty of assimilating speech during natural sleep was developed in three subjects, B. aged seventeen, Zh. aged seventeen and M. aged ten, during the daytime in a state of deep hypnotic sleep, by the methods already described.

In the evening the subjects went to bed as usual and fell asleep naturally. At 2.30 a.m., in the presence of S. L. Levin, there was read to all three subjects, who were sleeping in the same room, a story about the revolutionary Nechayev (his killing an *agent provocateur,* his flight to Switzerland, his handing over to the Tsarist authorities, his imprisonment in the fortress of Petropavlovsk, his attempted escape, etc.; thirty-two paragraphs in all). All three subjects went on sleeping, showing no external reaction to the reading of the story. Thirty minutes after the end of the reading of this story, the following sentence was uttered: 'Today you are riding in a car with Dr. Levin to Detskoye Selo and going very fast!'

Next morning, immediately on awakening, one of the subjects cried: 'Girls, what a dream I've had! I was going for a drive in a car with Dr. Levin.' 'No,' replied the second, 'I'm the one who was going for a drive!' 'It isn't true,' said the third, 'that's *my* dream.' They were then taken to separate rooms, after which they were questioned in turn in the presence of S. L. Levin.

We reproduce the shorthand report of the questioning.

B: What a thing happened today! I had such a quarrel with Shurka (subject M.)! I said she was cribbing, and she said *I* was.

I said, 'Girls, I dreamt that I was riding very fast in a car with Dr. Levin, fast enough to take your breath away. We were going to Detskoye Selo.' I slept on my side all night. That dream—it was so silly, you ought not to take it down!

We were going along and Dr. Levin said: 'I'm going to tell you a story.' And he began telling me about Nechayev the revolutionary.

B. went on to reproduce 70·5% of the text that had been read to her, and added: 'That's what Dr. Levin told me while we were going to Detskoye Selo. But when I woke up at seven o'clock this morning I woke Shurka and said, 'Fancy where I've been! I was riding in a car with Dr. Levin.' But she said, 'Silly, that's what I was doing; I was riding, not you. You cribbed it from me!' She said, 'I will tell Dr. Levin first.' 'No, I will,' I said. Then they separated us.'

The subject declared that the story about Nechayev had been told to her by Dr. Levin in the course of a drive with him to Detskoye Selo. In point of fact, the story about Nechayev was read thirty minutes before the story of the trip with Dr. Levin to Detskoye Selo.

We now reproduce the shorthand report of the questioning of subject Zh. on the 9th May 1936, at 10.30 a.m.:

S.: How did you sleep?

Zh.: Very well indeed. I was sound asleep.

S.: Did you dream? Tell me about it.

Zh.: I had not one dream but a good many; I've forgotten them all now; first one dream and then another. I remember about some revolutionary. He escaped abroad, and after that the government caught him and put him into the Petropavlovsk fortress. They put a gendarme in his cell so that he shouldn't escape, and did not let anyone speak to him. But he said to them, 'Do you know why I'm here, chaps? It's because of you!' He won them over. The gendarmes started to tell him that it wasn't their fault, they were obliged to guard him. They came over to Nechayev's side. Nechayev resolved to escape. He wrote a letter to the revolutionaries. The letter was held back. They knew it came from the fortress, but did not know who had written it. One of his neighbours betrayed him. They put him in chains, shackled him and didn't give him much to eat or drink. And so he died. That was the revolutionary Nechayev.

S.: Had you ever heard of Nechayev before?

Zh.: No, I had never heard of him. I've heard of Avdeyev, but it was Nechayev I dreamt about.

S.: Did you have any other dreams?

Zh.: They were all mixed up; everything was mixed up. I dreamt I was riding in a car with Dr. Levin to Detskoye Selo, going very fast. Then I dreamt I was playing volley-ball.

S.: Did anyone come to you during the night?

Zh.: No, nobody. Only in the morning Olga Vasiliyevna came to give me the thermometer and asked, 'How did you sleep?' I started to tell about Dr. Levin, and Shurka said, 'Don't tell lies, that's what *I* dreamt!' and they separated us.

S.: Where did the dream about Nechayev come from?

Zh.: I was reading 'Hadji-Murat' with Shurka; there's a soldier Avdeyev in that, only I dreamt about Nechayev.

S.: How did you sleep?

Zh.: Very well.

On being questioned during deep hypnotic sleep, all three subjects remembered that during the previous session it had been suggested to them that they would sleep, hear a count up to twelve and then a story. Nevertheless all three had forgotten that the story had been read during their sleep at night, and they did not remember the counting up to twelve. The subject B. continued to declare that she had heard the story about Nechayev from the doctor, in a dream. Subjects Zh. and M. did not know whether they had heard the story about Nechayev or seen it in the form of visual images.

In another experiment subject B. dreamt that she and K.E. (the nurse who had read a story at night) were sitting on a bench and that K.E. told her a story about a dog Nellie. In the dream B. asked K.E. why she was telling her a children's story of that sort, to which K.E. replied that she did not know any novels. Next morning B. reproduced the text of the story word for word.

A woman student to whom a lesson on the theory of the torsional pendulum was read during sleep knew it the next morning and even remembered some formulas, but did not know how she had assimilated it. 'I slept last night and was not thinking about anything. In the morning I guessed that you had probably read out this theory, because I had never heard of it before.'

Another subject, the schoolteacher O., on being asked whether she had dreamt at night, during the assimilation of a story, that she was lying in bed listening to the story, replied: 'No, I slept and did not dream anything or think about anything. In the morning I woke up and felt that I knew the story. So I must have heard it. When I woke up this morning I decided that it must have been you who read it. Why I decided that it must have been you I don't know; it was probably from your voice. I heard the story, but did not see it.'

In cases where the faculty of mastering speech during natural sleep had been developed by suggestion and auto-suggestion in the waking state, or by suggestion during a light hypnotic sleep, the subjects were previously aware that texts would be read during their sleep at night and so easily guessed the source of the information on awakening. *However, the fact that they had assimilated speech during sleep was not itself realised by them.*

Further observations showed that sometimes a story read in a low whisper might be taken in by the speaker as having been pronounced very loudly. The underlying basis for this is evidently the development of a paradoxical phase in the cortex of the sleeper's brain.

Certain texts, for example the 'Journey to Detskoye Selo in a car', readily underwent visualisation, while texts of an abstract nature (philosophical, technical or of complex literary character) did not undergo it.

Immediately after the conclusion of the assimilation of speech during sleep it was suggested to the three subjects that they should raise a hand. They did not do so. Muscular tone was found to be diminished. In the course of hypnotic sleep, all three subjects always carried out similar suggestions and catalepsy was always observed in all three.

The faculty of assimilating speech during sleep, once developed, may be retained for a considerable time. Thus, in one of the subjects it was observed sixty days after development. Taking luminal before sleep removed the faculty of assimilating speech during sleep, but afterwards it re-established itself.

For convenience in analysing the data obtained, we applied the conventional term 'high' to reproduction in which not less than 66% of the text was repeated (as in the experiment with Zh. described above), and 'low' to less than 66%. In a case of low reproduction, for example of the story of the revolutionary Nechayev, one subject remembered only that she had dreamt of some revolutionary; another entirely failed to master the story that was read, and only isolated fragments of it found expression in the visual images of dreaming (she dreamt of a dense forest and gold coins falling from above).

Out of twenty subjects who had mastered speech during natural sleep, high reproduction (on an average, 89·5% of the text) was observed in sixteen, and low reproduction (on an average 18·6% of the text) in four. High reproduction was observed in subjects of various ages (including children aged ten to thirteen). *It was observed in the recall of both simple texts and complicated texts of a literary character, as well as of texts with a philosophical or technical content, and independently of whether they were read by persons known or unknown to the subject.*

The quality of the learning of texts did not depend upon which method had been used to develop the faculty of assimilating speech during sleep.

High reproduction was observed not only when the first questioning took place immediately after the subjects awoke, but also twelve to forty-eight hours after their awakening from sleep.

Repeated reproduction was investigated in subjects after sixty hours and, in the case of two subjects, after one month from the time of assimilation of the speech. *The extent and accuracy of the reproduction of texts assimilated during sleep were found to be substantially the same as the extent and accuracy of reproduction of texts of similar difficulty assimilated by the same subjects in the daytime, in the waking state, and recalled after the same intervals of time.*

The actogram and pneumogram during the assimilation of speech in natural sleep differed sharply from those for subjects assimilating speech during a period of brief awakening from natural sleep. In nine out of thirteen subjects, during the reading of the text (usually at the beginning of the stimulus), only a brief, hardly perceptible breathing reaction was observed (slightly deeper breathing movements), after which the same even rhythm of breathing as had been observed in them before the reading of the texts was re-established.

In four subjects to whom an energetic suggestion had been made during hypnotic sleep that they should sleep peacefully, it was impossible to discern any distinct reaction, on the actogram and pneumogram, to the speech stimulus while they were assimilating speech during their sleep at night.

We made no special investigation into fatigue accompanying the assimilation of speech during natural sleep. To five subjects we read texts of a literary character for one hour on six consecutive nights. Each of the subjects went to bed and got up at his usual time. *No effects upon fatiguability or any signs of insufficient sleep were noticed in them.*

Our collaborator A. S. Romen tried to develop the faculty of assimilating speech during natural sleep in five healthy subjects (four male students and one female student) by means of two to four months of autogenous training according to the method described above. He succeded in obtaining positive results in three subjects (two male students and one female student); in two cases after a single session of auto-suggestion, and in one case after several sessions. In the course of the first experiments, one of the subjects, after auto-suggestion that he should sleep without waking and hear everything, nevertheless woke up as soon as the reading of the text to him was begun. After four experiments it was possible to suppress this reaction and obtain assimilation of speech during sleep. In this case the assimilated speech was transformed into the visual images of dreams.

It is of interest to mention that all three subjects who were able to develop in themselves the faculty of assimilating speech during sleep had learned, as a result of autogenous training, to change the temperature of their hands by two or three degrees, and also to bring about in themselves the condition of the cataleptic bridge, whereas this was not achieved by the two subjects who were unable to develop in themselves the faculty of assimilating speech during sleep.

EVALUATION OF THE RESULTS

The data obtained show that during natural nocturnal sleep it is possible to assimilate speech: lessons, stories, chapters from books with a literary, philosophical, technical, etc., content, and words of a foreign language, pronounced by known or unknown persons or communicated by sound recordings. *The assimilated speech in these cases is mastered without undergoing distortion, and can be reproduced upon awakening.*

In contrast to dreams, which are soon forgotten, the speech is preserved in the memory at least as well as speech assimilated in the waking state. It follows that there is a possibility, in principle, of acquiring knowledge during natural sleep.

The psychological peculiarity of the assimilation of speech during sleep is that *the fact of assimilation itself is not realised,* i.e., at the time of assimilating the speech the sleeper does not realise that he is lying in bed and listening to it. In the majority of our subjects the speech mastered during sleep was either experienced, on awakening, as thoughts arising spontaneously, 'coming into the head somehow or other', or else as being the outcome of a logical train of events unfolding in a dream. A minority of subjects noticed that they had heard speech while asleep, although at the time they did not realise that they were sleeping and hearing speech.

In contrast to this, in the control experiments in the course of which the subjects were awakened at night, had similar texts read to them and then resumed their sleep, the nature of the experience was quite different: the next day the subjects either did not remember at all that they had been roused, had awoken, had answered questions, heard texts and promised to remember them—they asserted that they had slept all night without waking up—or else they remembered the content of the story read to them, but *ipso facto* necessarily remembered that they had woken up and heard speech.

It never happened that subject remembered the content of a text read to him while failing to remember that he had woken up at night and heard speech. These cardinal psychological differences between assimilation during natural sleep and assimilation during a brief period of awakening undoubtedly point to the fact that the assimilation of speech by our subjects really did occur during sleep. They allow us to exclude the possibility that our subjects assimilated the speech during a period of brief awakening from sleep and next morning, under the influence of suggestion, mistakenly asserted that they had assimilated the speech while they were asleep.

It must be added that the data of actography and pneumography also confirmed that the speech *was assimilated during sleep* and not during a period of awakening from it. This is further confirmed by the fact that the texts assimilated during sleep were retained in the memory of the subjects distinctly better than similar texts assimilated by the same persons during brief awakening from sleep.

In most cases the experiencing of assimilated speech lacked any visual character. Only in a few cases did some easily visualised portion of the speech directly give rise to corresponding visual images in dreams.

In subjects who experienced the material assimilated during sleep as the outcome of some logical course of events developed in a dream, factual relations of cause and effect were sometimes violated. Thus, in point of fact, one of the subjects first heard the story about Nechayev and only thirty minutes later the story about a journey with Levin to Detskoye Selo; but she dreamt that it was on the way to Detskoye Selo that Levin told her about Nechayev.

It is evident that in such cases there is no question of pseudo-reminiscence, arising in the waking state, but that the subjects really experience in dreams what they afterwards recount. It is possible that speech assimilated during sleep gives rise to dreams a little while after being assimilated (possibly in connection with a diminution in the intensity of the trace excitation provoked by it, with development of a phase state). This dreaming remains in the memory after awakening; the process of assimilation of speech that actually took place is not realised. As a result, the dream content is experienced as the sole source of the information.

The experiences connected with the assimilation of speech during sleep may sometimes be reflected in subsequent dreams. Thus, a boy in whom the faculty of assimilating speech during sleep had been developed without the aid of hypnosis (by suggestion in the waking state and by auto-suggestion), next morning remembered word for word a story about the dog Nellie which had been read during his sleep.

'In the morning,' he said, 'I thought that I had dreamt it. Then I thought: How can I have dreamt it, since I didn't see anything? I remembered that they were going to tell me a story and I guessed that they had told it to me at night. And then, probably towards morning,' he went on, 'I dreamt that we were in class. The teacher told us a story about the dog Nellie. The teacher asked which of the children remembered this story. Then she began asking us all in turn. They all said they didn't remember it. They called me out. I stood and said nothing. I couldn't remember the story either. But when I woke up in the morning I remembered it.'

Evidently the desire to remember the assimilated speech and anxiety lest it should be forgotten brought about towards morning a dream that the teacher had read the story to the class and that all the children in the class, including himself, had forgotten it.

From the physiological point of view the natural sleep during which the assimilation of speech is possible is a partial sleep—a sleep with a 'point of alertness'. It is through the latter that the assimilation of speech takes place.

Underlying the development of the 'point of alertness' is the arising of a focus of inert excitation. This focus may be imagined as a complex system embracing both the cortical counterparts of the auditory analysor and the reticular substance, in particular the 'centres' of the orientation reflex. The 'feedback' set up between them ensures the selective reception of signals and the uninhibiting, by means of impulses proceeding from the reticular substance, of the portions of the brain which make possible the mastery of speech.

Hypnotic sleep, too, is sleep with a 'point of alertness'. Can we suppose that our subjects assimilated speech while in a state of hypnotic sleep? The answer to this must be negative, since hypnotic sleep is an artificially induced, suggested sleep. The onset of sleep in our subjects, on the contrary, was not artificially induced.

There were also clinical differences between hypnotic sleep and natural sleep with a 'point of alertness'. Thus, our subjects, during deep hypnotic sleep (somnambulism) were able to remember everything that had happened to them while in a similar condition during previous sessions.

In other words, amnesia for events during hypnotic sleep could be made to yield during subsequent sessions of hypnosis. However, amnesia for the fact of having assimilated speech during natural sleep could *not* be removed in hypnosis.

During natural sleep with the faculty of assimilating speech we were unsuccessful in suggesting to our subjects the execution of motor actions; nor was catalepsy observed in them, whereas it was regularly observed during hypnotic sleep. Obviously, the degree of propagation and the depth of inhibition (particularly of the motor analysor) were different during natural sleep with the faculty of remembering speech, and during hypnotic sleep.

Sleep with a 'point of alertness' may be not only hypnotic, but natural. During natural sleep the sleeper is capable of manifesting heightened selective sensitivity to a given stimulus or group of stimuli while other and sometimes more powerful stimuli may not be taken in. This is characteristic not only of man but of many animals. The faculty of selective reception evidently developed in the process of evolution, in the course of the struggle for existence, since it allows better adaption to changing conditions of the external environment. L. A. Orbeli (9) has described natural sleep with a 'point of alertness' in the octopus; Birman was able to observe such sleep in the dog.

Sleep with a 'point of alertness' is also met with in humans. Thus, for example, a tired mother, who has fallen fast asleep at the bedside of her sick child, may fail to awaken as a result of loud surrounding noise but will wake up at the least rustle from the child. A tired captain is not awakened by the rhythmic sound of the ship's engines; but the moment there is a pause in the sound, he wakes up.

Many people, sleeping soundly and not waking up as a result of some given stimulus, may wake up as a result of a far weaker stimulus, or at a given time, if they induce the appropriate mental attitude in themselves before going to sleep.

A. Forel (18) showed that the 'point of alertness', affording the possibility of awakening under the influence of a strictly specific stimulus, may be developed by means of post-hypnotic suggestion. He successfully suggested to nurses on duty by the bedside of a patient that they should sleep all night but should immediately wake up if the patient got out of bed. This in fact they did. The nurses had begun to sleep the same kind of sleep as the mother at the bedside of her sick child.

Our data showed that it is possible for such *a 'point of alertness' to arise during natural sleep,* during which the sleeper masters information *without* the onset of awakening. In most cases, what was biologically expedient was a 'point of alertness' leading to awakening on the reception of a stimulus (for example, the approach of a foe to an animal) rather than to the learning of a signal while sleep continued. This is probably why, in natural conditions, the faculty of assimilating speech during natural sleep is rarely encountered. It may arise when the sleeper falls asleep during the reception of speech and contact is maintained, or when a person falls asleep in the tense expectation of hearing speech. In the latter case the 'strained attention', i.e. emotion, proceeding from the subcortex, favours the development of a focus of inert excitation, which underlies the arising of the 'point of alertness'.

The state of strained attention is frequently met with in the mentally deranged, and as a result of it there may sometimes appear in them the faculty of assimilating speech (conversation of staff or patients) during sleep. In support of this we may cite our own observation that a patient, during the depressive phase of a manic-depressive psychosis, assimilated speech uttered during his sleep (some sentences about the arrival of a certain woman from Vinnitsa.) The next morning he declared that his wife and children had arrived from Vinnitsa (although they had never been there), and accounted for it in a setting of ideas of guilt. How he had learned of their arrival he was unable to explain.

Speech assimilated during sleep, in contrast to that assimilated in the waking state, is not subjected during assimilation to critical processing, and is experienced on awakening as a thought of which the source remained outside consciousness; to some extent, therefore, it is as if it belonged to an alien personality. In the mentally well, this does not lead to the occurrence of psychopathological experiences; in the mentally ill, it may obviously have an effect upon the content of delirious or semi-delirious ideas, and exert a greater inducive effect than speech assimilated in the waking state.

On the basis of our experiments it is not possible to judge how frequently the faculty of assimilating speech during sleep can be experimentally developed in persons. V. I. Lyashchenko, in 1958, developed at our suggestion the faculty of assimilating speech during natural sleep in ten children aged from seven to thirteen who were receiving treatment at the pediatric clinic of the Karaganda Medical Institute (director L. G. Leyvikov, reader) and obtained positive results in two children (girls of eleven and thirteen). Here, one of the stories assimilated during sleep was partially transformed into the visual images of dreaming.

The faculty of mastering speech during natural sleep may be developed artificially by appropriate suggestion to a person in the waking state or during hypnotic sleep; by auto-suggestion, accompanied by the *summoning up by efforts of will of an appropriate attitude towards the assimilation of speech;* by autogenous training; and also by applying to the patient, during sleep, weak stimuli which do not lead to awakening. It is easiest to develop it by using a combination of the above methods. It may be induced in persons of both sexes and of different ages and cultural levels.

The possibility of experimentally developing a 'point of alertness' allowing the assimilation of speech during natural sleep may be affected by a number of factors; in the first place, by the attitude of of the subject towards the experiment that is being carried out, which is in turn affected by his attitude towards the experimenter.

The occurrence of interest in the experiment carried out, or a positively coloured emotional attitude of the subject towards the experimenter, may assist the appearance of a 'point of alertness' during natural sleep. On the other hand, the occurrence of overt or covert resistance towards the development of the faculty of assimilating speech inhibits its formation, the mechanism being negative induction on the part of representations against awakening. Such resistance may also appear in the course of the development of a 'point of alertness' during hypnotic sleep.

The higher the suggestibility of the subject, the easier it is to induce in him the verbal operation of the concentrated focus of excitation in the brain which underlines the 'point of alertness'. During hypnotic sleep suggestibility is heightened, and it is therefore easier to form a 'point of alertness' by suggestion in hypnotic sleep than in the waking state. However, even during deep hypnotic sleep, with the occurrence of somnambulism, success is not always achieved in developing the faculty of assimilating speech during natural sleep. Possibly in such cases some part is played by a covert negative attitude towards the experimenter. In deep hypnotic sleep of the lethargic type there is a tendency towards irradiation of the inhibitory process, as a result of which it is very difficult to develop a stable concentrated focus of excitation allowing the assimilation of speech during natural sleep.

It may be suggested to the subject, during deep hypnotic sleep, that he will have a given dream during his natural sleep at night. In persons with whom this suggestion is successful, the faculty of assimilating speech during natural sleep is usually most easily induced by post-hypnotic suggestion.

In persons who possess the ability to wake up at will at a given time, or in response to a strictly defined stimulus, the faculty of assimilating speech during sleep can be developed more easily than in persons who have no such characteristic.

The faculty of assimilating speech during natural sleep, as further experiments showed, can be developed comparatively easily in children and young persons; this is possibly because their suggestibility is usually higher than that of older people. The impression has been formed that it is easiest of all to develop the faculty of assimilating speech in girls, particularly if the experimenter calls forth towards himself an emotionally coloured positive response.

According to contemporary accounts (M. Breizye (3), E. N. Sokolov (16), P. K. Anokhin (1), Adrian (20)), in the process of assimilation a stimulus passes from the peripheral analysor to the corresponding zone by two paths: a specific and a non-specific path. By the first path, information proper to the given analysor is transmitted directly to the corresponding zone of the cortex.

From this path, collateral paths branch off in a reticular formation. From this, impulses pass to the cortex by the non-specific path (Moruzzi and Magoun (27), Jasper (24), F. B. Bassin (2) and others). It is by this path that the transmission tonifying (activating) influences proceeds over the entire layer of the cortex. The building up of excitation along the specific path leads to the development in the cortex of an action potential (primary response of the cortex), while along the non-specific path it leads to a change in the background rhythm as a consequence of the appearance of rapid, high-amplitude oscillations.

During sleep, even deep sleep, and narcosis the conductivity of the specific path remains high and the primary response of the cortex is very distinctly recorded, whereas the electrical response called forth by the propagation of excitation along the non-specific path cannot be observed.

According to Adrian, the process of assimilation is possible only when there is interaction between the specific and non-specific systems of excitation.

During deep hypnotic sleep, if no assimilation of external stimuli is taking place, the occurrence of slow waves is observed, but at the time of the assimilation of speech these waves change to rapid high-amplitude oscillations.

The electrical activity of the brain accompanying the assimilation of speech during natural sleep has not yet been investigated. It may be surmised that in the assimilation of speech during natural nocturnal sleep the slow waves change into frequent high-voltage oscillations, either over the whole cortex (effect of the trunk reticular system) or, more selectively, in the front or rear regions of the cortex (effect of the reticular system of the thalamus). This, however, would by no means imply that assimilation takes place not during sleep but in a waking state; it would merely imply that the occurrence of high-frequency waves is a characteristic of assimilation in sleep, just as it is a characteristic, according to Adrian, of assimilation in the waking state.

The question of fatigue during the assimilation of speech in natural sleep presents great interest. Is fatiguability the same as in mastering speech in the waking state, or is it less? How far is rest provided by sleep during which speech is being mastered?

Our experiments with five subjects, who noticed no heightened fatigue in themselves after assimilating speech for an hour during six nights in succession, give us no right to answer this question.

It is highly probable that fatiguability in the mastering of speech during natural sleep will prove to be *less* than for assimilation in the waking state.

The fact is that although the brain functions as a single whole, not all its regions are in the same functional condition at any given moment. In both waking and sleeping some portions of the brain, may be in a state of inhibition while others are in a state of excitation. The cortex of the brain in the waking state presents a mosaic with moving points of excitation and inhibition; in other words it is constantly in a state of partial sleep. 'The section of optimal excitability,' 'the creative department of the great hemispheres,' in the words of I. P. Pavlov, is constantly changing. In this way the brain is at the same time awake and resting.

The cerebral cortex, like the heart (writes N. I. Krasnogorskiy (6)), continuously works and continuously rests. However, as we know, man cannot keep awake uninterruptedly. The explanation of this may be that during wakefulness some single definite system functions continuously; a system, that is, which ensures the state of wakefulness of the consciousness enabling man to give active direction to his attention. Fatigue arising in such a system would necessarily lead also to the onset of natural sleep, although the operational fitness of many cortical cells, now at work and now at rest for long periods during wakefulness, might nevertheless be potentially preserved. It is perhaps because of the working of these cells that the assimilation of speech during sleep is possible, even though the system ensuring the wakefulness of the state of consciousness is meanwhile inhibited and resting. For a final judgment on this question further experimental investigation is necessary.

REFERENCES

1. P. K. Anokhin, *Internal Inhibition as a Problem of Physiology*. Medgiz, 1958.
2. F. V. Bassin, *Concerning some Debatable in the Contemporary Theory of the Localization of Functions. The S.S. Korsakov Journal of Neuropathology and Psychiatry*, **7**, 1956.

3. M. Breizye, *The Electrical Activity of the Nervous System*. Medgiz (*State Medical Publications*), 1955.
4. B. N. Birman, *Experimental Sleep,* Giz, Leningrad, 1925.
5. N. V. Viazemskii, *Application of Medical Suggestion. Transactions of the Saratov Naturalists' Society,* 4, 2, 1903–1904.
6. N. I. Krasnogorskiy, *Teaching Developments in respect of the Physiological Activity of the Brain in Children.* Biomedgiz (*State Publication in Biological Medicine*), 1935.
7. S. L. Levin, *The Functional Exclusion of Analyzers and Conditioned Reflexes. Archives of the Biological Sciences,* **1**, 1958.
8. F. P. Maiorov, *The Physiological Theory of Dreams. Academy of Sciences Publications,* USSR, 1951.
9. L. A. Orbeli, *Lectures on the Physiology of the Nervous System.* **3**, 1938.
10. I. P. Pavlov, *Collected Works,* **3**, Books I, II, **4**, Moscow-Leningrad, *Academy of Sciences Publications,* USSR, 1951.
11. K. I. Platonov, *The Word as Physiological and Therapeutic Factor.* Moscow, Medgiz, 1957.
12. A. M. Svyadoshch, *Speech Perception during Natural Sleep. Thesis for Master's Degree,* Leningrad, 1940.
13. A. M. Sviadoshch, *Some Experimental Findings in the Psychology of the Creative Process. Transactions of the V.M. Bekhterev State Institute for Brain Research,* **18**, Leningrad, 1947.
14. A. M. Svyadoshch, *Neuroses and their Treatment.* Moscow, Medgiz, 1959.
15. A. M. Svyadoshch and S. G. Feinberg, *Hypnosis by Sound Recording. Leningradskaia Pravda* **223** (6508) of 27/X 1937, *Kurortnaia Gazeta* (Health-Resort Gazette) **27** (1410) of 2/II 1941; in book: N. I. Krasnogorskiy. *Papers on the Study of the Higher Nervous Activity of Man and Animals,* **1**, Medgiz., 1954.
16. E. N. Sokolov, *Perception and the Conditioned Reflex. Moscow State University Publication*, 1958.
17. I. E. Stepanov, *The Psychology of Dreams.* Berlin, 1922.
18. A. Forel, *Hypnotism or Suggestion and Psychotherapy.* Leningrad, 1928.
19. S. Freud, *The Interpretation of Dreams.* Moscow, 1913.
20. E. D. Adrian, *The Physiological Basis of Perception,* Journal *Brain Mechanisms and Consciousness.* Ed. J. Delafresnaye. Oxford, 1954, pp. 237–243 (group discuss. 234–248).
21. C. H. Burdon, *Etude sur la Staso-lasophobie* (*Research on Staso-lasophobia*) Lille, 1904.
22. Ch. R. Elliott, *Science Digest,* May 1948. (Note on the work of Charles R. Elliott, published without heading or indication of author).
23. W. H. Emmons and C, W. Simon, Non-recollection of Material presented during Sleep. *American Journal of Psychology,* 1956, **69**, p. 76.
24. H. Jasper, *Symposium; Thalmo-cortical Relationships; Diffuse Projection Systems; Integrative Action of Thalamic Reticular System. Electroencephalography and Clinical Neurophysiology,* 1949, **1**, pp. 455–473.
25. E. B. Leroy, *Les Visions de Demi-sommeil* (The Visions of Half Sleep). Paris, 1927.
26. L. Maury *et al., Le Sommeil et les Reves.* Paris 1878.

27. G. Moruzzi and H. W. Magoun, *Brain-stem Reticular Formation and Activation of EEG. Electroencephalography and Clinical Neurophysiology,* 1949, **1**, pp. 455–473.
28. D. Müller-Hegemann, *Psychotherapie,* **2**, Berlin, 1959.
29. C. W. Simon and W. H. Emmons, *EEG Consciousness and Sleep, Science,* 1956, **24**, 3231, pp. 1066–1069.
30. J. H. Schultz, *Das autogene training,* **10**, Stuttgart, 1960.

Editor's note: The re-educative application of hypnopaedic technique is favoured by several psychiatrists in the Western countries and in the USSR as well. Electrically induced sleep, which closely resembles natural sleep, is an aid to psychotherapy widely used in Russia, but no particular data on this method have appeared so far.

Psychotherapy, methodically applied during increased suggestibility (hypnosis), does not exclude the use of 'sleep-learning' techniques in a therapeutic sense. The two following Chapters provide some information on hypnopaedia used in the rehabilitation of two patients. They had to re-learn certain faculties which were lost due to pathological conditions.

Mar

8

SLEEP LEARNING AS AN AID IN TEACHING READING TO A BRAIN-INJURED BOY

Cecelia Pollack

(This experiment was performed at the Northside Centre for Child Development, New York City, in 1961.)

THE PROBLEM

In the course of teaching a brain-injured boy with serious reading problems how to read, there seemed to be one very basic problem. A normal amount of reinforcement in training to recognise sounds and synthesizing these sounds into words was totally inadequate. If there were years in which to provide this reinforcement, a phonic word attack could be taught, but Victor was already seventeen years of age and about to learn a trade. The method of sight recognition had been tried and found almost useless because of the boy's poor visual and auditory memory.

It was believed that sleep learning, in which the auditory blending of sounds into words could be repeated to the subject hundreds of times a night, might provide the necessary reinforcement.

SUMMARY OF PAST RESEARCH

Research on the subject brought to light a number of studies in sleep learning dating back to 1916 and before. A review of ten such cases was made, in which the critics analysed the experimental design, statistics, methodology and criteria of sleep.

Their conclusion, after exhaustive analysis of the studies, was that the conditions under which the results were found tended to support the contention that some learning takes place in a special kind of waking state, after which subjects apparently do not remember later if they had been awake. (Simon and Emmons, 1955.)

The authors do not construe this learning which takes place as sleep learning but they do admit that learning does take place. A very cursory summation of the ten studies and their results follow:

1. A study of sixteen navy men learning the Morse Code. The subjects finished the course three weeks earlier than had been expected. The investigator, Thurstone (1953), indicated 'some gain'.

2. An attempt by LeShan (1942) to break the finger-nail biting habit in twenty boy campers, aged eight to fourteen. Forty per cent of the experimental group stopped biting their nails, none of the control group. It was concluded that 'there is a possible therapeutic use of suggestion during sleep'.

3. A study also by LeShan (1953) with a single subject who had to learn a list of nonsense syllables each morning for twelve days. On the fifth and eighth nights, the list was repeated fifty times while the subject slept. It was found that 50 per cent fewer trials were required to learn the two sleep-learned lists than to learn the ten non-sleep-trained lists.

4. A study by Elliott (1947) involved two groups of male college students of equal learning ability who were given lists of three-lettered words to remember. The results indicated that the sleep-trained group received a greater percentage of savings than the control group. The author concluded that 'there is some retention of auditory material during sleep'.

5. An attempt was made by Hedges (1950) to improve the speech of three mentally retarded and aphasic children. Short sentences, paragraphs and simple consonant sounds were played to the children. Positive results were obtained in only one subject.

6. Fox and Robbins (1952) designed a study with thirty college men whose task it was to learn twenty-five pairs of English-Chinese vocabulary. The investigators concluded that 'learning could occur during sleep'.

7. Leuba and Bateman (1952) tested a lightly sleeping subject, teaching him the words of three songs. Given only the song title the next day, the subject was able to write the lyrics of two out of the three songs with no errors, and the third with minor errors. During and following the use of sedatives later on, no learning occurred.

8. Hoyt (1953) tried ten pairs of English-Chinese vocabulary words with twenty subjects, and found insignificant differences.

His findings indicated that 'learning during sleep was not detected'.

9. Stampfl (1953) tested six college men with ten nonsense syllables and found his 'hypothesis uncertain and improbable'.

10. Coyne (1953), in studying the reactions of six college students in learning some material, concluded that 'results are favourable for the sleep learners'.

THEORETICAL BASIS FOR SLEEP-LEARNING

Pavlovian theory on sleep should logically provide the basis for positive effects of sleep-learning. Pavlovians believe that the cells of the cerebral hemispheres are exceedingly sensitive and are therefore subject to damage resulting from excessive strain. Protection is afforded them by the inhibitory process, a physiological process which cuts off the acceptance of stimuli into the cortex. Sleep is a form of protective inhibition. To quote Pavlov directly:

'Sleep itself is nothing but internal inhibition which is widely irradiated, extending over the whole mass of the hemispheres and involving the lower centres of the brain as well.'

He indicates that sleep inhibition may be partial in depth and extensiveness and develop only in restricted areas of the cortex. One part of the cortex may be in a waking state and the other in a state of sleep inhibition, for example, during the transition from the waking state to sleep.

Platonov (1959), basing his work on Pavlovian theory, describes laboratory experiments conducted to prove that this waking section of the cortex is in a state of increased excitation and reacts strongly to external stimuli. With a brain-injured subject, unable consciously to shut out irrelevant stimuli, it is of decided advantage to inhibit such irrelevant stimuli in sleep, thus focusing and strengthening the desired stimuli.

HYPOTHESIS

In view of both the theoretical and research findings in the field, it was considered a hypothesis worth testing as to whether a brain-injured boy of seventeen, a non-reader, could learn to blend a sleep-learned list of twenty three-lettered words faster than one of equal difficulty without the benefit of sleep-learning.

PROCEDURE

The subject: Victor, the subject of the experiment, is a boy of seventeen with perceptual disabilities. He is a tall slender boy who, despite a disproportionately small head and asymmetrical features, does not present an unpleasant first impression. He is affable in manner and speaks buoyantly and enthusiastically about his plans for going to college, which are entirely unrealistic. He is a junior in high school but has been functioning on a very low level even in the modified courses provided by the high school for slow learners.

In 1958 he was tested with the following results: On the Wechsler-Bellevue Intelligence Scale, he tested full scale fifty-five. This was not considered entirely valid. Throughout the testing period he was anxious and unco-operative, expressing the desire to go home. He showed a social intelligence above that of a mentally defective boy.

The E.E.G. report was generalised, abnormal, which together with other findings suggested an organic brain syndrome of a developmental nature. It was felt that his emotional difficulties might be related to brain damage.

Achievement tests given him by the remedial reading therapist pictured him as a total non-reader with a short attention span.

After a six-month trial period of psychotherapy, Victor was again tested in March 1960. These diagnostic tests were in contrast to the psychological tests administered when Victor first came to the clinic. Among the outstanding features was an increase of sixteen points in the IQ (same test), and an absence of organic disturbances which permeated the first tests. In addition to these changes, Victor's motivation for help in reading was high.

In September, 1960, he was entered into the remedial reading programme. Whatever reading he did was on the basis of a small sight vocabulary which he had developed. Early in the programme he expressed his dislike for phonics, and it was found difficult to keep his attention on word analysis skills at all. Victor's visual perception showed some degree of training, however. He was able to discriminate letters of the alphabet, associating them with their names but not with their sounds. He was able to copy pages of cursive writing from manuscript without being able to read one word of either. An auditory discrimination test indicated that he had 'extreme difficulty in auditory discrimination'.

In April 1961, when the sleep learning experiment was begun, Victor's achievement in reading was as follows:

1. His sight vocabulary was composed of about forty or fifty words, although the amount of forgetting precluded any definite estimate.

2. He understood the concept that letters mean sounds which can be blended into spoken words. Though unsuccessful in most cases, he always started to attack a new word phonetically.

3. He learned the sounds of most of the consonants and all the short vowels, although again, there was an abnormal amount of forgetting.

4. His motivation remained high. He told his therapist that he had improved in reading and that he felt hopeful that he would finally learn to read (Northside Centre for Child Development, 1961).

RESEARCH DESIGN

The first step was to prepare two lists of twenty words each and of equal difficulty. These lists were made up of three-letter words with a short vowel between initial and final consonants. The subject was pre-tested on many words until two such lists of equal difficulty were obtained, one to be the 'experimental' list, the other the 'control' list.

The next step was to prepare a tape containing the experimental list prefaced by a statement of motivation. The list employed will be found below. A tape recorder was employed, complete with sleep-learning equipment of an automatic timer and a pillow-sleeper.

The procedure in teaching and testing for both lists was identical. On the first day, the control list was taught once and then tested. Errors and number of attempts were accurately recorded. A maximum of thirty seconds was given the subject to sound out and say each word. The subject attended the clinic twice a week. On his second visit, four days later, he was taught and tested in the same manner. Errors and number of attempts for each word were again recorded. Three days later, and again four days after that, the same procedure was followed with the control list, thus making four sessions in all.

The identical procedure of teaching and testing with recording of number of errors and attempts at each word was followed with the experimental list. In addition, however, every night during the period in which the experimental list was dealt with, the subject heard this list on tape for two periods of one half-hour each, one hour after retiring and again one hour before waking in the morning.

The timing was automatically set by the timer. All the errors and number of attempts made for both tests were then tabulated and appear below.

DISCUSSION OF RESULTS

The summary of quantitative data below indicates that, although the number of errors and the number of attempts were the same with both lists at the first trial of each list, the gain made with the sleep-learned list over the control list was significantly greater.

Test Attempts and Accuracy in Learning Lists

	Control List (without sleep-learning)				*Experimental List (with sleep-learning)*			
Session	*Words 1st Attempt*	*Correct 2nd Attempt*	*At . . . 3rd Attempt*	*Words Still Unknown*	*Words 1st Attempt*	*Correct 2nd Attempt*	*At . . . 3rd Attempt*	*Words Still Unknown*
1st	8	1	1	10	8	1	1	10
2nd	12	5	1	2	17	1	1	1
3rd	14	1	0	5	18	2	0	0
4th	13	2	0	5	18	2	0	0

At the subject's fourth trial with the control list, he had learned thirteen words out of twenty well enough to blend them at the first attempt while still unable to blend five words at all. Of the experimental list, however, he was able to blend on the first attempt, eighteen out of twenty at the third session and retained this high score at the fourth session. He was able to blend *all* the words at both the third and fourth sessions.

On the basis of the results of this study, therefore, it is possible to conclude that sleep-learning can hasten the process of learning to synthesize sounds into words.

By its very nature, however, a study such as this has a built-in limitation. There are many variants that affect a learning situation. Without a very specific knowledge of all the influences that affect the subject's performance of the task, there could be no absolute determination as to whether the sleep-learning in itself caused the improved performance. An argument with a father, food that disagreed with the subject, or simply a frustrated desire to be elsewhere than at the clinic might well have had a bearing on the test results.

Then, too, the experimental list was taught after the control list. This means that the subject had more general experience with the process of blending with which to start the experimental list than he had at the beginning of learning of the control list. Specifically in terms of the number of words he correctly blended, however, he scored equally at the very inception of the experiment.

The limitations of the study discussed above would lose their validity in direct proportion to the number of such studies made, with varied content and different subjects. A consistency of pattern in a dozen similar studies, protracted over a longer period of time and more comprehensive in scope, would certainly constitute a set of more valid conclusions than one limited test. There is no doubt, however, that though this fragmentary test cannot be conclusive, it has sufficient validity to influence the thinking of others in this direction.

SUMMARY

This study was designed to test whether sleep-learning could be productive as a supplement to conscious learning in teaching a brain-injured boy of seventeen the blending of short vowel sounds into words. The boy, a non-reader, was tested on two sets of words, pre-tested to assure their equal difficulty. Both lists were consciously learned, the experimental list sleep-learned in addition. Error and number of attempts were noted and scored. A significant difference was found in the accuracy of synthesizing words as well as in the number of attempts with which the words were attacked. The results of the study indicate that learning of auditory material does occur during partial sleep.

ACKNOWLEDGEMENTS

Appreciation is expressed to Dr. Paul Benedict, clinical director, who provided every facility for the investigation and to Mrs. Jeanne Karp, director of the clinic's remedial reading department, for her help and encouragement. Appreciative thanks are also offered to Mr. David Curtis at whose suggestion the study was undertaken.

APPENDIX

A. CONTROL LIST

1. jam	6. mat	11. nap	16. sad
2. him	7. cud	12. nod	17. cat
3. not	8. pit	13. sod	18. but
4. cup	9. dip	14. mix	19. big
5. pot	10. hub	15. fun	20. hot

B. EXPERIMENTAL LIST

Victor, this is your reading teacher, Mrs. Pollack, talking to you. I know you want to learn to read as quickly as possible. It will help you to read if you will learn the list of words I am about to read to you.

You are completely relaxed, but part of your mind is concentrating on what I am saying. Listen carefully, Victor. You will remember and keep on remembering the words I say to you even after you have awakened in the morning after a night's refreshing sleep.

1. sat	6. cap	11. rag	16. cab
2. hid	7. bud	12. sum	17. map
3. sob	8. fit	13. fob	18. pup
4. nut	9. sip	14. win	19. fig
5. hop	10. rut	15. dug	20. pod

SOURCES

M. L. Coyne (1953) *Some Problems and Parameters of Sleep Learning*. Unpublished Honours thesis, Wesleyan Coll., Conn.

C. R. Elliott (1947) *An Experimental Study of the Retention of Auditory Material Presented During Sleep*. Unpublished Master's thesis, Univ. of N. Carolina.

B. H. Fox and J. S. Robbins (1952) *The Retention of Material Presented During Sleep*. *J. Exp. Psychology,* **43**, 75.

T. A. Hedges (1950) *The Effect of Auditory Stimuli Presented During the Sleep of Children with Delayed Speech*. Unpublished Master's thesis, Univ. of Wichita.

W. G. Hoyt (1953) *The Effect on Learning of Auditory Material Presented During Sleep*. Unpublished Master's thesis, George Washington Univ.

L. LeShan (1942) *The Breaking of Habit by Suggestion During Sleep*. *J. Abnorm. Soc. Psychol.,* **37**, 406.

L. LeShan (1953) Personal communication with Simon and Emmons.

C. Leuba and D. Bateman (1952) *Learning During Sleep*. *Amer. J. Psychol.* **65**, 301.

Northside Centre for Child Development (1960). *Case History of Earl Pearson*. New York.

I. P. Pavlov (1960) *Conditioned Reflexes—An Investigation of the Psychological Activity of the Cerebral Cortex*. New York: Dover Publishing Co.

K. Platonov (1959) *The Word as a Physiological and Therapeutic Factor*. Moscow: Foreign Language Publishing House.

C. W. Simon and W. H. Emmons (1955) *Learning During Sleep. Psychological Bulletin*, **52**, 328.

T. Stampfl (1953) *The Effect of Frequency of Repetition on the Retention of Auditory Material Presented during Sleep*. Unpublished Master's thesis, Loyola Univ. Chicago. Read at an APA meeting.

L. L. Thurstone (1953) Personal communication with Simon and Emmons.

9

PRELIMINARY EXPERIMENT WITH SLEEP-LEARNING FOR DYSPHASIC PATIENT

Mary Warren, L.C.S.T.

Aphasia is the name given to a condition of total impairment of language, and dysphasia to partial impairment, caused by a lesion in the motor and receptive speech areas in the cortex of the brain. The lesion can be caused by cerebral haemorrhage, cerebral thrombosis or cerebral tumour, and is commonly known as a 'stroke'. Aphasia is often associated with paralysis of the right side and limbs in a right-handed person.

The effects of the lesion vary enormously, and may include one or all of the following: loss of comprehension, loss of reading power and ability to write, loss of 'spontaneous' speech and loss of the use of familiar objects.

The prognosis is equally variable and sometimes unpredictable. Degree of recovery depends on the site and extent of the lesion, the age and resilience of the patient and on his fortitude; rehabilitation is likely to take several years.

Mr. M. has been in the care of the Speech Therapy Department of St. Margaret's Hospital, Epping, since his 'stroke' in 1962. He was, at that time, fifty-one years old, and had been a highly educated articulate man, fond of reading, a bachelor, and a director of a shipping company.

The 'stroke' caused almost total aphasia and considerable receptive loss, as well as right hemiplegia. He had two spontaneous words: 'Yes' and 'No' (which were used correctly), and two reiterated words: 'When' and 'Shipping' (to which no meaning was attached). He could not comply with any command, such as pointing to a picture; he could not count, name any object nor match a name to a picture.

Over three years his progress has been slow but steady, and this is partly due to the unknown amount of healing in the damaged area of the brain, and partly to his own tremendous courage and determination. Speech therapy has consisted of continuous repetition of all aspects of speech and language, and much encouragement in reading, writing and calculation. Treatment cannot be given for too long a period, as he tires easily, but he has been greatly helped by the acquisition of a tape recorder. I have recorded a suitable tape each week, and he can then give himself a 'lesson' each day, at his own convenience. His facility for imitating words by listening to my voice made me wonder about the possibility of sleep-learning.

The difficulties in this experiment must be mentioned at once, so that no false impression may be given. It is impossible to estimate the exact rate of recovery in the brain, nor the amount, if any, of nerve-regeneration. One can only judge by results, and these may be caused by many factors. The store of language is so complex that it is very difficult to identify the exact amount of words which have been lost, and the reason for words having been recalled. This patient's recall was strongly affected by his emotional and physical condition, and words which had been learned in context were not necessarily related to their concept. For example, he might remember a word perfectly before his morning walk, only to find it had eluded him completely after lunch . . . or he might have learned to say 'Blue' in answer to the question 'What colour is a summer sky?' while being quite unable to answer 'What colour is a sapphire?' Therefore these series of tests were not in any way conclusive, nor were they based on any exact 'control'.

The state of the patient at the beginning of June was as follows:

Comprehension: Normal.

Reading silently: Normal (for short periods only).

Writing: Can copy anything, and can write spontaneously a few words at a time (with left hand).

Movement: Right arm and leg have limited movement but are very stiff.

Counting: 1, 2, 3 spontaneously; can imitate up to 10.

Singing: All tunes, but 'Dee, Dee' for words.

Spontaneous words: About 10 he can use.

Imitation: Can repeat almost any word he hears.

On June 25th he was provided with a series of control tests (Test I) to ascertain his rate of normal progress over a fortnight with help during the day only. The result showed the following increase: at the beginning, he could answer 4/28 questions, and at the end 13/28 (gain of nine). Only his first reply was counted, and no help was given with the answers. He was also provided with a song ('God save the Queen') to sing with his landlady each day; but, at the end of the fortnight, he showed no improvement in recall of the words.

July 8th: Control tests were stopped, and he was started with a 'conditioning' tape at night. The time-clock was set for 1.30–2.30, and again at 4.30–5.30 a.m. (his normal bedtime is 12.0 midnight). The first night, the volume was too loud for comfort, so it was turned down to a minimal whisper, to which, after four nights, he indicated complete indifference.

July 12th: (Test II) A new series on tape was provided, again of twenty-eight items, which included counting to twelve. Single word answers were again required, and I gave him a new song ('Keep Right on to the End of the Road'), which was an old favourite of his. Of the score of twenty-eight, he could already count to seven, and say his name at the beginning of this fortnight, but he could not answer any other of the questions nor sing one word of the song. His landlady did not know the words of the song, so she did not help him with this during the day. The questions, answers and song were put on to the endless tape, which was set by the time-clock, as before.

July 19th: After one week of the Sleep Tape at night and no help at all during the day, I tested him. He answered 18 items (including counting to twelve, leaving out seven—thus having gained ten new words.

The second week, he was given day and night help with Test II, and the results at the end of that week were 23/28, showing a gain of fifteen during the fortnight, as against a gain of nine during Test I. The song was still not recalled in words. He then went on holiday for a week, so was only given day-help then (with the same material), and when he came back he had the Sleep-Tape as well, at night. The results, after this fortnight, showed little gain on what he had already learnt of the list (24/28), but he did sing the song right through, with 50 per cent of the words quite accurate! He could also imitate phrases of three or four words, which he had never done before.

I then gave him Test III, based on entirely 'new' material, with which he had day and night help for one week, and day help for the second week. At the end of this fortnight he could answer twenty-five of the thirty-two items. The results in figures, therefore, are as follows:

1st Fortnight (Test I)	2nd Fortnight (Test II)
(Day Teaching only)	(Night and Day)
Gained nine.	Gained fifteen.
No words of song.	No words of song.
3rd Fortnight (Test II contd.)	4th Fortnight (Test III)
(Night and Day)	(Day and Night)
Retained fifteen, Gained one.	Gained twenty-five.
50 per cent of song and phrases.	

These figures show a steady increase in his ability to recall new words. It would also seem that he learnt the new words fairly quickly each time, and the second fortnight of teaching the same material had little effect (in Test II). The teaching of the song must have come through the Tape, as he had little day help with this. His landlady reports that he has started to use other words during the last few weeks, which he has never been 'taught'.

Summary: The purpose of sleep-learning in treating dysphasic patients was not to teach new material, but to aid recall of familiar words. It was thought that extra stimulation during sleep or partial-sleep might show better results than during the day when the patient was easily excited or distracted.

The results of these tests cannot be called conclusive, owing to the immeasurable nature of aphasia, the variations in the patient's attention and concentration, and the small amount of time allowed for the project. However, the results do seem to show that spontaneous recall was increased when the patient received day-and-night help. Recall of words given during sleep alone appeared to be similar in number to those gained from daytime alone. The patient himself thinks that he has been helped by this method, and wishes to obtain the equipment in order to continue.

I am very grateful to the Sleep-Learning Association for their help and advice, and for their kindness in lending me the necessary equipment.

10

THE QUESTION OF HYPNOPAEDIA

V. N. Kulikov

The question of hypnopaedia has only claimed scientific attention fairly recently, since the thirties. Scientists in various countries have been associated with this subject.

The first references to perception by sleeping people go back to the end of the nineteenth century and to the beginning of the twentieth century. Both Russian and foreign doctors obtained this data in the course of curing children by the method of relearning during natural sleep (1, 10, etc.). *Therapeutic effects of this method of curing have convincingly shown that the patients in the state of natural sleep absorbed, remembered and retained words suggested by the doctor.*

Workers in the area of the psychology of dreams (8 and 9, *et al.*) have also noticed similar evidence. They have observed that the content of dreams often connected with the content of words acting on the sleeping person. For instance, the word 'fire' often evoked a dream connected with a fire, the word 'water' was transformed into a picture in which perhaps a river, the sea or rain figured.

Scientific study of the problem of hypnopaedia has passed through three phases.

First stage was that of studying the question of hypnopaedia, that is accumulating tangible facts on the problem of learning during sleep. As late as 1932 A. Huxley carried out some special tests on memory with a sleeping person and obtained positive results. M. Shirover followed by doing experiments in teaching languages to sleeping students. His tests revealed that students who had experienced a preliminary learning during sleep absorbed words of the language as a result of subsequent work whilst awake, and this took place 25–30 per cent more rapidly than without the preliminary learning during sleep.

It has thus been established and confirmed that the sleeping person can absorb and retain speech. This increased interest in the question of hypnopaedia. Experiments took place in various countries, especially in the U.S.A.: Powers (14) in the U.S.A. mentions that tests were done in many universities and medical institutes.

A characteristic feature of most of the experiments of that time was combination of teaching in the condition of natural sleep with subsequent teaching whilst awake. The idea of this method emanated from the view that learning during sleep is a repetitive learning and a person temporarily forgets what he has learned (Elliott).

Many new facts came to light in the study of learning during sleep, and these have been written up in the psychological literature (6, 12, 13, 14, etc.). It was necessary to follow on with a second stage in the study of hypnopaedia, namely that of finding the basic facts underlying scientific explanation of generalisation. This work was started in the Soviet Union, whereas foreign workers as we will see below confine themselves to describing the facts.

Studies in the Soviet Union began in the forties. The first name associated with this project is that of A. M. Svyadoshch (6). As distinct from the foreign workers, Svyadoshch carried out teaching during sleep without the subsequent second teaching whilst awake. However, he developed by experimental methods a preliminary ability in his test subjects. As a result of observing these conditions he obtained good experimental results. Thus in one experiment, out of twenty test people, sixteen reproduced 89·5 per cent of the matter that was given to them whilst asleep and only four people reproduced about 18·6 per cent of the text.

In his latter work (7) the Soviet author not only describes results of tests on learning during sleep but also has made an attempt to explain the manifestations. From the point of view of I. P. Pavlov, Svyadoshch regards sleep during which learning takes place as sleep with a 'watch point'. It is suggested that absorption and retention of words during sleep is accomplished due to the functioning of the cells in the 'watch point' during a simultaneous inhibition of the other parts of the brain.

However, Svyadoshch has only been able to give a preliminary tentative explanation of the phenomenon. For the full solution of the problem further work by many scientists is required.

The third stage in studying hypnopaedia is that of experimental tests in using the method of learning during sleep in actual practical applications of education. The work was started in the forties and is now going on in various countries.

Curtiss (13) reports that the American LeShan in 1940 did tests in which he tried to cure children of bad habits such as biting their nails. Whilst they were asleep he suggested to the patients that their nails were very bitter. The suggestion was repeated six times during the night. The cure lasted fifty-four nights. As a result 40 per cent of the children lost the habit.

In 1947 the present author tested the method for teaching foreign languages. English expressions and their Russian equivalents were read to sleeping students. On the next day students of both this group and a control group were made to learn these expressions so as to be able to use them. It appeared that the experimental groups absorbed the expressions 80 per cent more rapidly than the control group (2).

In a similar experiment carried out in 1947 by Elliott it appeared that the people tested in an *experimental group learnt* 83 *per cent quicker* than those in a control group.

Curtiss (13) writes that Shirover succeeded in teaching during sleep not only languages but multiplication tables, tables and logarithms, chemical formulae, the Morse code, etc. He also mentions that the American P. Vinai succeeded in teaching Italian opera to people who did not know the Italian language.

The newspaper *New York Times,* July 6, 1952, stated that the U.S. War Ministry used this method in training the Staff Officers of the Army and Navy. The Morse code was taught to cadets in Army training schools by this method. It appears also that the Canadian Ministry of Defence uses this method of teaching. *The American Journal of Experimental Psychology* (16) described tests in which students of Washington University were taught Chinese during sleep. Experiments were done between two-thirty and three o'clock in the morning. The first group of students listened to the Chinese words without translation into English, whilst the second heard them with their English equivalents. As might have been anticipated, the second group learned the words much quicker than the first, after 5·6 repetitions as compared with 11·1.

Certain authors (7, 11), however, deny the inherent character of ability to absorb and retain during sleep. Thus Svyadoshch, for instance, concludes this from the following experiment which he cites. A story was read twice to subjects who beforehand were not told that an experiment was to take place. It appeared that whilst the story was read the subjects either continued to sleep and did not remember anything when they woke up, or they overslept. However, these authors did not deny that the ability to accept during sleep can be developed experimentally.

Now what have we learned from this historical outline?

First of all we see that the possibility of teaching during natural sleep has been demonstrated by many experiments. Hypnopaedia has been taken from the area of fantasy into an indisputable scientific fact.

Furthermore, it has become obvious that the problem of learning during sleep has attracted the attention of several sciences, and these include physiology, medical sciences, psychology and education. At the moment it is still difficult to see what the study can do in the sphere of psychology. Only some tentative suggestions can emanate from consideration of learning during sleep and the experimental data available.

In our view, hypnopaedia can give considerable assistance in solving several theoretical problems in psychology. For instance, it will be possible to use it to assist in studying the important and complicated question of the conscious and the unconscious. In particular it might help us to solve the problem of the transition between unconscious to conscious and vice versa. Experiments in teaching during sleep will make their own specific contributions to various psychic processes and will reveal the laws governing them.

In studying the history of hypnopaedia we are face to face with the problem of finding out the nature of this ability and the conditions under which it is manifest. Such problems became the subject of tests which are described below. In order to solve these problems seventy-two experiments were done in which thirty-six subjects took part (children from the first and second classes and students). The subjects were tested for their high suggestibility, and this was tested by the method of hand gripping (5). The interest of the subject in the experiments themselves was also taken into account.

The material used in the experiments was unknown to the subjects but was related to their capacity in its subject: for the children, a story by Tolstoy called 'Hop-O'-My-Thumb'; for the students, a text on the different types of nervous activities in animals from a psychological treatise. Experiments were done in the following order. First, all preliminary tests were made without any preparation, that is, the subjects were not prepared in advance for absorption and retention of text. Whilst asleep the subjects without any preliminary suggestions were presented with the corresponding text. They were questioned when they woke up.

The main experiments were then carried out. They differed somewhat from those quoted by other authors (6, 7). Thus we did tests without preliminary fostering in the subjects of ability to absorb and retain words in their sleep. We assumed that this ability is a natural characteristic of human beings, just as is the ability to absorb and retain when awake.

We used a tape recorder for the tests, and tape contained the whole course of the experiments. The experimenter controlled the experiment, and only when necessary introduced some changes which afterwards had to be accounted for in the results.

A special feature of our tests was that they took place with the volume of the tape recorder reproduction below the threshold of hearing when in the waking state. We assumed that disturbances, below threshold in the waking state, become threshold when asleep, and this was confirmed in 89 per cent of the cases. In doing this we attempted to avoid the failures which took place in Svyadoshch's tests (7) (i.e., the disturbance of the subjects at the beginning of the experiments).

Experiments in the second series started by establishing contact with the sleeping subjects. After the subjects had been sleeping naturally for some one or two hours, the tape recorder was switched on and this reproduced the suggestions which had been previously recorded. Thus: 'You are sleeping peacefully, sleep on, do not wake up, you are resting, you are breathing in a very rhythmic, slow and deep manner,' etc.; then the character of the suggestion was changed and the subject was urged to change his breathing: 'Your breathing is becoming deeper and deeper.' When this suggestion was adopted it was finally considered that contact had been established with the subject and the main work would start.

The subject was then conditioned to accept, memorise and retain the subsequent reproduction. The following suggestion was made: 'Now you will hear the text (story, etc.), listen to this and remember what is said, try and memorise it as much as possible, you will remember this all your life, and whenever wanted you will be able to relate it. Listen and memorise.' Then the experimental text was reproduced.

After the final reading of the text a final confirmatory suggestion was made to the subject that he retain it and that he remember it so well that it could be reproduced whenever required. 'You have heard and you have remembered the story, you have listened to it and you have memorised it and you will always remember it. Now you will be able to relate it at any time you like, and now go back to sleep, just rest.'

In assigning the text to the magnetic tape we tried to make the reproduction such that the subject was under the influence of a commanding, firm but quiet voice of great suggestibility.

The tests were all done under visual control and observation. Under laboratory conditions control was done by means of actography and pneumography. Observations showed that during the imparting of the text all the subjects continued to sleep just as they slept beforehand. Not one of them showed any overt reaction to the verbal disturbances. There were no movements of any noticeable kind nor any changes in breathing of the subject. The third series of experiments were the control experiments. The text was also imparted to the subjects, but in this case they were awake; this was also done by tape recorder.

In all the tests we tried to select subjects (up to twelve people) more or less of the same age, knowledge and ability. The same material was given to all of them. The texts were repeated the same number of times. The experiments were then completed by questioning the subjects about the texts. To get a quantitative evaluation of results the texts were broken up into nominal units, each expressing one definite sort. In the story about Hop-o'-My-Thumb we had fifteen such units, whereas in the text about the nervous system there were twenty-five such units.

Now, what are the results of the experiments?

In the preliminary tests in which the texts were read to the sleeping subjects straight away without preliminary suggestion, eleven of those who were questioned afterwards revealed complete ignorance of what was presented to them.

Only one of the twelve subjects who took part in these tests revealed some knowledge of the story which was read to him. This was actually a boy who had taken part beforehand in tests in hypnopaedic suggestion.

The experiments, however, in which the texts were only read after some preparatory suggestion give quite different results. In these tests all twelve subjects revealed knowledge of the text.

One of the students to whom the text about the nervous system of animals was read was interviewed and gave a good account of what was read to him. The experimenter asked how he came to know this. And the subject replied: 'You know I was waiting for this question. I've been thinking about it, but I just can't remember where I found out about this. I do recollect however that last night when I was dreaming I saw something to do with dogs and with Pavlov.' (The student smiled.) 'Perhaps this is what I saw in my sleep.' The main results of the experiments with the students are given in Table 1; there were five involved, the number of bits of text in all cases was twenty-five, whilst the scores memorised were as follows: 12, 18, 16, 14, 19. *The lowest percentage score was* 48, *the highest* 76.

The children also gave good results when tested. A little girl was questioned and she said that she had a funny dream in which she was wandering in a wood. A dream which seemed to be vaguely associated with the subject matter of a story which she actually recalled quite accurately.

The results of the tests on the children are shown in Table 2. Seven children each presented with fifteen bits of text remembered between eight and twelve, *lowest score was* 46·7 *and the highest* 80 *per cent.*

The control tests in learning text in the waking state gave very similar results to those in the foregoing experiment. These are shown in Tables 3 and 4. Here the *lowest score for the students was* 44 *per cent* and the *highest* 80 *per cent;* with the children the *lowest score was* 46·7 *per cent* and the *highest* 86·7 *per cent.* Now to discuss the results of these experiments.

What do the experiments reveal?

First of all it is important to note that our basic hypothesis on the ability to absorb speech whilst asleep has been confirmed; this ability is possessed by all people just as the ability to absorb knowledge in the waking state. Speech is absorbed, memorised and retained during sleep and can be reproduced when awake. The ability to do

Table 1

Results of teaching students the Typology of the Higher Nervous System

Subjects	*Number of units of text presented*	*Number of units of text reproduced*	*% reproduced*
1	25	12	48
2	25	18	72
3	25	16	64
4	25	14	56
5	25	19	76

Table 2

Results of fundamental experiments on teaching children the fairy-tale 'Hop-o'-My-Thumb'

Subjects	*Number of units of text presented*	*Number of units of text reproduced*	*% reproduced*
1	15	8	53·3
2	15	7	46·7
3	15	11	73·3
4	15	12	80·0
5	15	11	73·3
6	15	11	73·3
7	15	7	46·7

this was observed in all cases where the basic experiment took place. All those who attended revealed a good knowledge of what was read to them whilst asleep.

It would follow that if the ability to absorb and memorise whilst awake is a manifestation of the conscious mind, then it follows that the absorption and memorisation during sleep is an activity associated with the subconscious mind. The latter is performed in all probability by means of the cells in the 'watch point' in the cortex (3, 4, 7) whilst at the same time the basic mass of nerve cells are inhibited, i.e., those due to which waking consciousness occurs.

The above is confirmed by the fact that learning during sleep takes place unconsciously. The subjects as a rule experience this knowledge obtained whilst asleep *without* knowing where it came

Table 3

Results of control experiments on teaching students the Typology of the Higher Nervous System

Subjects	*Number of units of text presented*	*Number of units of text reproduced*	*% reproduced*
1	25	13	52
2	25	11	44
3	25	17	68
4	25	20	80
5	25	19	76

Table 4

Results of control experiments in teaching subjects Tolstoy's fairy-tale 'Hop-o'-My-Thumb'

Subjects	*Number of units of text presented*	*Number of units of text reproduced*	*% reproduced*
1	15	9	60
2	15	7	46·7
3	15	13	86·7
4	15	11	73·3
5	15	12	80
6	15	9	60
7	15	10	66·7

from. However, this unconsciously absorbed knowledge when the subject is awake transforms into consciousness, and it can then be reproduced at will. If we compare the results of the basic experiment and the control experiment it appears that the ability to absorb and to memorise in sleep in its effectiveness approaches that absorbed and retained whilst awake. Thus the subjects in the basic experiment reproduced about 63·8 per cent of the text of the story, that is the little children, whilst in the controlling experiment 67·6 per cent was reproduced. With the students the results were respectively 63·2 per cent and 64 per cent.

Tests 1 and 2 series allow us to cite the supposition that absorption and memorising in sleep is a potential ability of the subconcious. In order to obtain results this ability must be awoken or excited, it must be put into action and it must be given the corresponding direction. Strictly speaking, the same really takes place when we absorb and remember in the waking state. After all, in this condition it is imperative that the attention of the subject is called to the object. In the case of absorption and memorising during sleep the 'watch point' must be put into action. This is the reason why in ordinary life cases of absorption of speech whilst asleep are encountered so rarely.

To awaken and put into action the subconscious ability to absorb and memorise is much harder than to do the same in the waking state. The difficulty is that this has to be done without waking the subject. We managed this as we have already said by using preliminary suggestions before reading the text, and this was done with the tape recorder and related within the subsensory range.

It is therefore necessary to establish preliminary contact with a subject, i.e., to prepare him for absorbing speech and to create a situation for the subject in which he can accept what is presented. Only as a result of this is it possible to present the text which is to be learnt; no learning results without this preliminary preparatory stage.

It appeared from the experiments that with exercise and repetition the necessity for this preliminary preparatory stage decreases and it can possibly be eliminated altogether. This thesis is supported by the fact that one of the subjects with whom we had experimented before in the same hypnopaedic suggestion revealed knowledge of text although this was presented without preliminary suggestion.

Although everybody can absorb text in this way whilst asleep, the ability does vary from one person to another. At the moment we have found individual differences in ability to absorb, remember and retain material, and our observations allow us to suppose that this ability is better with those who are more suggestible.

The ability to absorb and to remember in sleep can be improved and developed. Inasmuch as ability depends on the degree of suggestibility of a person as Svyadoshch (7) remarks (a positive relationship between the subject and the experiments and the experimenters, facing the experimenter, etc.), so the absorption and retention in sleep improves.

Our tests in addition give some indication of the demands made on the type of speech which is given. The experimenter should limit himself to short prepositions and vivid verbs. His voice and pronunciation should be strong, firm, commanding but quiet. Bearing in mind that learning during sleep is associated with the subconscious, efforts should be made to make the speech highly emotional. To this end pauses, expressions which arouse feelings, and so on, are all to the good. [Editor's note: L. A. Bliznitchenko contra-indicates the use of highly emotional intonation of hypnopaedic speech.]

Improvements in ability to absorb and to memorise can be sought by using suggestion equipment. Our tests show that the whole success of the experiments may indeed depend on such equipment. In tests where no connection was established between the subjects and the experimenters results were very bad. Only one subject revealed a knowledge of what was read to him and he gave a score of 46·7 per cent. In the basic experiments where these situations were observed, knowledge of the text of the story was revealed by all the subjects and the average reproduction score was 63 per cent. The effect of the situation or equipment is probably due to the adjustment or tuning of the brain in which excitation in the watch point is concentrated.

In our first tests in learning during sleep transformation took place between the absorbed verbal material into dream images. In this connection the problem of the importance of subconscious visual enforcement of learning during sleep came up. If we analyse the material of these experiments we come to the conclusion that dream images supplement and improve the process of memorising what has been absorbed. The supposition is confirmed by the fact that the subjects who experienced dreams whilst the text was being absorbed usually gave higher scores in reproduction. For instance, one subject gave 76 per cent score in this case as against 46·7 per cent.

We noted the same thing as Svyadoshch (7, 6), namely that the transformation of verbal material absorbed during sleep into tangible or significant images depends first of all on the character of the material. For instance, the story which was given to the children was easily transformed into significant dream pictures, whereas the text about the upper nervous activity is not amenable to dream images. However, the transformation of verbal material into significant pictures depends not only on the characteristics of the subject material which is absorbed but also on those of the person who is absorbing it. Our observations allow us to suppose that the peculiarities which are important are not so much those of age as the individual type peculiarities of the subjects, in particular the peculiar feature of their higher nervous activity. Of subjects in our tests who represented arts or artists (this is of course our purely arbitrary definition), 66·4 per cent revealed a well-developed tendency to image creation. Representatives of the so-called intellectual types only showed this tendency to the extent of 16·6 per cent.

Our tests have confirmed that there is a great possibility to use the method of learning during sleep in various practical applications such as teaching and education. It can be used for teaching quite different subjects, especially such subjects which create heavy demands on the memory. For instance, multiplication tables, logarithms, formulae, historical facts, reproductions of literature, language and so on.

Learning during sleep can play a large part in education and subsequent re-education. Many bad habits can be cured by this method, too, both in adults as well as children, and also the inculcation of good habits can be fostered.

The method of learning during sleep can be applied in practice to cases where self-teaching and self-education is required. We do *not* think, however, that the method of learning during sleep will actually replace parents, teachers and educators altogether. The idea is merely to use the method as an ancillary, as an aid to those who are teaching and educating their fellow men.

REFERENCES

1. N. B. Vyazemskii, *Applications of Curative Suggestion* (*Trud. Saratovsk. Obshch. Estestv.*) **1b**, No. 2, 193–194.
2. V. N. Kulikov, *Teaching a Foreign Language During Sleep* (unpublished investigation).
3. I. P. Pavlov, *Poln. Sobr. Soch.* **3**, bk. 1 and 2. M L, Izd ANSSSR, 1951.
4. I. P. Pavlov, *Poln. Sobr. Soch.* **4**, M L , Izd Vo ANSSSR, 1951.
5. K. I. Platonov, *The Word as a Physiological and Curative Factor*. Medgiz, 1957.
6. A. M. Svyadoshch, *Perception of Speech During Natural Sleep*. Candidates Thesis, L 1940.
7. A. M. Svyadoshch, *Perception and Memorising Speech During Natural Sleep*. (*Vopros. Psykhol.*) No. 1, 1962.
8. I. E. Stepanov, *The Psychology of Dreams*. Berlin, 1922.
9. S. Freud, *Analysis of Dreams*. M, 1913.

10. C. H. Burdon, *Etude sur la Staso-lasophovie,* de Lille, 1940.
10. W. Emmons and C. W. Simons, *Non-Recall of Material Presented During Sleep* (*American Journal of Psychology*), 1956.
12. F. Kuhlmann, *On the Analysis of Auditory Memory Consciousness* (*The American Journal of Psychology*), **20**, 1909.
13. D. Curtiss, *Learn While You Sleep*. New York, 1960.
14. Melvin Powers, *Hypnotism Revealed.* 1952.
15. C. W. Simon and W. H. Emmons, *EEG, Consciousness and Sleep* (*Science*), 1956, 24, 32, 31.
16. *The American Journal of Experimental Psychology*, 1962.

Linda

11

THE QUESTION OF HYPNOPAEDIA

(Preliminary Communication)

N. D. Zabaloba, V. P. Zukhar, Yu A. Petrov

Hypnopaedia is a method which allows one to teach people during sleep and was applied first in 1922 by the instructor of radio technology in the American Navy College at Pensacola in Florida. The students were taught telegraph codes during sleep. The instructor taught the subjects definite signals several times repeated during the night, using earphones. In the morning it was found that when they were awake it was only necessary to have one repetition for the subjects to fully remember and reproduce the information which was imparted during sleep. In 1952 a similar experiment was carried out with trainee pilots in France.

Apparently the origins of hypnopaedia go back to a much earlier period. There is evidence that Buddhist monks in China used to whisper sacred texts into the ears of sleeping students, and it was found that it was very much easier and simpler to teach them this way than by means of the thousands of hieroglyphic characters in their language.

Various reports have come in giving evidence of absorption and reproduction of stories, actions and problems during the time of suggested sleep (Moll (5), Levenfeld (4), Boni (2), B. N. Birman (1), K. I. Platonov (6)). It is well known that a manifestation of post-hypnotic suggestion is the ability of the subject to absorb and reproduce simple or complicated texts, actions, etc., during the hypnotic sleep.

Several authors (Burdon (10) and Vyazemskii (3), 1904) suggested to children during natural sleep a negative attitude towards bad habits, troublesome behaviour and so on, and they achieved a very convincing therapeutic effect. The children when they went to sleep did not know that they would receive this suggestion during their normal sleep.

Absorption and memorising during natural sleep have been mentioned in works published in the last century as well as in the present century (Maury (14), 1878; S. Freud (9), 1913; Leroy (13), 1927; N. E. Stepanov, 1922; K. I. Platonov, 1930, 1957 (6); A. M. Svyadoshch, 1940, 1962, (7–8) and others). The evidence in these papers reveals that not only in speech recorded by the subjects but the ability to absorb knowledge is evinced. At the same time it was noticed that if the subjects were not warned, and were not turned up so to speak, for reception, they were unable to remember anything next morning. Thus, Svyadoshch (8), 1962, gives us the following case when 100 children not warned about the experiment beforehand were read a short story twice whilst asleep. It appears that during the reading of the story the subjects either continued to sleep and did not remember anything when they woke up or they overslept. This author was unable to reveal any absorption of the speech. In Emmons and Simon's (12) tests the sleeping subjects either did not absorb the speech or they overslept. Thus the test revealed that the spontaneous ability to receive speech during natural sleep is not a thing that often occurs.

In cases where there has been positive attuning of the subjects and corresponding suggestion before sleep it has been possible to obtain data which confirm the ability to receive speech during sleep and to reproduce it after waking [K. I. Platonov (6), *et al*].

In 1948 the psychologist Charles Elliott (11) (U.S.A.) succeeded in imparting speech during sleep. He recorded fifteen words on a gramophone disc, each one composed of three letters. The discs were played over thirty times during sleep to twenty students (sleep was confirmed by records from electro-encephalograph). On awaking all twenty students were found to have learnt the words much more rapidly than twenty control students.

Svyadoshch (1940, 1962 (7–8)) demonstrated that during natural sleep in some cases aborption of speech can take place, including lectures, stories, chapters from literature, philosophy and technical and other content, classical quotations coming from known as well as unknown sources, and also transmissions for recording. The author maintains that the absorption of speech is to such a degree of accuracy that it can be reproduced in the memory as well as that absorbed in the waking state.

Therefore all these past investigations afforded some basis for assuming an ability to absorb knowledge during sleep.

We tried the experiment of investigating absorption and memorising in natural sleep, using words from a text and reproducing when awake, and we also tried applications of hypnopaedia in a collective experiment where we endeavoured to teach a foreign language. The work was carried out February to May 1962.

METHODS OF STUDY

Ten simple words were read to the subjects (lamp, train, book, etc.) and then ten hard, unknown names of new types of medicines (sanazin, gvimeri, solutan, etc.). Additionally a difficult but meaningful text about the construction of logical cybernetic problems was read. Words and texts were put on tape in a uniform and clear voice. During the test the subjects were kept to a soundproofed room, information was relayed through a radio pillow or through earphones. The tape recorder was in another room, in order to eliminate disturbances when switching on and off.

During the night the experimental words and text were repeated from ten to twenty times. The relaying of the information was done one hour after the subject got to sleep (as observed and recorded by electro-encephalograph) and it lasted two hours. Furthermore the subject slept a further four hours without any information. Before waking up, for one and a half to two hours, the information was relayed again.

The depth of the sleep was recorded on the EEG, with a fifteen-channel alvar. Diopotentials were recorded in three positions; the crown and forehead right hand side, forehead to the back left hand side, left ear to the back right hand side. Additionally the electrocardiogram of the pulse was recorded. Records were also made of the articulograms, the skin galvanic reflex and breathing. Recording of the EEG was made before each experiment. Additionally, before each transmission, at the moment of relaying as well as at the moment of recording and of waking, EEG was noted. [Editor's note: Disclosing the results of EEG recording would greatly add to the scientific value of this paper.]

On waking up, the subject was questioned about sleep, and reproduction was checked. For this a selection of ten simple words and ten unknown words were used. He also checked to see whether he remembered the meaningful text.

CHARACTERISTICS OF THE SUBJECTS

Ten healthy individuals ranging in age from nineteen to thirty-seven were selected. Without making any special selection for hypnopaedia, the authors in recording the EEG in the waking state tried to obtain from the subjects a clear picture of the bio-electric activity of the brain. Before the experiment details of each subject's sleep were found, for instance, such as how he gets to sleep, if he oversleeps, how long, how deep, the effect and character of dreams, how he suffers from lack of sleep, does he use sleeping pills and their effect, does he like working at night time, how he tackles sleepiness, etc., any infantile deviations about sleep were also found.

To find out the possibility of teaching in sleep with normal and specially high suggestibility, special tests were done. To do this the subject was recommended to calm down, to relax the body, to concentrate on sleeping and to close the eyes. After supplementary suggestion about the approach of sleep, immobilisation of the body, suddenly a command was given to open the eyes. Using this last method, it was possible to establish high suggestibility in the case of four individuals (one of them was found to have a light hypnotic sleep whilst another one had cataleptic sleep).

It was explained to the subjects beforehand that during their sleep they were going to be instructed through the radio cushion (or earphone) words and text which they should retain without being disturbed. If they wake up and hear the word they should give the appropriate signal to the experimenter by pressing an appropriate button. Individuals with high suggestibility were given a verbal suggestion before the experiment which amounted to telling them that during their normal night's sleep they would clearly absorb and retain words and text and would be able to reproduce it accurately next morning, but without interference with their sleep.

RESULTS

The preliminary communication describes the first part of the experiments and data given which were obtained from ten subjects with sleep registered by EEG.

It has already been mentioned that after waking up the subjects were read a series of twenty simple words put up by the experimental and control groups, and a series of twenty unknown words also put together from the experimental and control groups in the same way.

With those individuals who for the start obtained verbal suggestions, the experimental groups remembered words much better, in some cases two to three times *better* than the control group. One should point out that simple words are reproduced better than unknown ones, although the percentage reproduction as between simple and unknown words on the first and second reading does not give any significant difference.

The textual meaningful material, which was given during sleep, after waking was not reproduced by the subjects. The last two individuals to whom suggestions were made before the test, in a verbal account afterwards said that during their sleep they heard all the time complicated logical discussions about the construction of cybernetics problems but they could not remember them.

DISCUSSION

In this paper we will not discuss the electro-encephalographic characteristics of sleep, we will only review data on absorption and memorising information.

Experiments show that during natural sleep there is absorption and memorising of speech, words, and stories of different kinds. In some cases when the subjects found it difficult at once to reproduce the information obtained during sleep when they were awake, they still found it easier than the control information which was not given during sleep. It is possible from this to talk about the essential ability of acquiring knowledge during natural sleep.

It is quite characteristic that the process of absorption of words and text during sleep is not conscious, and when awake it is explained away by a dream experience or thoughts which have come into the mind from an unknown source.

It has been shown that the ability to absorb during natural sleep is improved if, before the hypnopaedic session, constructive suggestions are made to the subject when he is awake, i.e., he is made receptive to information.

The physiological mechanism applying at the basis of hypnopaedia might be considered to be evidently due to the work of the separate waking sections of the cortex and the larger cerebral hemisphere, which are in a state of inhibition. The absorption of information from outside takes place through the aural analyser, when the 'watch point' develops in the sleeping individual due to the impact of sub-threshold verbal disturbances.

This table gives the results of memorization by subjects of both simple and difficult unknown words. The number of experimental-group and control-group words is shown which the subjects remembered at the first and the second reading. Under remarks those individuals are shown who were treated by hypnosis before the session of hypnopaedia.

Subjects	*Type of words*	*First reading*		*Second reading*		*Remarks*
		Experi-ment	*Control*	*Experi-ment*	*Control*	
1	simple	5	5	6	5	
	unknown	2	2	2	2	
2	simple	4	3	4	5	
	unknown	4	2	2	4	
3	simple	3	3	6	5	
	unknown	0	2	4	2	
4	simple	3	4	8	7	
	unknown	1	1	3	3	
5	simple	7	9	6	8	
	unknown	5	3	4	6	
6	simple	3	3	6	6	
	unknown	0	0	3	2	
7	simple	5	5	7	5	Hypnosis
	unknown	1	1	5	2	
8	simple	8	4	9	7	Hypnosis
	unknown	4	1	4	2	
9	simple	7	5	9	5	Hypnosis
	unknown	3	2	8	2	light hypnotic sleep
10	simple	6	2	10	5	Hypnosis
	unknown	5	1	5	2	Catalepsy

From the table we see that there is no significant difference in reproducing the experimental and control groups of words by certain individuals (without previous session of hypnosis). It is worth while to mention that two subjects remembered the experimental group of words better.

It is known that the higher the suggestibility of a subject the easier it is to arouse by verbal signal the concentrated force of excitation in the brain which lies at the basis of the 'watch point'. It is obvious that in this case the initial functional level, the activity of the different portions of the cortex in the cerebral hemisphere, is very important. Those individuals who have the characteristic of high suggestibility are good subjects for the application of hypnopaedia.

CONCLUSIONS

1. In principle there is a possibility of acquiring knowledge during sleep.

2. There are great possibilities for hypnopaedia in the case of individuals who have high suggestibility, those whom in the waking state are subject to attunement for acceptance of information (the creation of their specific 'watch point' during sleep).

3. Hypnopaedia has wide possible uses in various areas of knowledge; languages, learning formulae, codes and other types of information.

REFERENCES

1. B. N. Birman, *Experimental Sleep.* L. 1925.
2. G. Bonn, *Hypnotism. Physiological and Psychological Investigations.* Translation from French, 2nd Russian edition, 1889.
3. N. V. Vyazemskiy, *The Use of Therapeutic Hypnosis. Transactions of the Saratovskiy Society of Nature Research,* **4**, 2nd edition, 1903–1904.
4. L. Levenfeld, *Hypnotism.* Saratov, 1908.
5. A. Moll, *Hypnotism.* Translation from German. SPb, 1909.
6. K. I. Platonov, *The Word as Physiological and Therapeutic Factor.* M., 1962.
7. A. M. Svyadoslich, *Perception of Speech During Natural Sleep.* Thesis for a Master degree. L. 1940.
8. A. M. Svyadoslich, *Perception and Memorization of Speech During Natural Sleep. Problems of Psychology.* No. **1**, 1962.
9. S. Freud, *Interpretation of Dreams.* M., 1913.
10. Ch. Burdon, *Etude sur la Stase-lasophobie,* de Lille, 1904.
11. C. R. Elliott, *Science Digest,* May, 1948.
12. W. H. Emmons and C. W. Simon, *Non-Recall of Material Presented During Sleep. American Journal of Psychology,* 1956.
13. E. B. Leroy, *Les Visions de Demi-Someil.* Paris, 1927.
14. L.-F. A. Maury, *Le Someil et Les Reves.* Paris, 1878.

12

A COLLECTIVE EXPERIMENT ON HYPNOPAEDIA

V. P. Zukhar', Ye. Ya. Kaplan, Y. A. Maksimov, I. P. Pushkina

THE previous chapter considered the question of the possibility of the memorisation and reproduction of isolated words and texts unknown to the subjects by the action of hypnopaedic influence during the period of natural sleep.

The next stage of the work was, on the one hand, to ascertain the effectiveness of these sessions when group hypnopaedia was carried out, and on the other to determine the firmness of memorisation in relation to the number of sessions of hypnopaedia.

METHOD OF EXPERIMENT

Since the object of our work was teaching during natural sleep, all experiments were carried out under conditions of normal nocturnal repose. In each experiment six to eight subjects took part simultaneously; they were placed in rooms measuring fifteen to thirty square metres. The verbal information was communicated, as a rule, in two stages: during the act of falling asleep, in the period of first superficial sleep (23.30–0.30 hours), and before awakening (6–6.45 hours). The choice of these times for communicating hypnopaedic information was made on the basis of physiological investigations previously carried out to study the change in the activity of the biological potentials of the brains of subjects as sleep inhibition developed.

Carrying out hypnopaedic sessions according to this method made it possible to eliminate unpleasant subjective sensations after awakening, and also to preserve a normal capacity for work.

As hypnopaedic material, English and Latin words with their Russian translations were used, reproduced by means of a tape recorder and communicated to all the subjects by a loudspeaker, and to some of them by a pillow speaker as well. In all, the words were repeated twenty to thirty times in the course of an experiment.

The beds of the subjects were at different distances from the loudspeaker; the power of the acoustic stimulus thus varied from *twenty to forty-five decibels.*

In order to eliminate extraneous noise, the tape recorder was placed in another room.

CHARACTERISTICS OF THE SUBJECTS AND METHOD OF CONDUCTING THE EXPERIMENT

The experiments were performed upon fifty-seven males aged from nineteen to twenty-five, with no abnormalities of health and no disturbances of sleep. Before the beginning of the experiment each subject was questioned about how he felt and the work he had done the day before. Before sleep the subjects were told not to upset their usual routine of preparing for sleep, to be calm and to try not to think about the forthcoming experiment.

During the whole night the experimenters carried out a check on the sleep of the subjects, the nature of their breathing and their motor activity.

On waking, each of the subjects was asked how he felt, how he had slept and whether he had had dreams; the number of words reproduced by the subjects, both spontaneously and after a single repetition of them by the experimenter, was ascertained. These data were compared with the memory of the subjects for words of a control group after a single verbal presentation. Furthermore the reproduction of the material communicated was determined twenty-four and forty-eight hours after the experiment.

EXPERIMENTAL DATA

On the basis of this method, three series of experiments were carried out.

In the *first series* of experiments, the problem was to elucidate the effectiveness of memorisation of foreign words in collective hypnopaedia. The investigation was carried out with twenty-six subjects. During the period of imparting information to them, ten English and ten Latin words were repeated several times, with their Russian translations (e.g.: Man—muzschin; charta—bumaga, and so on). Other unknown foreign words made up a control group.

Analysis of the experimental data showed that spontaneous reproduction was negligible, and in most of the subjects did not exceed two or three words out of ten. Some subjects could not reproduce a single word. After one repetition of the words by the experimenter, the subjects reproduced four to five of the experimental words and only one to two of the control words.

Thus, as a result of hypnopaedic influence the reproduction of experimental words learned by the subjects was two or three times better than the learning of the control words.

In the *second series* of experiments, the problem was to elucidate not only the effectiveness of reproduction of foreign words immediately after the experiment, but also the firmness of their memorisation later on (reproduction after twenty-four and forty-eight hours). Moreover, the effectiveness of memorisation was investigated in relation to the mechanism of imparting the verbal information.

The investigations were carried out with twenty-seven subjects. During natural sleep, in the period of falling asleep and before awakening (from 23.00 hours to 0.30 and from 6.00 to 6.30), only ten Latin words were repeated many times, with their Russian translations. Latin words were chosen because some of the subjects had previously studied English and this might have been reflected in the results of the experiment. The data obtained allow the determination of the different effectiveness of memorisation with reference to whether the verbal information was imparted by means of both a pillow speaker and a loudspeaker, or by means of a loudspeaker alone (Table 1).

Table 1

Number of words reproduced

Method of imparting verbal information	*Spontaneous reproduction*					*Reproduction after a single repetition of the words by the experimenter*								
	5	4	2	1	0	9	7	6	5	4	3	2	1	0
By pillow speaker and loudspeaker . .	1	1	3	1	3	1	1	1	–	1	1	–	2	2
By loudspeaker . .	–	–	–	4	14				2	4	3	2	2	5

Comparison of the experimental data given in Table 1 shows that hypnopaedic influence gives more effective results when the verbal information is given simultaneously by pillow speaker and loudspeaker.

The results given in Tables 2 and 3 are evidence that the experimental group of words is learned distinctly *better* by the subjects. The data give indications of spontaneous reproduction, and reproduction after a single repetition of the words by the experimenter, both immediately after the experiment and after longer intervals.

Table 2

Reproduction directly after the experiment

	Spontaneous				*After a single repetition by the experimenter*							
					Experimental group of words				*Control group of words*			
Number of words reproduced .	10–7	6–4	3–1	0	10–7	6–4	3–1	0	10–7	6–4	3–1	0
Number of subjects	–	2	8	17	2	8	10	7	–	–	12	15

Table 3

Reproduction twenty-four hours after the experiment

	Spontaneous								*After a single repetition by the experimenter*							
	Experimental group of words				*Control group of words*				*Experimental group of words*				*Control group of words*			
Number of words reproduced	10–7	6–4	3–1	0	10–7	6–4	3–1	0	10–7	6–4	3–1	0	10–7	6–4	3–1	0
Number of subjects	1	–	12	14	–	–	–	27	3	7	9	8	1	–	13	13

In one of the groups of this series (five persons), accuracy of reproduction of verbal information was ascertained after forty-eight hours. The data are given in Table 4.

Table 4

Reproduction forty-eight hours after the experiment

	Spontaneous								*After a single repetition by the experimenter*							
	Experimental group of words				*Control group of words*				*Experimental group of words*				*Control group of words*			
Number of words reproduced	10–7	6–4	3–1	0	10–7	6–4	3–1	0	10–7	6–4	3–1	0	10–7	6–4	3–1	0
Number of subjects	–	–	–	–	–	–	–	–	1	2	2	–	–	–	5	–

It may be seen from Table 4 that after forty-eight hours no spontaneous reproduction of either experimental or control words was observed. After a single repetition, from two to seven of the experimental words were reproduced and from one to three of the control words.

Thus, reproduction of words imparted during a hypnopaedic session can be observed after a single reading, and after a long time.

In the *third series* of experiments, the effectiveness of the memorisation of foreign words was investigated in relation to the number of hypnopaedic sessions.

With four subjects, five sessions of hypnopaedia were conducted, with an interval of from two to four days between them. As verbal material, thirty Latin words with their Russian translations were taken. The control group also consisted of thirty words. In the course of hypnopaedia, the groups of experimental and control words were not changed. In other respects, the method of conducting the investigation did not differ from that of the experiments in the second series.

It can be seen from Table 5 that the reproduction of experimental material, both spontaneously and after a single repetition of the words by the experimenter, bears a direct relation to the number of hypnopaedic sessions. Thus, whereas after the first session the subjects, after a single repetition, reproduced an average of three to five words, after the fifth session they reproduced up to fifteen to twenty-one words. Meanwhile, the memorisation of the control group of words by the same subjects showed an insignificant increase: one to four words after the first session and five to ten after the fifth.

No substantial differences in the learning of the material were observed when verbal information was imparted by means of the loudspeaker and pillow speaker simultaneously, and by means of the loudspeaker alone.

It must be added in conclusion that, in all the experiments, observations of the majority of subjects showed even, peaceful sleep *without* particular motor reactions or changes in breathing during the verbal influence. On waking, the subjects made *no* complaints of not feeling well, and their capacity for work in the daytime remained normal. Some individual subjects noticed the occurrence of dreams, directly or obliquely concerned with the hypnopaedia that was being carried out. [Note. In contrast to the methods used at that stage of the investigation, the authors have now adopted as a basic the method developed by L. A. Bliznichenko,

Table 5

Subjects	*First Session* (26.2)				*Second Session* (1.3)				*Third Session* (4.3)	
	Spontaneous reproduction		*Reproduction after a single reading*		*Spontaneous reproduction*		*Reproduction after a single reading*		*Spontaneous reproduction*	
	Experimental group of words	Control group of words	Experimental group of words	Control group of words	Experimental group of words	Control group of words	Experimental group of words	Control group of words	Experimental group of words	Control group of words
1	0		4	4	2	2	7	6	4	
2	1		5	2	1		9	2	6	
3	2		3	3	2	4	9	8	5	
4	2		3	1			8	5	8	

Table 5—*continued*

Subjects	*Third Session* (4.3)		*Fourth Session* (6.3)				*Fifth Session* (10.3)			
	Reproduction after a single reading		*Spontaneous reproduction*		*Reproduction after a single reading*		*Spontaneous reproduction*		*Reproduction after a single reading*	
	Experimental group of words	Control group of words	Experimental group of words	Control group of words	Experimental group of words	Control group of words	Experimental group of words	Control group of words	Experimental group of words	Control group of words
1	8	5	5		8	6	11	4	15	5
2	13	3	12		16	2	17	4	19	6
3	11	3	14	2	19	7	19	9	21	11
4	13	5	12	2	16	7	17	6	19	9

Note: The information was given to subjects 1 and 2 by pillow speaker and loudspeaker, to subjects 3 and 4 by loudspeaker.

director of the Laboratory of Experimental Phonetics of the Institute of Linguistics of the Academy of Sciences of the U.S.S.R., for imparting information to a person and fixing it in his memory during natural sleep.]

CONCLUSIONS

1. The experiments carried out demonstrated the possibility of using hypnopaedia as a method of teaching large groups.

2. In the course of the hypnopaedic sessions, no signs of fatigue or diminution of capacity for work were observed in the subjects.

3. The experimental material used in conducting hypnopaedia with a large number of subjects showed the effect of memorisation, recognition and reproduction of the verbal information (foreign words).

4. The possibility was experimentally established of delayed reproduction of the verbal information imparted during the hypnopaedic sessions.

5. With successive repetitions of the verbal information in the course of hypnopaedia, the number of words reproduced correspondingly increases.

13

THE RAPID TEACHING OF A FOREIGN LANGUAGE BY LESSONS HEARD DURING SLEEP

(a personal experiment)

I. Balkhashov

THE wide discussion of the possibility of teaching foreign languages during sleep is evidence of the prospects for this method.

In this personal experiment, the task set was to learn to read and translate scientific medical literature in Italian. For this purpose, Italian lessons from a German textbook (Wladimiro Macchi: Lehrbuch der italienischen Sprache) were recorded on magnetic tape (type 2, of which four reels were used). Thirty lessons were recorded; because of a shortage of tape, the speed of reading was as high as possible. An MG-56 tape recorder, type 'Melodiya', which reproduced the recorded speech, was automatically switched on by means of an electromechanical time relay ('timer') consisting of an ordinary clock to which was attached an alternating-current relay type RPT-100. It was also automatically switched off. The tape speed through the drive mechanism was 9·5 cm per second. The volume was set at mark 8, and the tone control at mark 9, on the graduated scales. Listening took place during the morning hours of sleep (6.00 to 7.00), and took, on an average, fifty-five to sixty minutes. The experiments were carried out from November 1963 to May 1964. Each lesson was heard, on an average, seven or eight times.

The subject was a doctor, aged twenty-seven, in good health. The experiments took place under the usual working conditions of an intern. The duration of natural sleep (without listening to lessons) averaged five to six hours. In all, thirty lessons had been heard during sleep after sixty hours.

From the first lessons, a change in general well-being was observed. Marked heaviness in the head frequently appeared, together with increased fatigue upon mental and physical exertion. The moment of falling asleep was characterised by the onset of disconnected dreams, consisting of fanciful intertwinings of scenes of ordinary life, sometimes with an erotic content. During the first experiments the switching on of the relay produced sudden awakening, which gradually gave place to falling asleep. In one of the first experiments, hypnagogic hallucinations were noted: 'voices' were distinctly heard, pronouncing words of a foreign language with emphatic articulation. These 'voices' were projected outside the subject, and accompanied by strange, unfamiliar sounds which gave the impression of infinite turbulence; they called forth a state of unaccountable terror and nightmare which resulted in awakening. After awakening the 'voices' were not heard. Sometimes momentary awakening alternated with the onset of drowsiness and falling asleep. Similar dreams, with nightmares of pursuit, were noticed throughout nearly all the experiments (sixty hours of listening during sleep). Some of the experiments had unfortunate results. In the seventeenth experiment the recorded lessons produced extraordinary effects. After four hours of listening, intense headaches of a bursting, suffocating nature set in; heaviness in the head gave cause for anxiety; fatigue was observed, together with loss of appetite and an increase in pulse rate to eighty per minute. This condition lasted for three days and went away of its own accord without treatment. Something similar was observed at the twenty-third experiment. Towards evening, after listening, diffused headaches developed, which were calmed after a deep sleep with a wet cloth round the head. Feelings of this kind did not thereafter recur and capacity for work was *not* lowered, although the experiments, as before, gave rise to vivid and arresting dreams.

In the last experiments, the appearance of hyper-aesthetic sensations in the finger-tips was observed (tingling, 'creeping' and crawling sensations). A chance consumption of alcohol proved to have extremely adverse effects on well-being. It was observed that tolerance for the experiments deteriorated when listening took place during the middle of sleep, between 3 and 4 a.m.

The spontaneous reproduction in the memory of all the material heard was difficult or even impossible. At the same time, one could not fail to observe that approximately forty hours *after* listening during sleep, a more or less marked facility in reading and understanding original medical literature, social and political articles and broadcasts appeared. The ideas of the material read or heard were grasped immediately and taken in intuitively. Texts and speech which had formerly been difficult of access were understood relatively quickly and, as a rule, *without* resort to a dictionary, although there was no question of freely mastering the Italian language or being able to 'think in it'. The author translated a number of Italian articles from the journal *Rivista di Medicina Aeronautica e Spaziale* (Review of aeronautical and space medicine); papers on them were published in the appropriate journals of the All-Union Institute for Scientific and Technical Information of the Academy of Sciences of the USSR. It should be observed that written forms and simple semantic constructions were remembered easily. Memory was improved by simultaneously listening to and looking at the text of the lessons. It was characteristic that, after listening for a long time, 'inner tension' was experienced.

In spite of some objections regarding the way in which the experiment was conducted, it may be considered that this single observation was to some extent a verification which affirmed the effectiveness of learning during sleep (the language to be learned was acquired through an 'intermediary', namely the German language, which was not the author's native one).

The experiments afford evidence that this kind of research may in some cases produce exhausting effects on the nervous system and lead to asthenia through inadequate rest. Moreover, it calls for great effort, firmness of purpose and perseverance. It is connected with the processes of a sudden transition from psychic relaxation (sleep) to tension and 'stress'—mental activity during sleep. A number of writers on psychology have demonstrated the possibility of self-regulated intervention, on the principle of 'rest activity'—the contrary of the autogenous training of Schultz-Hegemann, widely used in clinical practice, of 'activity-rest', relaxation. The possibility of training (M. Machac: Relaxation—self-regulated activity (sděleni 2. 'Československa psychologie', 2, 1964) allows teaching during sleep to be regarded as an available and genuine method of teaching.

Editor's note: I. Balkhashov's experiment is an example of an individual case, where dilettantism produced some undesirable acute side-effects. The results are ambiguous and a warning on the necessity for properly and skilfully administered hypnopaedic procedures, although the subject's improved performance in translating showed evidence of the effectiveness of hypnopaedic memorisation. It seems that the experimenter did not follow any recently established method of this technique as it is done by

L. A. Bliznitchenko and others. No information was given upon the subject's knowledge of German (which was the 'intermediary') but it leads to speculation on the possibility of presenting simultaneously lexicographical information in two foreign languages. It is likely that the subject had a good aptitude for foreign languages generally, but because of the lack of 'professionalism' in presenting the data, conclusions of Balkhashov's experiment can be considered as being only tentative.

14

AN INVESTIGATION INTO THE FUNCTIONAL STATE OF THE BRAIN CORTEX—PERSONS TAUGHT BY THE METHOD OF HYPNOPAEDIA

A. E. Khil'chenko, S. I. Moldavskaya,
N. V. Kol'chenko, G. N. Shevko

REFERENCE is made in many writings to assimilation and memorisation during natural sleep (I. E. Stepanov, 1922 (8); K. I. Platonov, 1957 (4); A. M. Svyadoshch, 1940, 1962 (6), (7); V. N. Kulikov, 1964 (3) and others).

A. M. Svyadoshch (6), (7), who began to investigate the problem of hypnopaedia in the nineteen-forties in the USSR, explains the facts arrived at from the point of view of the teaching of I. P. Pavlov about sleep with a 'point of vigilance'. It is supposed that learning during sleep takes place because of the functioning of the cells of the 'point of vigilance' with simultaneous inhibition of the remaining departments of the brain.

The method of hypnopaedia has recently begun to be widely used for the teaching of foreign languages and for other disciplines.

In the Institute of Linguistics of the Academy of Sciences of the USSR (Kiev), L. A. Bliznitchenko has developed a method of teaching persons during natural sleep which is becoming more and more widespread, not only in Kiev but beyond the borders of the Ukraine.

Teaching during natural sleep by L. A. Bliznitchenko's method is carried out as follows, in general outline: before sleep, while lying in bed, the learners listen to a text recorded on magnetic tape, lasting five minutes. Then, after the light in the room has been turned off, the same text is read through three times more; normal sleep then follows. For the first forty-five minutes of sleep the text is read through a further nine times, more and more quietly. At the conclusion of the lesson the following sentence is pronounced: 'Sleep peacefully; do not wake up.'

In view of the fact that the method used alters the circumstances and the usual course of the process of drowsiness and sleep, the question arises whether the method of hypnopaedia is not in itself harmful to healthy students and, above all, whether it may not give rise to serious disturbances in the functional state of the brain cortex.

The work now presented is devoted to the clarification of the question of the influence of teaching by the method of hypnopaedia upon the functional state of the brain cortex of man.

METHOD OF INVESTIGATION

Two groups of persons were submitted to the investigation: (1) a group of students by the method of hypnopaedia (fifteen persons); (2) a group studying by ordinary methods during the day-time (fifteen persons). All the subjects in both groups were aged from nineteen to twenty-four, had a complete intermediate education and lived in identical conditions. Teaching by the method of hypnopaedia lasted about two months. The lessons occupied five days a week; on Saturdays and Sundays the subjects rested.

Investigation of the functional state of the brain cortex was carried out with the help of the method developed by A. Ye. Khil'chenko (10) at the 'A. A. Bogomolets' Institute of Physiology of the Academy of Sciences of the USSR. This method makes it possible to obtain the qualitative characteristics of certain properties of the nervous system, in particular the mobility of nervous processes and the work capacity of the brain cortex in both the primary and the second signal systems.

The method we used is based on the demonstrations of I. P. Pavlov of mobility as a property of nervous processes, manifest in a whole series of time characteristics of the central nervous system (the rapidity with which nervous processes arise, the rapidity with which they are cut off, the rapidity of their movement, i.e., irradiation and concentration, the rapidity with which excitation turns into inhibition, etc.). At the same time, I. P. Pavlov introduced into the concept of mobility his general biological line of thought, observing that a greater or lesser marginal rapidity in the thoughts, movements or actions inherent in a given man is conditioned by greater or lesser mobility of the nervous processes.

The essence of the method used for investigating the mobility of the nervous processes and the work capacity of the cortical cells is as follows. A cinematograph film is moved onwards, in front of the subject, on which are recorded geometrical figures (stimuli addressed primarily to the first signal system), or else simple two-syllable words (stimuli addressed to the second signal system).

Before the experiment begins, the subject is instructed to press a button on the left with his left hand when a circle appears, a button on the right with his right hand when a square appears, and to press neither button when a triangle appears.

In investigating the second signal system, the subject is told to press the left-hand button for words designating plants, the right-hand button for words designating animals and neither for words designating inanimate objects.

Motor reaction to a stimulus was recorded by means of marking pens on a verification strip, moved in synchronism with and parallel to the demonstration film.

At first the film is moved on at a slow speed (forty to fifty frames per minute). As the task is mastered, the speed of moving on the frames with the recorded stimuli is gradually increased, i.e., the time of exposure of each frame before the eyes of the subject is diminished. After a few practice experiments, it was possible to determine for each subject the limiting speed of moving on the frames of stimuli at which the subject could still give correct responses according to his instructions, with no more than three errors in fifty frames. That limiting frequency of presentation of the stimuli at which the subject made no more than three mistakes per fifty stimuli was taken as the quantitative expression of the level of mobility.

The work capacity of the brain cortex was determined by counting the number of errors shown by subjects when a series of 800 stimuli was presented to them at a speed corresponding to the level of mobility of the nerve processes for each subject.

As is well known, I. P. Pavlov already considered that the best criterion of the strength of the cortical processes in man is the work capacity of the cortical cells. A number of physiologists hold the same view, and have used the work capacity of the cortical cells as one of the fundamental indices of the strength of the cortical processes. Thus, B. M. Teplov (9) points out that the strength of a stimulating process is characterised by the limit of work capacity of the nerve cells, i.e., by their capacity to retain a prolonged, concentrated excitation without passing over into a state of inhibition.

The determination of the index of work capacity of the brain cortex by the method of A. E. Khil'chenko is based on the fact that the concentration of attention, when a large number of stimuli are presented in succession, is reflected physiologically as the concentrated excitation of identical nerve elements. If the nerve cells are weak, attention will be shorter than with a stronger nervous system; this is revealed by an increase in the number of erroneous reactions. By determining the work capacity of the cortical cells before and after a given influence, it is possible to judge what changes have been brought about as a result of that factor.

In the case of our subjects, the mobility of the nervous processes and the work capacity of the cortical cells were determined first for the first signal system, and then for the second.

All investigations were carried out in three stages: (1) at the beginning of teaching by the hypnopaedic method; (2) just before the conclusion of teaching; (3) one and a half months after teaching had ended.

The control group also underwent a threefold investigation: (1) during studies (before the examinations); (2) after the end of the examination session; (3) after a rest of one and a half months.

In the case of the fifteen persons studying by the method of hypnopaedia, a determination was also made of the length of the latent period of conditioned motor reflexes during the teaching period, after it had ended and again after a rest of a month and a half.

The length of the latent period was measured in milliseconds by an electronic reflex-meter with a PS-100 counter. The preliminary instructions given to the subject explained that he should press a button on a portable push-button device and release it as quickly as possible in response to the lighting up of a small lamp. In each experiment the stimulus was applied ten times, and the mean length of the latent period for the ten experiments was taken as the final result.

RESULTS OF THE INVESTIGATIONS

The investigation of the state of mobility of the nervous processes and the work capacity of the cells of the cortex in the first signal system in the persons of the experimental group, after teaching by the method of hypnopaedia, showed no statistically significant changes; neither were statistically significant changes in the same indices for the first signal system shown when the persons of the control group were investigated after the examination session.

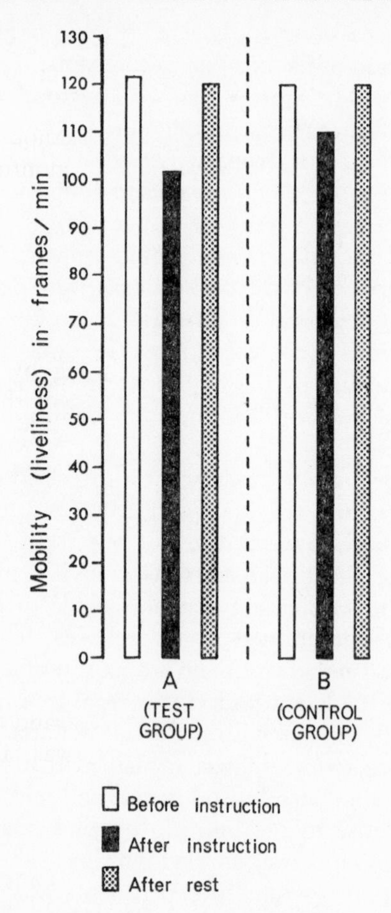

Fig. 14.1. Change in liveliness of the neural processes in persons of test and control groups.

A—test group B—control group
WHITE COLUMN—average index of liveliness before instruction
BLACK COLUMN—average index of liveliness after instruction
DOTTED COLUMN—average index of liveliness after rest

For the second message system, in the case both of the experimental group of persons and the control group, marked changes in the indices of mobility of the nervous processes and the work capacity of the cells of the brain cortex were observed. Thus, from Fig. 14.1, which shows the mean indices of the mobility of the nervous processes in the second signal system in persons of the experimental and control groups at all three stages of the investigation, it may be seen that mobility after teaching by the hypnopaedic method (or for the control group after the examinations) has diminished. After the period of rest, a re-establishment of the indices of mobility is observed for both groups.

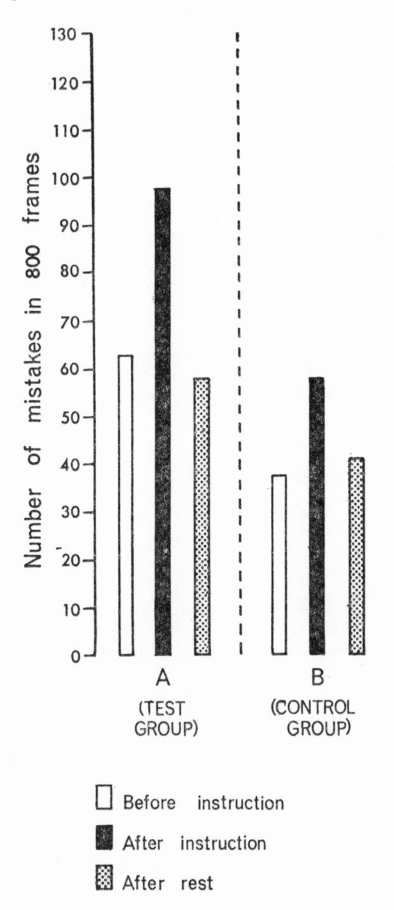

Fig. 14.2. Change in the working capacity of the cortical cells of the brain in persons of test and control groups

A—test group B—control group
Significance of columns the same as in 14.1

Fig. 14.2 shows the change in the work capacity of the cortical cells in the second signal system in persons of the experimental and control groups. Both after teaching by the hypnopaedic method and after the examinations (in the case of the control group), the number of errors in carrying out a lengthy task rises sharply. After rest, the work capacity of the brain cortex, for persons of both groups, is restored to its original level.

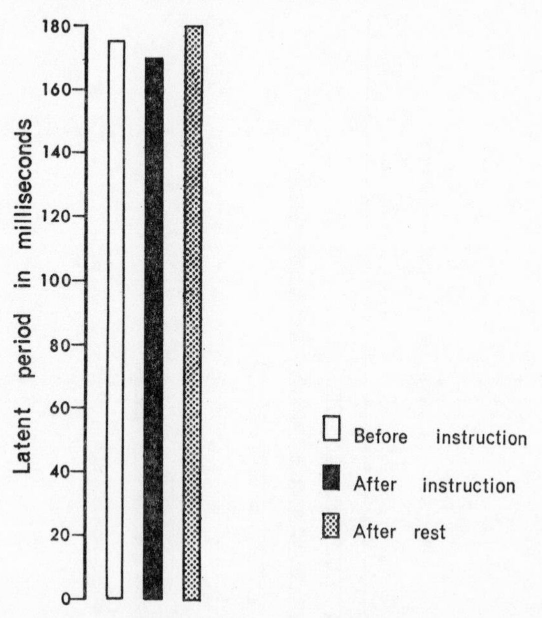

Fig. 14.3. Change in the duration of the latent period of the motor conditioned reflex in persons of the test group

WHITE COLUMN—average duration of the latent period before instruction
BLACK COLUMN—average duration of the latent period after instruction
DOTTED COLUMN—average duration of the latent period after rest

Fig. 14.3 shows the mean indices of motor conditioned reflexes in persons of the experimental group. After teaching by the hypnopaedic method the latent period diminishes, returning to its initial level after rest.

In order to evaluate the significance of the differences between the arithmetical means of the indices of mobility and work capacity in the first and second signal systems at all three stages of the investigation, a statistical analysis of the data was carried out. In establishing the significance of differences between the arithmetic means, we used standard deviations derived from the following formula:

$$t = \frac{\bar{x}_1 - \bar{x}_2}{\delta\bar{x}_1 - \bar{x}_2} = \frac{d}{ds}.$$

The mean error of differences was determined according to the formula for groups with a small '*n*' (P. F. Rokitiskii, 1961 (5)):

$$Sd = \sqrt{\left[\frac{\Sigma_1(x_1 - \bar{x}_1) + \Sigma_2(x_2 - \bar{x}_2)}{(n_1 - 1) + (n_2 - 1)} \cdot \frac{(n_1 + n_2)}{n_1 \cdot n_2}\right]}$$

The results of statistical analysis were as follows.

In the first signal system: the differences between arithmetical means and indices for the mobility of nervous processes and work capacity of the cortical cells, before teaching and after, were not significant.

In the second signal system, the probability of significance of the various mean indices of work capacity of the cortical cells before and after teaching (or for the control group, before and after the examinations), proved to be quite large—0·977 for the experimental group and 0·970 for the control group). The probability of significance of the differences in the indices of mobility before and after teaching was slightly less: 0·811 in the experimental group, 0·784 in the control group.

The probability of differences between the mean values for the latent period of motor conditioned reflexes, in persons of the experimental group before and after teaching, was also high (0·990).

Analysis of the data obtained shows that, in persons who have been learning for two months by the method of hypnopaedia, towards the end of the training the mobility of the nervous processes decreases, and there is a marked deterioration in the work capacity of the cortex of the brain. These shifts find expression, generally speaking, in the second signal system. At the same time, in the majority of subjects, a diminution of the latent period of motor conditioned reflexes is observed. As a rule, a diminution in the latent period is regarded as a positive reaction of the nervous system to the action of various factors; however, the causes and mechanisms of the diminution of the latent period are extremely diverse, and it is by no means always possible to interpret this phenomenon as a positive one (L. S. Bogachenko (1), M. P. Ivanovna (2)). Starting from I. P. Pavlov's position that the process of internal inhibition is much more labile than the process of excitation, and may suffer more than the latter from the effects of unfavourable conditions, the diminution of the latent period after training by the method of hypnopaedia may be explained as a weakening of the inhibitory process. The balance of the fundamental nervous processes is upset in the direction of the prevalence of the excitation process, and this finds reflection in the diminution of the latent period of motor conditioned reflexes.

Thus, under the influence of the study load, which included a two-months' course of teaching by the method of hypnopaedia, a lowering of the full value of the functional condition of the brain cortex was observed; in other words, fatigue, which showed itself as a diminution of the mobility of the nervous processes, a lowering in the work capacity of the cortical cells of the brain, especially in the second signal system, and a diminution of the latent period of motor-conditioned reflexes caused by a weakening of internal inhibition. However, all these phenomena are reversible; one and a half months after the cessation of teaching by the method of hypnopaedia (normal daily activity meanwhile not being interrupted), all the indices under investigation returned to their initial level.

In the control group, under the influence of the heavy study load during the examination session, a similar deterioration of the functional state of the brain cortex was observed; this too was reversible in character.

Consequently, the fatigue produced by a two-months' course of teaching by hypnopaedia may be equated with the fatigue produced by an intensive study load (the examination session), and since it is reversible in character it does *not* represent any threat to the functional state of the brain cortex in man, or to his health.

CONCLUSIONS

1. Teaching by the method of hypnopaedia leads to changes in the functional state of the brain cortex in man, showing themselves as a lowering of the mobility of the fundamental nervous processes, of the work capacity of the cortical cells in the second signal system and the shortening of the latent period of motor-conditioned reflexes.

2. The intensified study load taken on in the daytime only (the examination session) leads to changes in the functional state of the

brain cortex which are similar to those which arise in persons studying for two months by means of hypnopaedia.

3. The changes observed, both in teaching by the method of hypnopaedia and in teaching by the usual method, are reversible in character. The functional state of the brain cortex is restored after rest.

4. Teaching by the method of hypnopaedia for a period of two months does not exert any specifically harmful influence upon the functional state of the brain cortex in man.

REFERENCES

1. L. S. Bogachenko, *Zhurnal Vysshei Nervnoi Deiatel'nosti* (Journal of the Higher Nervous Activity), **3**, 2nd Ed., 1953.
2. M. P. Ivanova, Some data concerning reduction of the latent period of the motor reaction. Voprosy *Psikhologii* (Problems of Psychology), No. 2, 1958.
3. V. N. Kulikov, *The Problems of Hypnopaedia. Voprosy Psikhologii* (Problems of Psychology), No. 2, 1964.
4. K. I. Platonov, *Slovo kak fisiogicheskii i lechebnyi faktor.* (The Word as Physiological and Therapeutic Factor.) Moscow, Medgiz, 1957.
5. P. F. Rokitskii, *Osnovy Variatsionnoi Statistiki Dlia Biologov.* (Principles of Variation Statistics for Biologists.) Moscow, 1961.
6. A. M. Svyadoshch, The Assimilation of Speech During Natural Sleep. Thesis for Master's degree. Leningrad, 1940.
7. A. M. Svyadoshch, *Assimilation and Memorization of Speech During Natural Sleep. Voprosy psikhologii* (Problems of Psychology), No. 1, 1962.
8. I. E. Stepanov, *Psikhologiia Snovidenii.* (The Psychology of Dreams.) Berlin, 1922.
9. B. M. Teplov, *Tipologicheskie Osobennosti Vysshei Nervnoi Deiatel' nosti Cheloveka* (Typological features of the higher nervous activity in man), **3**, 1963.
10. A. E. Khil'chenko, *Zhurnal Vysshei Nervnoi Deiatel'nosti* (Journal of the Higher Nervous Activity), **8**, 6th Ed., 1958.

mar

15

INVESTIGATIONS INTO THE THEORY AND PRACTICE OF SLEEP-LEARNING

V. N. Kulikov

Editor's Note: This study of Kulikov's is an unabridged translation that he wrote for summing up further results of his extensive experimental work. Although the reader may find some repetitions of what he mentioned in his former work, the informative value of this paper (with the Tables 1 to 4) is more comprehensive than his previous monograph.

A BRIEF RESUME OF THE PROBLEMS OF SLEEP-LEARNING

THE subject of sleep-learning became of particular interest in the nineteen-thirties, although early mentions of cases of retention of the spoken word by a sleeping individual date back to the end of the nineteenth and beginning of the twentieth centuries (Maury, L., Vjazemskij, N. V., Moll, A., Stepanov, I. J.).

The interest was brought about by the necessities of existence. With the growth of the sciences, so typical of the twentieth century, the number of facts required in the life and employment of an individual grew rapidly. New ways for the acquisition of facts had to be sought and experiments into the possibilities of teaching people in their sleep were started in many countries.

These experiments employed various methods. Most researchers (Kulikov, V. N., Elliott, C., Emmons, W. H. and Simon, C. W.) started their first experiments by combining teaching during sleep with subsequent revision while awake. The method was roughly as follows: Sleeping subjects from an experimental group were presented with the chosen material (e.g. foreign words and their meanings). Later, while awake, subjects from both the experimental and the control group were invited to learn the material. It was found that subjects from the first group mastered the material much faster than subjects from the second group (e.g., in our experiments, on the average 84 per cent faster, in the experiments of C. Elliott 83 per cent faster).

Simultaneously, experiments were carried out using the method of revision during normal sleep (Kulikov, V. N., Bliznitchenko, L. A.). During these experiments the material was read to subjects from both experimental groups while awake (before going to sleep). The same material was then presented to the members of the experimental group only, while they were asleep. When checking retention, it was found that the members of the experimental group retained far more of the subject matter than members of the second group (in our experiments, 84 per cent against 16 per cent).

The above experimental results show that methods which combine sleep-learning with additional learning while awake are relatively effective. Such methods, however, still deprive a person of some of his waking time.

Some experimenters, prompted by this realisation, initiated sleep-learning experiments without previous teaching or subsequent revision while awake. One of the first researchers to attempt such experiments was A. M. Svyadoshch. This author, however, precedes his work by experimentally enhancing in his subjects (by a method of 'autogenic training') their ability to absorb verbal information while asleep. Under these conditions the experimental results were good. For example, during one experiment, sixteen subjects out of twenty reproduced on the average 89·5 per cent of the material presented to them while they were asleep and only four subjects scored the low average of 18·6 per cent of subject matter reproduced.

The method which relies on prior training of the ability to absorb verbal information while asleep is inseparably connected with the understanding of the nature of this ability. Some authors (Svyadoshch, A. M., Zuchar, V. P.) deny that the ability to sleep-learn is a natural one. A. M. Svyadoshch reaches this conclusion on the basis of the following experiment: sleeping experimental subjects, who were not previously warned of the experiment, were twice read a fable. The experimental subjects either slept through the reading and did not remember anything the next morning, or they woke up during the reading.

Our experiments, however, disproved this attitude towards sleep-learning. We found that the ability to learn while asleep is a natural one and as much a heritage of every human being as the ability to learn while awake. However, the ability to sleep-learn is a potential ability of the subconscious levels of the human psyche. To achieve results, it must be 'awakened', activated and directed towards the appropriate subject matter. This is why spontaneous cases of retention of the spoken word by sleeping persons are so uncommon in everyday life. Here, too, lies the reason for the lack of success of the experiments of A. M. Svyadoshch, to which he refers, when he denies that sleep-learning is a natural ability.

The discovery of the above fundamental facts enabled us to modify our method of sleep-teaching. Our latest experiments make no use of any learning while awake or of previous training of the sleep-learning ability, yet our experimental results are good.

Sleep-learning covers learning not only during normal sleep, but also during hypnotic sleep. Such experiments were, and are, being carried out by a number of workers (Powers, M., Hollander, B., Kulikov, V. N.), who have had very good results. The French magazine *Science et la vie* announced, for example, that M. Bellini employs hypnotism to help students prepare for, and successfully pass, examinations. The same author carried out an experiment, during which fifteen students were taught simultaneously while in a hypnotic sleep. All the experimental subjects showed good knowledge of the subject matter.

It must be emphasised that all workers concerned with teaching with the aid of hypnotism carry out experiments without any additional teaching while the subjects are awake and without any previous training of the sleep-learning ability in the subjects of their experiments.

Suggestions implanted during normal and hypnotic sleep can also be used for purposes of training and reorientation of human beings. Many authors (LeShan, L., Kulikov, V. N.) use such methods to eliminate successfully undesirable habits (smoking, chronic mendacity, nail biting and others) and to strengthen positive habits and characteristics of the personality (obedience, meticulousness, ability to take decisions, memory and others).

Since the beginning of the study of sleep-learning, Soviet workers (Svyadoshch, A. M., Kulikov, V. N.) have tried to explain its existence, in the light of the teachings of I. P. Pavlov. The kind of sleep during which learning or training is possible is assumed to be supervised by a 'guard centre'. This means that the absorption and retention of verbal information during sleep is carried out by the cells of the 'guard centre', while the activity of the remainder of the cerebral mass is damped. The process is one of the formation of temporary nerve paths.

What, then, does this brief historical resume tell us? It shows that the possibility of teaching human beings during normal and hypnotic sleep has been experimentally proven. Also proven is the use of suggestion during normal and hypnotic sleep for purposes of orientation and re-orientation. This means that sleep-learning methods can be of great practical value.

Sleep-learning is also of theoretical importance. Its study may help us solve many problems in psychology, not the least of these being the complex and scientifically important interaction of the subconscious and the conscious in the human psyche.

RESEARCH AIMS AND METHODS

The requirements of the study of sleep-learning itself led us to the problem of the nature of this human ability and the conditions of its realisation.

The problem also arose of the specific peculiarities of those properties of the psyche which take part in the process of sleep-learning. This was, then, the background of our work, the results of which are described in this article.

In the years 1962–1964 four series of experiments with teaching subjects in normal and hypnotic sleep were undertaken, to help clarify some of the above problems. We conducted a total of eight collective experiments, in which forty experimental subjects took part pupils of sixth and seventh forms and students from the Institute of Pedagogy.

When selecting experimental subjects, we investigated not only the overall state of their health, but also any peculiarities of their sleep: how they fell asleep, the length and depth of sleep, dreams and their nature, awakening, etc. Their degree of suggestibility was also taken into account.

The subject matter used in the experiments was previously unkown to the experimental subjects, but comprehensible to them in its content and scope. With the pupils, we used the fable 'Wounded by a word' from the book *The Wisdom of Whimsy* (S. S. Orbeliani), with the students, a text in psychology on the constancy of perception (special version, par. 5, chapter V, *Textbook of Psychology for Institutes of Pedagogy*).

The first series comprised experiments on teaching during normal sleep. They were preceded by no attempt at any preliminary training of the ability to sleep-learn in the experimental subject. Each experiment was begun by establishing contact with the sleeping experimental subject. To this end, the following suggestion was used: 'You are peacefully asleep. . . . You are asleep and not going to wake up. . . . You are asleep and you are listening to my voice. . . .'

After establishing contact, the experimental subjects were directed towards good understanding and perception, to facilitate their retention and subsequent recall of the subject matter. This was done as follows: 'You will now hear the subject matter. . . . You will grasp and remember its contents. . . . You will remember it well, you will remember forever. . . . You will be able to recall it at will. . . . Now listen and remember!' (With experimental subjects who had taken part in previous experiments, this particular suggestion was omitted.)

After this introduction came the actual subject matter. This was repeated twice and followed by a suggestion of successful absorption, understanding, memorisation and retention of the subject matter: 'You have heard the subject matter. . . . You have understood it and remembered it for ever. . . . You will be able to recall it at will. . . .'

During all these experiments the voice used was not the direct voice of the experimenter, but a previously prepared tape-recording of all the experimental matter. The tape-recording was played at the lowest possible level. This not only prevented waking up the experimental subjects, as happened during the experiments of other authors, but, in our opinion, reduced the loading and stress of the nervous system of the experimental subjects.

The second series comprised experiments with teaching during hypnotic sleep. The necessary degree of hypnotic sleep was induced in the experimental subjects by the method of influencing the visual centre together with verbal suggestion. The various instructions given to the subjects were then exactly the same as in the experiments of the first series. The subject matter was presented from the same tape, repeated the same number of times as during the normal-sleep experiments. (To check the permanence of memorisation and recall, the normal subject matter was, in some experiments, followed by material totally foreign to the subject.) The concluding instructions were the same in the second series of experiments as in the first series.

During the experiments, a check was kept of the movements and respiration of experimental subjects. Observations (visual, recordings of motility and respiration) showed that, while the subject matter was being presented, all the experimental subjects slept exactly as before. None showed any external reaction to verbal stimuli. There was no particular change in motility or in respiration. In particular, the respiration rate remained exactly the same before, during and after the experiment.

The experiment ended for each subject with a determination of his knowledge of the subject matter. This was done immediately after the experiment, one day later and one week later. To make the classification of results more objective, the subject matter was divided into units, each unit expressing a particular idea or concept.

EXPERIMENTAL RESULTS

Examination of the knowledge of the subject matter learnt by subjects during normal sleep showed a high degree of retention in all the subjects. We shall give, as an example, the complete interview with a subject who listened to the text on the constancy of perception:

Experimenter: Well, how are you? How did you sleep?

Subject M.: I slept well and I feel fine.

Exp.: Well, in that case, tell me what you know about the constancy of perception.

Sub.: The constancy of perception is the relative constancy of certain properties of perceived objects when the conditions of perception have changed. It manifests itself in the perception of colour, size and shape of an object. . . . The constancy of perception of the size of objects means that the size of an object does not change when our distance from the object changes. For example, a person at a distance of three, five or ten metres is seen as a full-size adult. This happens, because we are always comparing the size of the person we are looking at with size of other objects already known to us. . . .

The constancy of perception of the shape of objects means that the shape of the object does not change when the direction of observation changes. For example, a circle looks round even from one side. This happens, because we know the real

	shape of objects from previous observation.
Exp.:	Give another example of the constancy of perception of the shape of an object.
Sub.:	(thinks) For example, a plate. When we look at it from one side, it looks like an ellipse, but we perceive it as being round.
Exp.:	And why is that, then?
Sub.:	Because we know from previous perception that the plate is round. And the previous experience affects our perception of the plate and makes it correct.

The summary of this series of experiments is given in Table 1. Good results were also obtained with the pupils who were presented with the fable 'Wounded by a word'. The interview with one of the experimental subjects went as follows:

Experimenter:	How do you feel, young man?
Subject B.:	Fine.
Exp.:	Do you know the story 'Wounded by a word'?
Sub.:	Yes.
Exp.:	Come on then, tell it to me.
Sub.:	There was a man who made friends with a bear and asked him home. . . . When the bear was leaving, the man kissed him on both cheeks. The man's wife then said, that she would not kiss a bear for anything. The bear went away. . . . One day the man went back to the forest and he met the bear again. The bear asked the man to hit him with his axe. . . . A month later the man met the bear again. The bear told the man that the cut the man gave him was all right again, but the words of the wife were still hurting. A word can kill a person.
Exp.:	You know the story well. But where did you learn it?
Sub.:	I dreamt it, I think.
Exp.:	And what exactly did you dream?
Sub.:	Well, what I have just said: How a bear came to visit a 'mujik' . . . (subject re-tells story).

The summary of the results of this series of experiments is given in Table 2.

Even better results were obtained with experimental subjects who were learning during hypnotic sleep. Here is part of the record of an interview with a subject who had listened to the text on the constancy of perception:

Experimenter: Well, how do you feel?

Subject J.: I feel fine.

Exp.: Tell me, do you know anything about the constancy of perception?

Sub.: I do.

Exp.: Tell me, then.

Sub.: One of the laws of perception is constancy. . . . In psychology, the concept of constancy expresses the lack of change of properties of perceived objects under changing conditions of perception. Constancy is observed in the perception of colour, size and shape of objects.

The constancy of perception of a colour manifests itself in the unchanged colour of an object under different conditions of illumination. A piece of white paper, for example, appears white in bright sunlight, as well as at dusk. This is a consequence of previous experience. The observer knows the real colour of the object. . . . The constancy of perception of the size of an object manifests itself in the unaltered size of an object with varying distance. For example, a man at a distance of three, five and ten metres is perceived as the same size. This can be explained by the contraction of the optic muscles and by the fact that we always compare the size of objects with the size of other objects already known to us. . . .

The constancy of perception of the shape of objects manifests itself in the constant apparent shape of objects with changing angles of view. For example, when we observe a circle at an angle to its plane, it is projected on our retina as an ellipse. In spite of this, we perceive a circle as being round. This can be explained as the effect of perceptions, which occurred previously, of past experience.

A summary of this series of experiments is shown in Table 3.

Similarly good results were obtained when teaching pupils in a hypnotic sleep the fable 'Wounded by a word'. Here again is the interview with one experimental subject from this group:

Experimenter: How do you feel?
Subject G.: Fine.
Exp.: Do you know the story 'Wounded by a word'?
Sub.: Yes.
Exp.: Tell me, then.
Sub.: A man once befriended a bear. He arranged a feast and invited the bear for a visit. When the bear was getting ready to go home, the man kissed him on both cheeks. He then told his wife to kiss the bear too. But when the wife smelt the bear, she said: 'I can't stand your stinking guests.' The bear went away without a word. . . . After some time, the man picked up his axe and said to the wife: 'I am going to the forest to chop some wood'. As soon as the man entered the forest, he met the bear. They greeted each other—each in his own way. But the bear then insistently demanded that the man wound him on the head with his axe. The man kept refusing but the bear insisted. And so, the man hit him on the head with his axe and went home.

About a month later, the man and the bear met again. And the bear said to the man: 'Come and look. The wound you gave me with your axe has healed, but my heart, wounded by the words of your wife, is still bleeding'. A word can kill a man. The wound caused by a word does not heal.

Exp.: You know the story well. Where did you learn it?
Sub.: I don't know.

A summary of this series of experiments is shown in Table 4.

EVALUATION OF EXPERIMENTAL RESULTS

The data from these experiments again confirms the already stated conclusion that the ability to sleep-learn is a *natural* one and *inherent* in all human beings. All experimental subjects demonstrated a good knowledge of the text presented to them during sleep, although the experiments were conducted *without* a preliminary training of the ability in question.

There are reasons for considering the ability to sleep-learn to be a function of the subconscious level of the human psyche. This is confirmed by the fact that the experimental subjects were not aware of the process of acquiring knowledge while asleep. Where the experimental subjects had not been previously informed of the nature of the experiments conducted on them, they could not explain the origin of the knowledge they had acquired. However, the knowledge gained in this way, through the subconscious, is transferred, as a result of the experimenters questions in the waking state, into the region of conscious knowledge and becomes a part of its contents.

The transfer of subconsciously acquired knowledge into the conscious mind does not take place immediately after the awakening of the experimental subjects. It occupies a definite time. This is why attempts at recall postponed by a day were more productive. See Table 1 (subjects 3,4,5,6,8,9,10), and Table 2 (subjects 4,7,8,9,10.)

This leads one to suppose, that the process of sleep-learning requires not only perception and memory, but also thought. The need of conscious thought is borne out by the reconstruction of the sleep-learned knowledge (changes in the sequence of ideas explained in the subject matter), and by the answers given by experimental subjects to special questions which required understanding (see replies to questions in interviews).

The experiments uncovered some peculiarities of retention and recall by sleep-learning. They showed an exceptional lack of stability of these processes immediately after the presentation of the subject matter. When we exposed an experimental subject, immediately after the presentation of the subject matter, to other stimuli, the subject matter was easily forgotten—see Table 3 (subjects 9, 10) and Table 4 (subject 10). This can clearly be explained by the high 'vulnerability' of freshly formed paths which can be easily and quickly damped.

Together with this lack of stability immediately after exposure, sleep-learning is characterised by a rapid fixing of the acquired knowledge after the initial period. Experiments show that even a few minutes after presentation, other stimuli no longer erase the acquired subject matter—see Table 3 (subjects 4, and 5). The temporary paths, clearly very 'vulnerable' at the beginning, strengthen very rapidly and gain considerable stability. This can probably be explained by postulating, that the brain subconsciously continuously reinforces paths, once they have formed. It is known that paths in the brain are fixed by a process of reverberation and that they are continuously repeated in the central part of the brain and so kept permanently active.

Our work further defines our previous conclusions that, when teaching during normal sleep, the presentation of the subject matter to the experimental subject should be preceded by a suggestion of perception, retention and recall. It was found, that the need for such instructions is reduced with repeated experiments and ultimately disappears entirely. This is further emphasised by subjects 2, 3, and 4 in the first series of experiments, in whose case the instructions were omitted but who, nevertheless, showed good results (see Table 1).

A comparison of the results of the first and second series of experiments demonstrates the difference in the ability to acquire knowledge during normal and hypnotic sleep. These abilities would seem to be the result of the operation of the subconscious on different levels, which is also connected with the different level of activity of the cells. There is substantiation for an assumption that learning during hypnotic sleep occurs in a condition of higher activity of cerebral cells then is the case in normal sleep-learning. This is supported by the fact that the subjects taught in hypnotic sleep showed better results than subjects taught in normal sleep (compare Tables 1 and 3, 2, and 4). Although the ability to learn during sleep is inherent in all human beings, the degree differs among people. Experimental subjects in the first and second series of experiments show substantially different amounts of acquired knowledge (see Tables 1, 2, 3, 4). These individual differences are associated with different degrees of suggestibility among the subjects. In our experiments, the more suggestible persons gave better results.

We must not omit the very important fact, that *not one* of our experimental subjects complained of tiredness or mental upset after experiments during both normal and hypnotic sleep. All the persons concerned mentioned a pleasant state of mind and a feeling of having slept restfully.

Table 1

Final Results of Experiments on Teaching Subjects in Normal Sleep about 'The Constancy of Perception'

P.O. Subjects	*Quantity of textual units presented*	*Qunatity of textual units reproduced*			*Reproduction as a percentage*		
		after experiment	*in a day*	*in a week*	*after experiment*	*in a day*	*in a week*
1	25	21	21	21	84	84	84
2	25	21	21	20	84	84	80
3	25	20	21	20	80	84	80
4	25	19	21	21	76	84	84
5	25	19	20	20	76	80	80
6	25	19	20	20	76	80	80
7	25	19	19	19	76	76	76
8	25	17	18	17	68	72	68
9	25	17	18	18	68	72	72
10	25	15	20	20	60	80	80

Table 2

Final Results of Experiments of Teaching Subjects in Normal Sleep The Fairy Tale 'Wounded by a Word'

P.O. Subjects	*Quantity of textual units presented*	*Quantity of textual units reproduced*			*Reproduction as a percentage*		
		after experiment	*in a day*	*in a week*	*after experiment*	*in a day*	*in a week*
1	20	18	18	18	90	90	90
2	20	17	17	17	85	85	85
3	20	17	17	16	85	85	80
4	20	17	18	18	85	90	90
5	20	17	17	17	85	85	85
6	20	17	17	17	85	85	85
7	20	16	18	17	80	90	85
8	20	15	17	17	75	85	85
9	20	15	16	15	75	80	75
10	20	11	19	18	55	95	90

Table 3

Final Results of Experiments on Teaching Subjects in Hypnotic Sleep about The Constancy of Perception

P.O. Subjects	Quantity of textual units presented	Quantity of textual units reproduced			Reproduction as a percentage		
		after experiment	*in a day*	*in a week*	*after experiment*	*in a day*	*in a week*
1	25	23	23	21	92	92	84
2	25	23	23	23	92	92	92
3	25	22	22	21	88	88	84
4	25	22	22	22	88	88	88
5	25	22	22	22	88	88	84
6	25	20	20	20	80	80	80
7	25	19	19	19	76	76	76
8	25	19	19	19	76	76	76
9	25	16	16	16	64	64	64
10	25	16	16	16	64	64	64

Table 4

Final Results of Experiments on Teaching Subjects in Hypnotic Sleep The Fairy Tale 'Wounded by a Word'

P.O. Subjects	Quantity of textual units presented	Quantity of textual units reproduced			Reproduction as a percentage		
		after experiment	*in a day*	*in a week*	*after experiment*	*in a day*	*in a week*
1	20	19	19	17	95	95	85
2	20	19	19	18	95	95	90
3	20	18	18	17	90	90	85
4	20	18	18	17	90	90	85
5	20	18	18	18	90	90	90
6	20	17	17	17	85	85	85
7	20	16	16	16	80	80	80
8	20	16	16	14	80	80	70
9	20	16	16	16	80	80	80
10	20	10	10	9	50	50	45

16

REPORT ON THE PROBLEM OF ABSORBING IDEAS DURING SLEEP

M. Hradecky, V. Barton, V. Brezinova, M. Burian,
S. Stepanek, B. Mikuleckz

WE regard sleep generally as a condition when the contact of the subject with his surroundings is reduced and the capacity of absorbing information from outside is more difficult compared to the waking state. That this isolation of the subject is not complete is shown by current experience as well as by experiments: e.g., the differentiation between one's own name and other names (Oswald 1960); the carrying out of a simple motor reaction on a given stimulus even when fast asleep (Fischgold 1961, Granda 1961, Williams 1963); and the influencing of dreams by outside stimuli, even verbal ones (Kleiman 1961, Shevrin 1963, Berger 1963). With these experiments the effect of outside stimuli becomes frequently obvious through changes of the electric action of the brain, either by periodic actions, as shown by vertex sharp waves and K-complexes, or by general changes of the electric activity, change-over of the sleep level, usually towards the waking state, sometimes even up to the picture of the alpha rhythm which is typical for the waking state. Some reactions, however, were observed, e.g., instrumentally caused even in the so-called high-voltage sleep, in the electro-encephalogram without any signs of waking.

In our studies we observed the changes of the electro-encephalogram associated with word stimuli which were unknown and offered during sleep, and we evaluated the quality and frequency of these electric reactions in relation to the absorption of the words offered in the waking state, i.e., in learning them. We presumed that if learning during sleep was due mainly to absorption—that is, the impregnation of the proffered words—and that no other factors (e.g. emotional) were involved, there should be evident a difference in numbers, and possibly in the type of electric reactions, between the group of words absorbed later and the group of unsuccessful words. We were particularly interested in any possible difference between the occurrence of K-complexes, which represent a sign of aural stimulation whilst maintaining sleep, and the occurrence of the waking reaction—that is, a disturbance frequently only temporary—during the ordinary course of the sleep.

We evaluated the EEG records of a whole night's sleep of twenty test persons. These were normal volunteers who were subjected to the tape recording of a series of twenty-five or fifty individual words of a language unknown to them, mainly Japanese, together with the Czech translation; according to the length of sleep this series was repeated during the night one to twelve times. During the initial experiments on seven persons we found that of the whole number of 990 possibilities proffered there was not one instance proved by the EEG of a direct absorption of the recorded unknown word in the sleep. Therefore we evaluated in the experiments only the difference in learning two equally long and complicated series of individual words which were both replayed to the persons tested in the waking state and of which one was repeated during sleep. The statistical evaluation of the results (with the chi^2 test) showed that of twenty-eight proferred during the night, six series were more successful than the respective control series; with sixteen series there was no essential difference, and with the remaining six series the result was worse than with the control series. The EEG data was obtained on the Kaiser apparatus, with cemented electrodes arranged in accordance with the 'ten-twenty' diagram up to the front-polar electrodes, pushed up to the eyebrows. The following results were obtained: type of curve during the stimulus (high-voltage sleep, low-voltage sleep, alpha-rhythm); k-complexes in the high-voltage sleep; waking in the low-voltage sleep; occurrence of the alpha-rhythm during part of the stimulus.

We could not keep to our original intention of concentrating mainly on the period of the so-called paradox sleep, because we soon found that noise stimuli, whether spoken or indifferent noise transmitted during the intervals, severely impair the cyclic course of sleep, as was described by Dement and Kleitman, markedly reducing the high-voltage sleep and rendering the rapid eye movement period unclear, ending in an almost chronically flattened curve of most of the persons tested during the major part of the night.

Altogether we evaluated the EEG reaction on 5982 stimuli; of these 40 per cent referred to successful words, 60 per cent to unsuccessful ones. Table 1 shows the type of EEG curve during the offering of these stimuli. A comparison of all the successful and unsuccessful words showed a more frequent occurrence of the low-voltage sleep in the group of successful words, and the high-voltage sleep in the unsuccessful group. The division of whole series into groups according to the influence of sleep exposition on the result of learning provided, however, much more pronounced differences which were no longer influenced by the new division of successful and unsuccessful words. The group with positive results shows particularly little high-voltage sleep, which is again frequently above-average in the negative group.

Table 1

EEG Curve at Time of Preferring a Word Stimulus

EEG Group	*High-voltage Sleep*	*Low-voltage Sleep*	*Alpha rhythm*
+ (% of 1579 stimuli) .	5	89	6
0 (% of 3300 stimuli) .	11	86	3
− (% of 1103 stimuli) .	33	62	5

When observing the EEG reactions the group of successful words had a considerably larger number of cases with alpha-rhythm in the course of the waking stimulus in low-voltage sleep, smaller number of K-complexes in the low-voltage sleep; the unsuccessful words had the opposite reaction. A further analysis showed again a closer correlation of these reactions on the division, according to the result of the whole series (Table 2): the positive group showed an above-average occurrence with alpha rhythm during the stimulus, above-average K-complexes in the high and low voltage sleep, with successful as well as with unsuccessful words (Table 3); on the other hand, however, the group without a pronounced difference, and especially the negative group had even with the successful words little alpha rhythm occurrence with only few K-complexes in the low-voltage sleep. In the high-voltage sleep there occurred an inversion of the negative group by more K-complexes in the high-voltage sleep than in the zero-group.

Table 2

EEG Reaction of Successful Words (2338 stimuli)
% of number of possible reactions

EEG Group	+ *Total* 829 *stim.*	0 *Total* 1158 *stim.*	— *Total* 351 *stim.*
Alpha rhythm during part of stimuli . . .	21	17	3
Waking during high-voltage sleep . . .	2	8	1
Waking during low-voltage sleep	9	7	8
K-complexes during high-voltage sleep . . .	54	24	36
K-complexes in low-voltage sleep . . .	52	40	27

Table 3

EEG Reaction of Unsuccessful Words (3645 stimuli)
% of number of possible reactions

EEG Group	+ *Total* 750 *stim.*	0 *Total* 2143 *stim.*	— *Total* 752 *stim.*
Alpha-rhythm during part of stimuli . . .	21	8	2
Waking during high-voltage sleep . . .	5	3	1
K-complexes in high-voltage sleep . . .	53	22	35
K-complexes in low-voltage sleep . . .	59	44	28

It therefore appears that a certain statistically proven correlation of the EEG reactions to the result of learning is expressed less in the relation to the individual words; rather it is a question of a relation to the characteristics of the entire word series. It is not impossible that the favourable or unfavourable effect of the hypothetical happening expressing itself also in a change of the EEG does not affect the word proffered at the moment of the EEG change, but another word, perhaps near with regard to time; for instance, the previous or the subsequent one. In this case it is possible that there may be little pronounced (or zero) relationship to the word proffered during the EEG reaction, but a pronounced relationship to the output of the entire series of words. It is, however, also possible that it is an influence of another factor without direct inter-relation to the process of sleeping, for instance, selectively directed attention which could then even cause difference in the reaction to hearing stimuli during sleep. The evaluation of the group with negative result in conjunction with the values of high-voltage sleep exceeding all expectations, and the K-complexes in high-voltage sleep, brings to mind the experience of Kleitman about the attenuated influence and short period (five to ten minutes) of the high-voltage sleep on remembering dreams. It is, however, possible even in this case that this is an incidental result influenced by other factors, and it would be necessary to verify it with a larger number of cases.

CONCLUSION

1. It did not succeed in proving that foreign words were absorbed only in electro-encephalographically proven sleep.
2. From twenty-eight comparisons between learning series proffered during the waking state and during sleep there was no significant difference in 60 per cent; the sleeping series was better in 20 per cent of the cases and worse also in 20 per cent.
3. The EEG data were more closely connected to the result of learning a whole series than to the result with individual words.
4. The successful words occurred more frequently with the alpha-rhythm during the stimulus, more subjects waking in the low-voltage sleep.
5. Series better than the control series showed more with alpha-rhythm during stimulus, more K-complexes in high-voltage and low-voltage sleep, a greater number in low-voltage sleep.
6. The series which were worse than the control series were more frequent in high-voltage sleep, and more K-complexes in high-voltage sleep.
7. The results obtained seem to us to be theoretically interesting, but do not, however, support the possibilities of practical application of so-called learning during high-voltage EEG sleep.

In conclusion we wish to express our thanks to J. Vedralova, EEG laboratory assistant at the Clinic, the Instrument Centre VSPE, and all the persons tested for their co-operation.

Dr. V. Brezinova sent the following personal observations to the Editor:

'There were no psychologists participating in our first trial; however several psychological and clinical variables (e.g. subjective appraisal of the quality and quantity of the sleep, the recall of the dreams, Taylor's anxiety scale etc.) were evaluated by me.

'Before my actual function of electro-encephalographist I worked eight years as psychiatrist and I also have experience in clinical psychiatric research. Some results dealing with these psychological variables were reported at the Conference of the Czechoslovakian EEG Commission in May 1966 (Brezinova, Barton, Hradecky, Bechoucek, Simandl: Subjective appraisal and EEG record of the night sleep disturbed by sounds in normals). We found that subjects who evaluated their sleep (during the experimental night) as having deteriorated, did not differ (statistically) from subjects with subjective good sleep in regard to the quantity of EEG vigilance patterns, EEG sleep patterns and number of EEG arousals. Subjects who felt drowsy in the morning showed a smaller number of the EEG awakenings and better preserved high-voltage slow-wave periods during the experimental night; they also had a more frequent incidence of very good sleep in the last six months (comparison with subjects who did not feel drowsy in the morning).

'In regard to the EEG sleep cycles we found that continuous verbal stimulation or the indifferent noise—at least in the intensity applied by us, that is about 40 dcb—disturbed the development of normal EEG sleep patterns and even reduced the amount of the high-voltage slow waves. Our "low-voltage sleep" cannot be directly identified with the REM phase. The true REM phase was found rather seldom and mostly when stimulation was interrupted. During acoustic stimulation, however, predominance of very low-voltage record was found, with mixed fast and slow waves but there were also episodes during this time of phase rhythms which do not exist in the true REM phase. We could also distinguish two types of reactivity in this state, one with marked K-complexes after the sound stimuli, another without those reactions (which is similar to the REM phase). I believe that our low-voltage sleep is not a physiological unity and I prepare a further evaluation of it.

'I agree with your emphasis on the inter-disciplinary team investigation of the very complex problem of hypnopaedia. I believe that on the first step the true role of the sleep in the hypnopaedic procedure is to be testified. Is it not possible that the effect of a "placebo" situation is involved, enhancing the motivation and the zest in the learning during the wakefulness? I might ask you if a double blind trial exists in this regard, as it is applied in the psycho-pharmacological research.

'I agree with your opinion that the success of the Russians might rest on applying the hypnopaedic technique during behavioural sleep and not EEG sleep only. In some papers (e.g., Kulikov, Ivanovo, USSR) hypnopaedia means also learning in the state of the hypnosis, which does not differ from the wakefulness in regard to EEG patterns.'

[Editor's note: The paper presented next contradicts the conclusions of the Czechs and shows certain inadequacies in their conditions of experimental recall, although practically it is not convenient to use classically induced hypnosis to recall events experienced during deeper or high-voltage, slow-wave sleep.]

17

STATES OF AWARENESS DURING GENERAL ANAESTHESIA

Preliminary Communication

BY

B. W. Levinson

Ten patients were exposed during deep surgical anaesthesia to a suggestion indicative of an anaesthetic crisis. One month later the patients were hypnotized and regressed to the operation. Four were able to reproduce the words spoken by the anaesthetist. Four became anxious and woke from hypnosis. Two did not reproduce the suggestion.

THIS preliminary communication describes a method of investigating the nature of awareness during anaesthesia. It is based on the application of a memory stimulus during anaesthesia, the depth of anaesthesia being monitored by electro-encephalography, and patients' recollection of the stimulus being investigated later under hypnosis.

METHOD

Ten patients over 21, in whom hypnosis could be induced, volunteered to take part in this study. They were all told that their brain waves would be examined during their anaesthetic and that hypnosis would be used to explore their feelings about the operation. Thiopentone, nitrous oxide, oxygen and ether were used to anaesthetize the patients, all of whom were undergoing dental operations.

Encephalography was used to monitor the depth of anaesthesia throughout each operation and when the record consisted entirely of irregular slow high-voltage waves indicating very deep anaesthesia, the anaesthetist stopped the operation with the following words: 'Just a moment! I don't like the patient's colour. Much too blue. His (or her) lips are very blue. I'm going to give a little more oxygen.' The anaesthetist then paused, hyperventilated the lungs and then after a moment or two said, 'There, that's better now. You can carry on with the operation.' The theatre and ward staff were warned not to discuss any aspect of the operation with any patient.

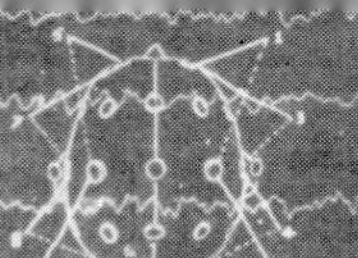

Just a moment! I don't like the patient's colour! The lips are too blue, very blue! More oxygen please!

...at's better, much better now

You may carry on with the operation

Fig. 17.1. An eight-channel electro-encephalogram recorded during third-plane anaesthesia.
This section of the record is cut at the point when the signal is given to the anaesthetist to read his script. The first few seconds show the slow high-voltage waves of deep anaesthesia. The theatre is suddenly silent. At this point the record changes markedly in all eight channels. A moment later the anaesthetist announces with alarm that the patient's lips are too blue. There is an augmentation of high-voltage slow waves throughout the anaesthetist's announcement. The section is cut and continued beneath the first part. In spite of the anaesthetist being satisfied and allowing the operation to proceed, the altered electro-encephalogram continues for many minutes. It slowly returns to the usual third-plane pattern. This recording is of one of the patients who could not recall the words of the anaesthetist under hypnosis. This patient became anxious and awoke from the trance.

One month after operation the patients were interviewed. All could remember entering the anaesthetic room and receiving an injection, but none of them could recall anything of the operation and their first memories were of waking in the ward. The patients were then hypnotized and regressed to the actual operation. A tape recording was made of the patient's description of the events during anaesthesia.

RESULTS

Of ten patients, four were able to repeat almost exactly the words used by the anaesthetist. Four patients remembered hearing something or somebody talking, and some identified the speaker as the anaesthetist. All this group displayed marked anxiety and either woke from hypnosis or blocked any further investigation. The remaining two patients denied hearing anything.

DISCUSSION

It would seem that patients who are deeply anaesthetized retain memories of events occurring during anaesthesia which can be described under hypnosis at some time after the anaesthetic. It is interesting that the patient's encephalogram indicates a response to a suggestion during anaesthesia (Fig. 17.1). It can be seen that as the suggestion was given there was suppression and subsequent augmentation of slow waves. The irregular slow waves seen just before the suggestions indicate third-plane third-stage surgical anaesthesia. It is also interesting to observe that the change in the record occurred before the anaesthetist began to speak, in the silence when the theatre staff waited for him to read his script. The change in record increased as he spoke and persisted for many minutes after he had finished.

The following is a transcription of the hypnosis session of one of the subjects. She was deeply hypnotized and indicated to me that she could hear someone talking. 'Who is it who's talking?' 'Dr. Viljoen. He's saying that my colour is grey.' 'Yes?' 'He's going to give me some oxygen.' 'What are his words?' Long pause following this question. 'He said that I will be all right now.' 'Yes?' 'They're going to start again now. I can feel him bending close to me.'

18

THE HISTORY OF HYPNOPAEDIA

A. M. Svyadoshch

Apropos V. N. Kulikov's article 'The Question of Hypnopaedia' and the article by N. D. Zabalova, V. P. Zukhar' and Iu. A. Petrov, 'The Problem of Hypnopaedia', published in Problems of Psychology, *No.* 2, 1964.

HYPNOPAEDIA—instruction during natural sleep—is beginning more and more to attract the attention of investigators, and this, of course, has given rise to an interest in its history. Apropos the latter, some erroneous assertions contained in V. N. Kulikov's article (4) and in the article by N. D. Zabalova, V. P. Zukhar' and Iu. A. Petrov (1) constrain us to refer to this question.

V. N. Kulikov (4; 87) writes that the first scientific investigations concerning hypnopaedia were allegedly carried out in 1932 by A. Huxley, who performed special tests in the memorization of words by sleeping persons. In reality, hypnopaedic tests were not carried out by Huxley. In 1932 he wrote the science-fiction novel *Brave New World*, in which he described hypnopaedia—instruction during sleep. After Huxley, writes V. N. Kulikov, experimental language-instruction of sleeping students was begun by M. Sherower. Nor is this true. M. Sherower is the author of a science-fiction novel *Cerebrophone, Inc.*, in which is described an imaginary apparatus for instruction during sleep. It was not until 1947, in San Francisco, that the engineer E. Brown constructed in the line of his work a 'dormiphone' apparatus—a combination of gramophone with an electric clock and ear-phones, to be placed under the pillow, and in 1948 C. R. Elliott (10) used this apparatus for instructing students during sleep. V. N. Kulikov erroneously attributed to Curtis what the latter did not say about the work of Sherower. With Curtis it is stated: 'In 1948 Sherower *predicted*' (my italics—A.S.) 'that his apparatus could be used for teaching the multiplication table, chemical formulae, the Morse alphabet, logarithms, speeches, vocabulary and languages'. V. N. Kulikov (4; 88) translated this paragraph of Curtis's in the following way: 'Curtis writes that M. Sherower has *succeeded*' (my italics—A.S.) 'in teaching, during sleep, not only languages, but the multiplication table, logarithms, chemical formulae, the Morse alphabet'. Whence, misunderstanding. V. N. Kulikov's assertion to the effect that A. M. Huxley and M. Sherower were in fact the founders of hypnopaedia is unfounded.

N. D. Zabalova, V. P. Zukhar' and I. A. Petrov (1) write that 'hypnopaedia is a method used for the first time in 1922 by a radio instructor of the American Naval School in Pensacola (Florida). Students of the school were instructed in the telegraphic code during sleep'. And allegedly, 'on awakening in the morning a single repetition sufficed for the student to recall completely and to reproduce information assimilated during sleep'. This can create the impression that they are quoting scientific data. In fact this is not so.

In 1911, in several numbers of the journal *Modern Electrics,* there was published a science-fiction novel by Hugo Gernsbeck, *Ralph* 124*C*41—. In this it is stated that in the year 2660 people will be able to learn during sleep by means of ear-phones worn by the sleeper. In 1921 and 1923 part of it was published in somewhat altered form under the title *Learn While You Sleep*, and by way of publicity the letter of the radio technician of the naval base in Pensacola was included. The radio technician wrote that he had read this novel, and he certifies that everything that is written in it can in fact come to pass: in 1922, while some men who were learning the Morse alphabet in the base were sleeping, he made a transmission in respect of this alphabet. In the morning some of the sleepers were able more quickly than usual to take up the symbols of the alphabet by ear. The letter was accompanied by an illustration taken from the novel (a sleeping man, with ear-phones). This ill-founded amateur experiment cannot be considered to constitute scientific data. [There is no mention of it in the American works on hypnopaedia by Curtis (9), or by Simon and Emmons either (12), (13). The latter, giving a detailed review of the literature, indicate that they make no reference either to the Press or publicity reports or to the reports of popular scientific journals.] The French journalist I. Pichon, in the popular journal *Science et Vie*, No. 511, 1960, in an article entitled 'Peut-on apprendre pendant le sommeil?', gave an abridged report on it.

The assertion to the effect that 'on awakening in the morning, a single repetition was enough for the student to be able fully to recall and reproduce the information assimilated during sleep', is contained neither in the radio technician's letter nor in the article by Pichon.

N. D. Zabalova, V. P. Zukhar' and I. A. Petrov (1; 99) state that K. I. Platonov 'on an occasion of positive attuning of subjects and of suitable suggestion before sleep had succeeded in obtaining data confirming the possibility of perception of speech during sleep and of reproducing it on awakening'. This is a misunderstanding. K. I. Platonov is an outstanding Soviet psychotherapist, but he has carried out no experiments in hypnopaedia of any kind, not excluding tests confirming the possibility of perception of speech during sleep and its reproduction on awakening.

The authors assert (1; 98) that 'there are references to the ability to perceive and remember speech during natural sleep both in works of last century and in our own time (Maury, 1878; S. Freud 1913; Leroy, 1927; I. E. Stepanov, 1922; K. I. Platonov, 1930, 1957; A. M. Svyadoshch, 1940 and 1962, and others). At the same time, data have been obtained, not only about the perception of speech by subjects, but also about the possibility of acquiring various kinds of knowledge'. This is not so. Maury, S. Freud, Leroi, I. E. Stepanov, having studied the psychology of dreams, have recorded that the sleeping person can sometimes hear a word, but the semantic value of the latter is distorted, being converted into the visual forms of dreams (they say 'cold' to the sleeper and he dreams of snow). He can remember the dream, but the word itself he cannot. Instruction with spoken material during sleep cannot be derived from these works.

Vetterstrand (1893) in Germany, N. V. Viazemskii (1903) in Russia, Burdon (1904) in France, and others, have healed children by suggestion during sleep. Judging by the therapeutic effect (the criterion is highly unreliable), the children perceived the speech during sleep, but in the morning they did not remember its contents. On awakening, those operations which during sleep it was attempted to suggest to the hypnotized sleepers are not remembered. None of these experiments prove the possibility of hypnopaedia either.

The first scientific research on hypnopaedia was carried out, not abroad, but in the USSR in 1936 by the author of the articles (5), (6), (7), (14), (15), (16) and presented by him in the form of a thesis in 1940, *Perception of Speech during Natural Sleep*. In this work it is for the first time experimentally demonstrated that man can perceive speech during natural sleep—words of a foreign language, texts with a literary, philosophic, technical content, lectures, transmitted to the subject both by known and unknown persons and also reproduced in sound-recordings. Perceived speech can be assimilated without distortion and can be reproduced on awakening. It is retained in the memory no less perfectly than what is perceived in the waking state. In the perception of texts an hour at a time for six days in succession no increase of fatigue was observed in the subjects. It has been noted that the sleep during which the perception of speech takes place is sleep 'with a sentry point' and that it is possible to 'cultivate' the 'sentry point' securing perception of speech by different methods—by means of preliminary suggestion or auto-suggestion ('attuning' to the perception of speech), or by sound-diffusion of the speech which is to be perceived, or by the transmission of faint stimuli in the rhythm of the sleeper's breathing. In this way, not only was the possibility of instruction during sleep demonstrated for the first time, but the teaching of spoken material was actually realized.

In the sequel, the possibility of hypnopaedia was confirmed by a number of authors (1), (2), (3), (4), (8), (9), (10), (11).

Wide-scale research on hypnopaedia is being carried out at present by the Ukraine Academy of Sciences. In Kiev, under the direction of L. A. Bliznitchenko, experimental classes have been formed in which systematic collective instruction in foreign languages is carried out during sleep. According to the Press reports (3), (8), Bliznitchenko has worked out a technique of instruction, while much that is new has been introduced into the method of presenting the information to the sleeper-in particular optimal physical and phonetic parameters of the spoken signals have been established, making it easier to achieve speech perception without intervention of an awakening. According to these data, in night studies of one hour per night in three nights of the week, a two- to three-fold acceleration in the learning of foreign languages is achieved.

Thus, a new stage now begins in the history of hypnopaedia—the stage of its introduction to practice.

REFERENCES

1. N. D. Zabalova, V. P. Zukhar', I. A. Petrov, The Problem of Hypnopaedia. *Problems of Psychology,* No. 2, 1964.
2. V. P. Zukhar', I. Pushkina, Hypnopaedia. *Science and Life,* No. 4, 1964.

3. M. Konstantinovskii, Summons to the Lesson . . . Sleep peacefully. *Knowledge is Power,* No. 3, 1964.
4. V. N. Kulikov, On the Problem of Hypnopaedia. *Problems of Psychology,* No. 2, 1964.
5. A. M. Svyadoshch, *The Perception of Speech during Natural Sleep.* Thesis for master's degree. Leningrad, 1940; *Kurortnaia Gazeta* (Health-Resort Gazette), No. 27, of 2/II 1941.
6. A. M. Svyadoshch, Perception and Memorization of Speech during Natural Sleep. *Problems of Psychology,* No. 1, 1962.
7. A. M. Svadoshch, Hypnopaedia. *Meditsinskaia Gazeta* (Medical Gazette), July 10, 1964, No. 55 (2322).
8. 'I Learn While I Sleep'. *Nedelia* (The Week), No. 14, March 29–April 4, 1964.
9. D. Curtis, *Learn While You Sleep.* New York, 1960.
10. *Sciences Digest,* May, 1948.
11. J. Genevay, Hypnopaedie. *Revue du Son* (Sound Review), Jan. 1959, Feb. 1959.
12. C. W. Simon and W. H. Emmons, *Consideration for Research in a Sleep-Learning Programme.*
13. C. W. Simon and W. H. Emmons, *U.S. Air Force Project Rand Research Memorandum.* Responses to material presented during various levels of sleep. The Rand Corporation. Santa Monica, California, 1954.
14. A. M. Svyadoshch, Peut-on apprendre en dormant? (Can one learn while sleeping?) *Information UNESCO,* Paris, September 6, 1963.
15. A. M. Svyadoshch, Can you learn while sleeping? *UNESCO Features.* N 42223, Sept. 1963.
16. A. M. Svyadoshch, Kan men lernen tijdens het slapen. (Can one learn while sleeping?) *UNESCO Features* in *Jeugdnieuws,* Amsterdam, Dec. 1963–Jan. 1964.

19

HYPNOPAEDIA AND ITS PRACTICE IN THE USSR

Leonid Bliznitchenko

Mass-scale, daily (except for Saturdays and Sundays) radio-instruction of the English language by means of the hypnopaedic method was carried out for the first time in the USSR from December 21, 1965, to February 16, 1966. This experiment embraced some 2,000 residents of Dubna, a town not far from Moscow known as a centre of nuclear physicists.

The experiment was organised by the State Radio and Television Committee, with the participation and support of the Ukrainian Academy of Sciences and several other Soviet scientific organisations.

Among those who took part in the experiment were a group of scientists consisting of the author of this article (the scientific head of the experiment, Ukrainian Academy of Sciences), candidate of medical sciences V. P. Zukhar, neurophysiologist Y. A. Maximov, psychologist I. P. Pushkina (USSR Academy of Sciences), and specialists in German philology M. P. Dvorzhetskaya (Ukrainian Academy of Sciences), and B. A. Zhebelev (First Moscow State Foreign Languages Pedagogical Institute).

The method used in the experiment was that of introducing and consolidating information in the memory of a person during his natural sleep. The method was developed by the author of this article. The many years of research work conducted by Soviet scholars in the field of hypnopaedia made it possible to conduct this experiment.

I would note that the term 'hypnopaedia' is obviously not a fortunate one inasmuch as the uninitiated person will immediately associate it with hypnosis. However, we must take into consideration that some scientists (including the author of this article) consider hypnopaedia to be a science about the introduction of information into a person's memory and its consolidation during his natural physiological sleep, and others—during artificial sleep as the specific use of hypnosis, pharmacology or electro-sleep. Both of these trends are of equal force and require the further research work applicable to hypnopaedia.

However, whereas science has long studied questions concerning hypnotic sleep, and its theoretical bases and application are becoming ever clearer, questions concerning the introduction of information into man's memory during natural sleep have, as yet, been little studied inasmuch as the elaboration of this new trend began relatively recently both in the USSR and in other countries.

Research in hypnopaedia was first undertaken in the USSR in the 1930's by Professor A. M. Svyadoshch in his thesis for the degree of Master of Science, which was devoted to the theme: 'Perception of Speech during Natural Sleep'. This work was carried out in the Laboratory of Higher Nervous Activity of the Leningrad Research Institute for the Protection of the Health of Children and Adolescents, in the Laboratory on the Study of Sleep of the Ivan Pavlov Institute of Physiology of the USSR Academy of Sciences, and also in the clinics of Professors N. I. Krasnogorsky, N. I. Ozeretsky, and others.

Considerably later I continued this research along the line of studying hypnopaedic speech, in particular, the specific features of its intonation, as the basis of a method for introducing and consolidating information in a person's memory during natural sleep. Research by other Soviet scientists was continued in parallel. The latter were interested chiefly in the psychological-physiological and pedagogical aspects of this problem.

The research conducted by Soviet scientists showed that the consolidation of information under 'unusual conditions'—during natural sleep—calls for the intricate interaction of a number of sciences: linguistics (information that is sonic, its trend and structure); physiology (higher nervous activity during sleep, the reaction to a sound stimulus); psychology (the desire and readiness to perceive); radio-engineering (sound recording, sound reproduction of the programmes); and pedagogy (the elaboration of hypnopaedic programmes). It must be noted that we interpret hypnopaedia as absolutely presupposing the closest tie with the pedagogical process, with a critical realisation of the person's activity in the state of wakefulness that precedes the night séance.

The possibility of man perceiving information during definite stages of natural sleep is connected with the existence of alpha-rhythms in most sleeping people. This was proved by numerous electro-encephalographic researches by a number of scientists: C. Simon, W. H. Emmons, V.P. Zukhar, Y. A. Maximov, and others.

From the viewpoint of physiology, sleep that is used for hypnopaedic work is partial sleep with a 'sentry post' which ensures that the learner will tune in at a definite signal. According to the Soviet scientists Zukhar and Pushkina, the work of the individual wakeful parts of the cerebral cortex when the latter is in a state of inhibition, can be considered the physiological mechanism that serves as the basis of hypnopaedia.

The hypnopaedic introduction and consolidation of information in a person's memory demands that special attention be paid to the elaboration of the sound programmes for the night séances. Numerous experiments have shown that ordinary speech is poorly perceived by the learners during natural sleep. This is quite understandable inasmuch as such speech presupposes a wakeful state. It is conditioned by the entire intricate complex of communication. The speaker and the listener take part in it, and the conditions of communication are of great significance: who is speaking, why he is speaking, how he is speaking, to whom he is speaking.

Such speech presupposes an active reciprocal reaction from the person being spoken to (which is excluded in hypnopaedia). That is why sharp changes sometimes take place in ordinary speech in the physical parameters of its intonation—the movement of the basic tone, the force of the utterance and the time of the phonation.

In hypnopaedia, the communication with the learner is effected without any considerable drops in the physical characteristics of the speech signal. It resembles the communication between a prompter and an actor on the stage, or the prompting of a pupil in school. True, as a rule, the theatre prompter introduces the actor's cue once, repeating it two or three times only in unfortunate cases. In hypnopaedia, however, frequent repetition is absolutely obligatory. *Thus the intonational structure of hypnopaedic speech performs the functions of helping the learner to remember the information given through speech.* Hence, it seems to me, linguistics plays a primary and organisational role in hypnopaedia.

Does not the presentation of material in this way disturb the normal sleep of the person? Is it not harmful to his health?

Numerous observations of hypnopaedic séances, which were conducted strictly according to the method we proposed, showed that hypnopaedia helps to normalise sleep and that the learners sleep soundly. The investigations conducted in the Laboratory of Higher Nervous Activity of the Institute of Physiology of the Ukrainian Academy of Sciences, under the direction of Professor A. E. Khilchenko, have also confirmed that the given method does not have any specifically harmful effect on the cerebral cortex. This was again confirmed by the experiment in Dubna.

The method of introducing and consolidating information in a person's memory during natural sleep was tried out in the USSR not only under many laboratory and semi-laboratory conditions, but also in work with learners' groups of three-to-four and eight-to-ten people and even with groups of thirty-to-forty people, whereas in the Dubna experiment it was conducted with a group of about 2,000 people. The learners included people ranging in age from sixteen to fifty-eight, men and women, factory and office workers, engineers, technologists, actors, scientists, college students and writers.

The method is becoming ever more widespread in Soviet schools. In a number of universities, colleges and technical schools, hypnopaedia is employed experimentally during foreign language instruction. The use of hypnopaedia as an additional method of studying a foreign language makes it possible to cut down the period of instruction to one-half of what it was and to even less. A student in the philology department, who studies a foreign language as his speciality, usually during the first year of instruction memorises in one day thirteen to eighteen words and expressions for active use and he spends about one and a half to two hours of his wakeful time on this in addition to classroom lessons. The average student usually memorises thirty-five to sixty words and expressions during one hypnopaedic séance, and this is by no means the limit to the number he can memorise.

A preliminary analysis of the results of the work of a control group in the Dubna experiment (100 people) showed:

1. Those people who had studied the English language earlier (in school, college, or in other courses) activated their knowledge of the language, especially their skills in oral speech.

2. People who had never studied the English language previously received a knowledge of the fundamentals of the language (phonetics, vocabulary, grammar), and in most cases they can now conduct an

active conversation within the limits of the material they have learned (about 1,000 words and phrases and the basic models of sentences).

Characteristic of the second group is that they mastered the first ten lessons (of the total number of thirty-six), almost completely; from ten to twenty lessons they mastered within the limits of 90 per cent; from twenty to thirty lessons—within the limits of 85 per cent; and from thirty to thirty-six lessons—80 per cent. These are very convincing results, especially if we bear in mind that the learners were at home where there was no control by a teacher.

Even better results were obtained when class-room studies were combined with hypnopaedia in the work of the experienced hypnopaedist and methods specialist L. Y. Garbuz; twelve of his students received marks of 'excellent' at the examination and one received a mark of 'good' for their knowledge of the programme for the German language even though the time devoted to their instruction had been considerably reduced.

The attraction of this method of applied linguistics lies in the fact that when used in rational combination with the usual methods of work, those employed in classroom instruction or independent study, it is possible considerably to hasten the process of soundly memorising the information in much less time.

What is most important, when the hypnopaedic method of language instruction is used, is the quantitative and qualitative selection of the material to be memorised, and the sequence and continuity of this material in its organic tie with the usual classroom studies.

The following is a brief description of the method of work in the Dubna experiment:

(a) Morning—7.25–8.5 a.m.—radio lesson, check-up on the mastery of the material of the previous lesson and the introduction of new material;

(b) In the pre-sleep state (10.45–11.0 p.m.) the learners, who are already in bed, read the material given them at the lesson in the morning (visual memory); they listen to a tape recording read at special sound parameters (aural memory); repeat aloud the study material during pauses especially set aside by the announcer for this purpose (motor memory).

(c) In stages of drowsiness, of light sleep, and sleep of average deepness (11.5–11.55 p.m.) the learners perceive the same programme which is repeated frequently.

(d) In the period just before they awaken (6.30–6.55 a.m.) the study material is again given to the learners in the respective sound parameters.

The cycle of instruction is completed at the morning lesson, when the learners are in a wakeful state, as indicated above (7.25–8.5 a.m.).

As regards the study material, it consisted of thirty-six lessons which contained Russian-English linguistic equivalents that became more difficult with each new lesson.

Of course a number of questions concerning hypnopaedia have not as yet been sufficiently studied. However, I feel that further comprehensive research work of linguists, physiologists, psychologists, radioelectronic specialists and acoustics specialists will lead to the greater perfection of the hypnopaedic method in studying various subjects: languages, mathematics, anatomy, history, pharmacology, and the like.

PART II

A series of eight papers written by the editor, in which he clarifies and expands some of the conclusions presented in the earlier chapters.

20

IMPROVEMENT OF MEMORY BY SLEEP

THE results of the studies on the effect of sleep upon retention are of great theoretical and practical importance in hypnopaedia. If a person memorises certain kinds of material, and goes to sleep immediately afterwards, he will recall more of it—and also relearn the whole task more economically after a lapse of twenty-four hours—than if he waits even a few hours before he goes to sleep, according to Dr. H. M. Johnson, Professor of psychology at the American University, Washington, D.C.

As the American, French and Russian papers on hypnopaedia do not contain specific references to the significant findings of experiments conducted by E. A. Graves, Edward B. van Ormer and J. G. Jenkins and K. M. Dallenbach on the effect of sleep upon retention, I begin my section of the book by quoting from the conclusions reported by the authors above. *There is evidence, conjunctively based on the following reports, that hypnopaedic speech could be perceived in the EEG waking, transitory, or light stages of sleep, which were generally followed by deeper phases, and indeed that the whole process of hypnopaedia has a positive effect on memorisation.*

E. A. Graves: 'There have been several experimental studies concerned with the effect of sleep upon retention although a good many years ago Foucault, in considering the data of Ebbinghaus, suggested that the smaller amount of forgetting in his results for the eight to twenty-four hour period might have been due to the greater predominance of sleep. While working with G. E. Muller, Heine conducted an experiment to determine the effect of sleep and waking on retention as a function of retroactive inhibition. She compared retention after twenty-four hours when syllables were learned just before going to bed with retention when waking intervals were interpolated between learning and sleep. Her results indicated that when learning occurred shortly before sleep there was an average saving in relearning after twenty-four hours of 47 per cent, while there was an average savings of only 36 per cent when waking intervals were interpolated between learning and sleep.

'The results of these studies show rather definitely that sleep in comparison with waking does have a beneficial effect upon the retention of nonsense syllables. The longest period studies for the effect of sleep on retention has been twenty-four hours. It seemed desirable, therefore, to determine the differential effect of interpolated periods upon retention when learning immediately precedes a sleeping period [as it is the case in hypopaedia—*Editor*] and when it precedes a waking period during much longer intervals of time.'

Edward B. van Ormer: 'In consideration of the studies of Heine, Jenkins and Dallenbach, and van Ormer, the conclusion seems established that the usual amount of daily sleep (about eight hours) favours retention of nonsense syllables over that time interval.

'In view of some fundamental similarity between the learning of nonsense syllables and other verbal material, the suggestion seems to be warranted that these conclusions may apply to other verbal material. Accordingly, the four studies, combined with Spight's suggestive results, indicate that retention of any verbal material is probably better after four hours or eight hours sleep than after the same time intervals of waking. Further study with meaningful material is very desirable.

'If the before-said conclusion is thoroughly established, a new principle of efficient study will be clearly indicated. Assuming that a possible decrease in the learning efficiency at the late evening hours is overbalanced by the better retention following sleep, the advantage of night study, as suggested by Jenkins and Dallenbach, will be evident. Much less is forgotten during sleep, and on waking the learner may take up the task refreshed and with renewed vigour.'

J. G. Jenkins and K. M. Dallenbach: 'Our experimental data show that there is a marked difference in the rate of forgetting during sleep and waking. On an average, more than twice as many syllables are reproduced by both after intervals of sleep than after intervals of waking. On an average, 5·8 and 6·0 syllables were reported by H. and Mc. respectively in the sleep experiments, and only 2·4 and 2·8 syllables in the waking experiments. The superiority of the reproductions after intervals of sleep is also shown at every one of the experimental intervals. At the end of one hour of sleep an average of 7·1 and 7·0 syllables were reproduced, whereas an average of only 4·4 and 4·8 syllables were reproduced after a like interval of waking. At the two-hour interval, both sleep and waking, there is a corresponding drop in the averages of each 0; but the reproductions after sleep still maintains a decided superiority. *This superiority becomes more pronounced as the length of the interval increases.* Our results also indicate, so far as they go, that a similar condition of retention exists in the hypnotic and in normal sleep'.

SOURCES

Graves Elizabeth A., *Effect of Sleep upon Retention, Journal of Experimental Psychology,* **19**, 316–322, 1936.

Van Ormer E. B., *Sleep and Retention, Psychological Bulletin,* **30**, 415–439, 1933.

Jenkins J. G. and Dallenbach K. M., *Obliviscence During Sleep and Waking, American Journal of Psychology,* **35,** 605–612, 1924.

21

PSYCHOLOGICAL ASPECTS OF THE PERCEPTION AND REPRODUCTION OF HYPNOPAEDIC SPEECH

THE ROLE OF THE ORIENTATION AND ADAPTIVE REFLEXES

Y. N. Sokolov* states: 'The action of a stimulus on any sensory system brings about a number of changes in its different parts, including the receptor itself, as a result of which the sensitivity of the system to external stimulation changes. On this account, during the action of the stimulus, its effect on the system is altered, and this in turn produces further changes in sensitivity. In this way, the reception of a stimulus takes place as a series of reflex acts occurring within the sensory systems concerned in the perception of any particular stimulus. A very important part in the perception is played by the orienting and adaptive reflexes.'

Soviet psychological conceptions on Pavlov's paradoxical phases occurring during certain stages of sleep support the views of Sokolov concerning the alteration of sensitivity. This may play a major part in hypnopaedic phenomena, considering the role of habitual attention involved in the set for perception of acoustic stimuli. There are several examples of the significance of increased sensitivity and habitual attention in certain types of behaviour, such as the sleeping mother's readiness to hear a 'weak' stimulus, i.e., the faintest sound of her baby, or the sleeping soldier's pre-conditioned habitual ability to hear and arouse himself when his wireless apparatus signals.

Pavlov's pattern of the dynamic aspect of sleep with an 'alert post on guard' in hypnosis and applied to hypnopaedia is incidentally supported by the conclusions drawn by H. I. Williams and others.

* Ye. N. Sokolov (Dept. of Psychology, Moscow State Univ.) *The Orienting Reflex and Problems of Reception.* (Reports to the Conference on Problems of Psychology, 3–8 July, 1953).

Sokolov's views on establishing certain properties of the orienting and adapting reflexes—to the effect that: 'they develop in response to a wide range of stimuli; they include many components affecting many different organs; they may be divided into general and special orienting reactions; *they are maintained during the whole of the period of application of the stimulus*'—can be coordinated with the continuation of discriminative sensitivity during all stages of sleep (H. L. Williams, 1963). The interaction of receptor and effector adjustment at a cortical level which takes place for establishing contact with the voice of a hypnopaedic instructor during certain stages of sleep, makes it possible to carry on associative learning of rote material. A simplified pattern of how this occurs is presented as follows:

Learning, from a physiological point of view, is also a continuous phenomenon of acquiring conditioned responses. Learning on the human level can be primitive or high grade, but the neural functioning of all learning is based on the same dynamics as are the unconditioned-conditioned stimuli and unconditioned-conditioned response of the organism. In this aspect, learning during certain stages of sleep is based on the anticipation of conditioned auditory-verbal stimuli used in habituated circumstances. For instance, the individual who communicates by speech uses first his mother tongue as being his interpretative instrument as a coded symbol for recognising objects, ideas, etc., on the level of the Pavlovian second signalling system. This process begins in early childhood as a completely natural function; therefore communication in one's mother tongue is to be considered in hypnopaedic learning as acting as the unconditioned stimulus and response mechanism, although in a superimposed form of the first signalling system. New expressions and unknown words of a foreign language being memorized by presenting them in paired associates with their equivalents from the mother tongue, in the case of hypnopaedia, will act as the conditioned response in verbal behaviour.

Thus, when the individual anticipates the meaning of one word (heard for instance in English as his mother tongue) e.g., TABLE, the previously acquired conceptual image of it appears in his memory recognized and recalled as

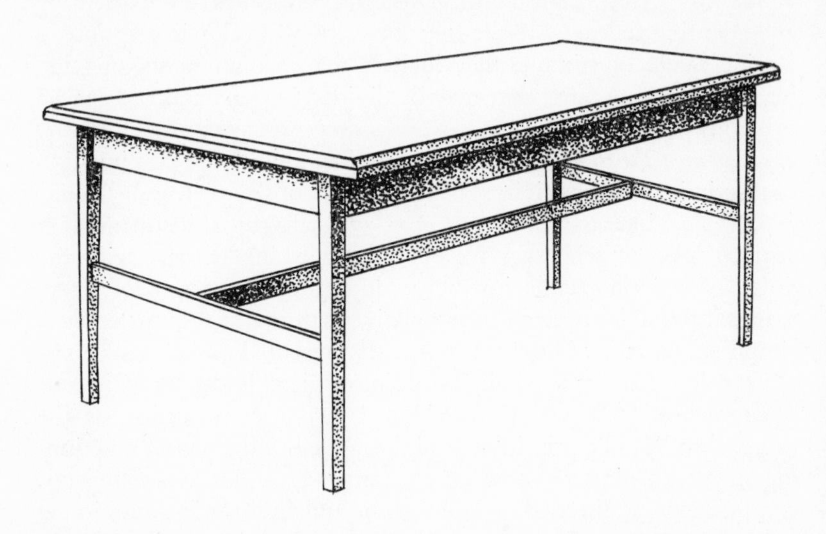

By accepting the German words for THE TABLE-DER TISCH, he learns to use a new verbal symbol, a newly acquired conditioned response for understanding and anticipating the previously acquired conceptual image recognized again as

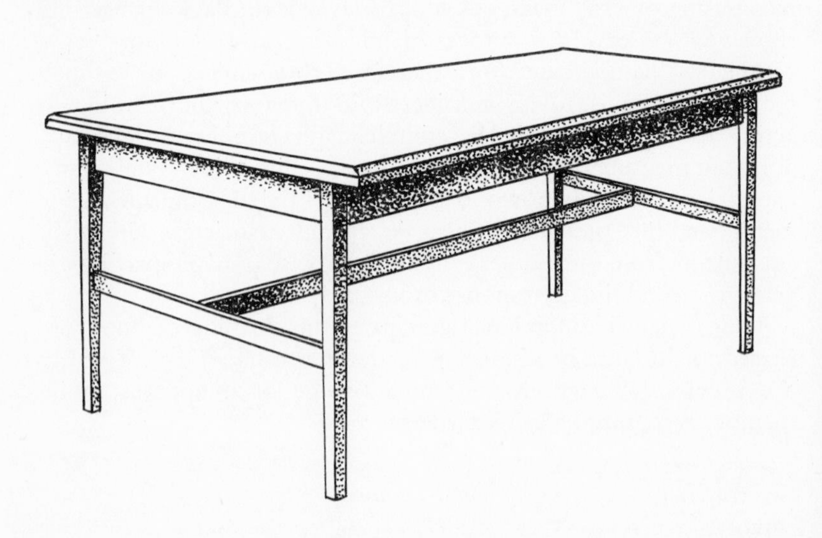

The presentation of paired verbal associates, THE TABLE-DER TISCH, in frequent continuous repetition during the perceptive stages of sleep, facilitates the memorization of *the second part* of the paired associate, DER TISCH, upon the complex process of hearing and imaging the original concept, which is THE TABLE. Using the words DER TISCH instead of THE TABLE acts now also as a newly learned (conditioned) verbal response.

Hypnopaedic memorization of rote material aids conventional study techniques. The detection of hypnopaedic learning by the 'saving method', mentioned by Fox and Robbin (1952), can be followed by studying the Russian papers and experimental results. Both will lead to a broader understanding of the recall value of hypnogenically memorized material when it comes to practical use. The apparent discrepancies in savings during day-time study seem to be connected with the experimental recall (aided recall in Russian hypnopaedia) in a quantitative proportion. The concepts (as shown in details below) of (A) active, (B) partial and (C) latent types of memories in hypnopaedia (Svyadoshch, 1962) will clarify the practical aspects of programmed hypnopaedic learning as a means of reducing the time of day-time studies, which, it is claimed, has already been achieved in the method of teaching English used and developed by Professor L. A. Bliznitchenko, Director of Linguistic Studies, Ukrainian Scientific Academy, Kiev.

MEMORY AND THE SEQUENCE OF THE SLEEP-LEARNING METHOD

Whenever material is retained, there must be a correlated change of some kind in the nervous system. This is referred to theoretically as a 'memory trace', 'neurogram' or an 'engram'. ['Development of Memory Engrams and Qualified Word Elements During Sleep' is the name and main task of the State Plan of the Academy of Sciences in Czechoslovakia for the development of hypnopaedia.] How the brain cells store information is not exactly known, but it has been suggested that the 'engram' is a modification analogous in some ways, to the molecular changes in a magnetic tape which enable us to play back what is recorded. Pavlov's model of what takes place in the nervous system when conditioned response is acquired involves the concept of a neural connection. Essentially the same idea has been held by some to account for verbal associations, as when the student learns that the German equivalent of THE TABLE is DER TISCH. In view of our ignorance of what actually takes place in the nervous system when we learn, some investigators prefer to make no assumptions about neural traces. With respect to the THE TABLE-DER TISCH association, for example, they are satisfied to speak of associative strength of the connection, by which they mean merely that, as practice continues, there is an increasing probability that, given the stimulus word TABLE, the response word TISCH will follow. It is agreed by most neurologists that memory involves the making of an impression by an experience, the retention of some record of this impression and the re-entry of this record into consciousness as recognition and recall.

Hypnopaedic memorization is usually tested by aided recall using, for instance, TABLE as an eliciting stimulus for recalling TISCH. Scoring, in tests for subjects in hypnopaedia, is obtained from the quantitative variables of unknown or foreign expressions recognized or recalled, (Fox and Robbin, 1952, Svyadoshch, 1962, Kulikov, 1964.)

The sequence of the practically applied Sleep-Learning Method is as follows:

First Phase: Subconscious data processing (assimilation) takes place during hypnopaedic sessions. Study material, if memorized, can be recognized or recalled experimentally or practically in the next morning or after an interval of days, weeks or even months. Saving (Fox and Robbin) during day-time study will depend upon the score of subjects, who will be divided into three main groups, namely those who have: (A) an *active memory* by remembering and recalling 65 to 100 per cent of items; (B) *partial memory* by remembering and recalling 35 to 65 per cent of items; (C) *latent memory,* recalling 0 to 35 per cent of items. (Re-learning of the non-recalled remaining parts in cases of partial or latent memory can also be detected by the saving method.)

Second Phase: Conscious and analytical application of the re-activated hypnogenically acquired (memorized) data will reduce the time usually needed during day-time studies. (L. A. Bliznitchenko, 1966.)

Third Phase: Colloquial exercises, written studies, composition of essays, etc., if the study material belongs to arts or sciences, for achieving progress in praxis as an extension of the combined technique mentioned above.

Auditory phenomena, which in certain conditions can mobilize the central nervous system and the organism for its responding behaviour, involve also the selective functions of higher (psychic) centres in the cerebrum when assimilating speech in acoustic signals. The significance of acoustic stimuli does not always depend purely on the physical properties of the signals. Psychological attunement with its conjunctive physiological functions may play an important role in the understanding of hypnopaedics. The interaction between the primary and secondary auditory centres (activated via the non-specific and specific pathways) may be decisive for the memorization of hypnopaedic speech.

The auditory process during sleep-learning may not differ from its basic functioning (as it is in the waking state), but it is most likely that qualitative and quantitative changes do occur within certain levels. Sleep, with a 'point of vigilance' (term used in Russian literature on sleep), affects the excitation and inhibition of the secondary auditory and psychic centres, which does not arouse behaviourally the organism.

Phonetic and acoustic skill in specially preparing the intonation of hypnopaedic lessons is very important according to L. A. Bliznitchenko, but it is considered to be negligible according to Professor V. Vachmistrov, who is another leading authority. Although the Russians have not published any controlled experiments in memorising speech which was reproduced ordinarily or altered by hypnopaedic intonation, it seems that acoustic aspects of hypnopaedic speech may have an important role in making this technique practical and available for collective use.

It is known, that for instance the fundamental frequency of voice is not usually a critical factor for communication in normal circumstances. In hypnopaedic speech, which is limited in its volume, the communicative properties of the hypnopaedic texts will be optimal within those volume levels which are generally used in hypnopaedia, to avoid arousing behaviourally the subject but in the meantime making the speech 'effective'. According to L. A. Bliznitchenko, a constant frequency characteristic, an even acoustic level and an unvarying time characteristic are important features of the intonation of the speaker conducting the hypnopaedic lesson.

The perception and reproduction of hypnopaedic speech are the two final stations in learning during certain stages of sleep. The experimental and practical value of this technique may depend on the co-ordination of a two-factor basis, namely between the specific perceptive state of the subject and the acoustic properties of the stimulus. Experiments conducted in the United States were not methodologically pursued as was similar work done in Russia.

SOURCES

Jasper, H. *Reticular-Cortical Systems and Theories of the Integrative Actions of the Brain. Biological and Biochemical Bases of Behaviour,* Univ. of Wisconsin Press, 1958.

Hunter, W. S. *The Symbolic Process, Psychol. Review,* 1924, **31**, 478–494.

McConnell, Cutler, R. L., McNeil, E. B. *Sublimal Perception, American Psychologist,* 1958, **13**, 229–242.

Sokolov, Y. N. *Reflex Receptor Mechanisms, Recent Soviet Psychology,* Pergamon Press, 1961.

Pavlov, I. P. *Lectures on Conditioned Reflexes,* Lawrence & Wishart, Ltd., London, 1941.

Svyadoshch, A. M. *The Assimilation and Memorization of Speech During Natural Sleep, Voprosy Psikhologii,* No. 1, 1962.

Rubin, F. *The Perception and Anticipation of Speech During Sleep, The Journal of the Sleep-Learning Association,* July, 1965.

22

REPORT ON A SELF-ADMINISTERED HYPNOPAEDIC EXPERIMENT

Subject:	Mr. Zs. Köhalmi
Age:	21
Occupation:	Student of Electronic Engineering (Technical University)
Address:	Budapest, Rákosliget-VIII-36, Hungary.

The subject (*S*) conducted self-administered sleep-learning experiments to assess and evaluate the retention and aided recall of *English* words and phrases which were presented to him during apparent sleep. The English expressions were recorded in paired associates with their Hungarian equivalents. Every paired associate was followed by a pause. The *S* is of Hungarian nationality, born and brought up in Budapest. An ordinary double-track domestic tape recorder was used with an endless tape cartridge (for uninterrupted repetition) controlled by a time-switch. The *S* made his own recordings on the endless tape cartridge as he was not a beginner in English. His pronunciation and grammar were developed before the experiment—which lasted for six weeks—took place.

Hypnopaedic sessions were programmed for every night of the week, except Saturday. The *S* arranged and programmed 1,284 *new* English words to be memorised either as vocabulary or by placing them into short phrases of known material. The average hypnopaedic session in one night of eight to nine hours sleep lasted approximately 120 minutes, and they commenced shortly after retiring at a regular time between 10–11 p.m. (The *S* observed himself as a light-medium sleeper.) The average nightly intake was thirty-five words or textual units recorded in six to seven minutes giving seventeen to twenty repetitions during one hypnopaedic session. The volume, selected by the *S*, was below his waking threshold. Each session contained new material.

Table 1

Quantity of textual units presented each night	*Recalled next morning*	*Recalled next evening*
36	36	36
28	28	28
35	35	35
35	30	30
36	36	36
36	36	36
35	35	35
34	29	30
29	24	26
30	27	27
21	15	18
20	16	17
38	28	32
30	29	29
35	32	34
29	12	26
32	23	28
35	33	34
30	28	28
30	25	27
33	25	28
36	30	30
31	26	28
38	30	34
30	20	22
40	28	29
37	30	33
31	29	30
43	39	40
44	39	40
41	33	36
38	31	31
33	27	28
33	29	30
43	36	37
33	27	27
36	29	31
Total 1,284	1,065	1,126

Table 2

The Recall of Sleep-Learned Material after One Month of the Experiment

	Quantity of textual units forgotten after one month:
	1
	0
	2
	2
	1
	1
	0
	0
	1
	3
	6
	0
	2
	2
	0
	3
	2
	2
	5
	3
	5
	8
	2
	5
	4
	7
	0
	0
	3
	3
	5
	7
	2
	2
	0
	9
	2
Total	100

Table 2 is continued on page 224

Table 2, continued

Total quantity of textual units presented during thirty-six nights	1,284
Recalled after twelve hours interval	1,126
Forgotten after twelve hours	158
Forgotten after thirty days	100
Total quantity forgotten	258
Total quantity learned and memorized for long term	1,026

Tests of recall were carried out by the *S* himself during the morning following a hypnopaedic sessions, the next evening and finally, thirty days later, from a bilingually typed script by responding in English upon seeing the Hungarian cues only. Original learning in this case may be considered as the process of preparing the material for recording, and relearning took place during hypnopaedic sessions. The *S* did *not* observe any apparent acute side effects or interferences in the efficiency of his university studies of other subject material.

SUMMARY

Material was transferred by the experimenter into his consciousness and became part of its contents: this resulted from information being consolidated unconsciously or, as presumably happened in this case, being re-learned or even over-learned during hypnopaedic sessions. As we can see, this transfer may not occur immediately upon the awakening of the subject. Reproductions postponed for a short or longer period of time became more productive. The increase of the recall with approximately twelve hours interval is self-evident. The apparent success of this experiment was also due to the subject's high motivation. He was interested in hypnopaedic phenomena and he *needed* further knowledge in English to win a BBC English competition contest carrying with it the reward of a visit to the U.K. He succeeded. Professor A. L. Bliznitchenko's report confirms similar outstanding results of hypnopaedic techniques achieved with highly motivated subjects. (See also Ch. 19 and also *New Education*, March, 1965.)

23

THE SIGNIFICANCE OF REPETITION IN CONVENTIONAL LEARNING AND HYPNOPADIA

'There is no question about the importance of repetition in memorising. When information is received and must be retained for use a short time hence, the retaining appears to be accomplished by some sort of repetitive rehearsal of the information. Furthermore, it was seen that if, say, a digit sequence could be recalled immediately after being received, this was no guarantee that it could be retained for a matter of minutes: it must usually be repeated several more times. And even then, still longer retaining often requires that the information be repeated yet again from time to time if it is not to be forgotten. So, repetition plays a crucial part in acquiring mastery of the material and, subsequently, in maintaining this mastery.'

These are the words of Professor Ian Hunter, Professor of Psychology, in his book *Memory* (Penguin). He continues: 'As a general practical rule, it may be said that repetition must involve appropriate practical activity on the part of the memoriser if it is to be effective. In memorising many kinds of material, one such appropriate procedure involves active anticipation.'

Comparing the before-mentioned criterion with corresponding behavioural aspects of memorising material via auditory channels during reduced states of awareness, or—shall it be said?—during the light stages of sleep, it seems that a contradiction may arise. As the effectiveness of hypnopaedic repetition is already established by several sets of experimental data, is it necessary to contradict the views of Professor Hunter? My answer is Yes, insofar as the cerebral tone for assimilating repeatedly presented texts or messages does not correspond in *all* occasions with the behavioural concomitant of conscious anticipation. (Conditions of learning without awareness or even by subliminary stimulation also enter into hypnopaedia and will be mentioned in Chapter 24). The behavioural appearance of repetitive memorising, by reading the text silently or loudly with conscious attention, does not finally indicate that these circumstances are the only conditions for retention.

Psychological experiments in memorising were mostly conducted during the waking state until the Russians involved themselves in special investigations of hypnopaedic memorisation techniques. As the hypnopaedic study method is conjunctive with the day-time learning and relearning of previously familiarised texts of rote material, the following views of Professor Hunter again incidentally support hypnopaedia:

'Consider, for example, the task of memorising the Morse code equivalents of English letters, or the foreign language equivalent of English words. One way of proceeding is to read each English item and then its equivalent, and to do this repeatedly.

'Familiarised material is favourable for relearning and therefore it is easier to memorise than unfamiliar material. This obvious fact would need no discussion if it did not have so many practical and theoretical implications for memory in general.'

Hypnopaedic pre-presentation of material may act psychologically as a cumulatively built up past experience which can result in long-term patterns of retaining. Experiments conducted in the dormitories of the Sleep-Learning Association, in Russian psychological laboratories and by individuals, resulted in long-term patterns of retaining. It is rightly claimed by Russian educational scientists that hypnopaedically acquired material is memorised and retained better than via the conventional method. The effectiveness of repetition during the paradoxical phases is self-explanatory, because the weak stimulus from a sensory and associative (psychic) angle evokes string responses affecting the conditioned reflexes and the complex functional chain of cerebral events, which are the physiological concomitants of memorising and learning.

Further controlled experiments would be necessary for obtaining scores of diurnal and nocturnal memorisation by presenting texts repeatedly to subjects for long-term retention.

THE EBBINGHAUS EXPERIMENT

The Ebbinghaus experiment provides an illustrative example of memorisation and learning by repetition, which is indirectly applicable for investigating certain motions in hypnopaedics. The practical values of the hypnopaedic study method from an efficiency and economic point of view had been proved by the retention of '1,000 words of English with grammar and pronunciation in 36–40 days', a result achieved by Professor A. L. Bliznitchenko; but to obtain data and 'saving score' further experiments are necessary. The combined hypnopaedic-diurnal study method of foreign languages was actually developed on the basic findings of the Ebbinghaus experiment, and therefore it is worth while to quote some parts of it, as a supporting issue for Sleep-Learning. *Ebbinghaus's combination of original learning and re-learning occurs also in the subconscious (sleep-learning) and conscious (day-time study) assimilation of study material.*

The reduced efforts of day-time study will naturally depend on the 'active', 'partial' and 'latent' memorisation of hypnopaedic material by the students, as their 'saving scores' in qualitative and quantitative aspects should be conjunctive with their individual types of hypnopaedagogic memory.

Herman Ebbinghaus (1850–1909) made several contributions to psychology, but is best known for his work on memorising. This work, involving six years of arduous research, was published in 1885 in a book, *Über das Gedächtnis,* which is now a landmark in the history of inquiry into mental life. It was the first systematic study of memory activities, and most of our present-day knowledge about memorising stems more or less directly from this pioneer investigation. He conducted experiments during the state of conscious awareness and he may not have known or was not informed of the existence of the paradoxical phases or similar mental conditions. This, however, does not reduce the importance of his contributions to the psychology of learning and their indirect link with hypnopaedia. Ebbinghaus approached the problems of memory in the spirit of an experimental physical scientist. His aim was to introduce into the study of human functioning the methods of strict experimental control and quantitative treatment of his results. These methods had previously reaped rich rewards in physics and physiology and so he deployed them to psychology.

By comparing the re-learning time with the original learning time, Ebbinghaus derived a measure of the retained effects of the original memorising. For example, if 1,000 seconds were required for original learning, and if re-learning took 600 seconds, then the saving of effort was 400 seconds, or 40 per cent of the original time. This 40 per cent exemplifies a 'saving score'. It reflects the amount of learning time or efforts saved in consequence of previous learning. If this material had not been learned before, the student would require 1,000 seconds for its mastery. But because it had been learned once before, he saved himself 40 per cent of his time.

These experiments were carried out by memorisation of nonsense syllables and were not motivated by the urge for educational gain: therefore this reference applies only to pure experimental psychology, (studying the basic foundations of memorisation) which is then subsequently applied to educational procedures. During practical studies we usually do not analyse or dissect our material into parts that have been originally learned or re-learned when preparing for examinations which are actually practical tests of memorisation and retention.

NUMBER OF LEARNING TRIALS AND REPETITIONS

What happens if the number of learnings given to a particular list is either less than or more than the number required to reach the criterion of effortless recital? If, for a particular list, twelve repetitions are needed to reach the criterion, what would happen if we took twenty-four repetitions? Or if we took only six?

To answer this question, Ebbinghaus conducted tests in which, in each case, the material was read a given number of times. This figure was varied from test to test, between eight and sixty-four. Then a day later he applied his usual re-learning method to determine the amount of saving. He found that the surplus repetition was not wasted. Over-learning made it easier to re-learn the material on a subsequent occasion. Even a few readings made the material easier to master on a future occasion. Ebbinghaus described these findings by saying that it was as though each repetition engraved the material more and more deeply on the nervous system. We can thus see quite clearly the tremendous potentialities dormant in hypnopaedia in providing a subconscious repetitive learning technique during the time of sleep.

AMOUNT OF MATERIAL TO BE MEMORISED

If it required so many readings to memorise a list of twelve foreign words, how many readings will be required to memorise a list of twenty-four? It might be expected that, if the amount to be memorised is doubled, then the time to memorise would also be doubled. In fact, this expectation is not borne out. It takes more than twice as long—in conventional learning conditions. Experiments show that as the amount of the material increases learning time not only increases but does so at a disproportionate rate. It takes more than twice as long to memorise twenty-four items as to memorise twelve. Again, it takes more than twice as long to memorise two hundred as to memorise one hundred items.

Where lists of nonsense syllables are concerned, a fairly general finding is that the learning time per syllable increases in proportion to the square root of the number of syllables in the list. Broadly speaking, the above rule applies to the memorising of any kind of material. These are the findings of day-time memorisation tests. The Editor has no knowledge of data comparing such formulae between conventional and hypnopaedic memorisation by means of repetitions, but it is likely that in hypnopaedia the formula alters towards the reduction of time required, or the quantity of items may be increased without effecting the sleep-learning time.

The Ebbinghaus experiment also provides interesting and applicable information concerning the spacing of the interval between memorising sessions, namely: 'The results showed that increasing the interval between memorising sessions progressively reduced the time actually devoted to memorising'.

This very brief survey of the Ebbinghaus experiment shows that his work established a number of 'laws' which have been confirmed over and over again whenever his procedures have been followed. Furthermore, these 'laws' have been found, with certain modifications, to apply to memorising activities, such as hypnopaedia, even where these activities do not conform to his structures.

24

LINGUISTIC PROBLEMS IN HYPNOPAEDIC TEACHING

I

Linguists and educational psychologists are continually searching for the best technique of teaching foreign languages. The followers of different methods praise the advantages of their technique whilst criticising the weak spots of others, and this applies to hypnopaedia as well, quite independently as to whether they accept memorisation during certain stages of sleep or not. The Editor does not intend here to enter into discussion as to which method is the best, but he wishes to mention some significant conclusions resulting from scientific investigations in this field.

A detailed description of oral speech in a foreign language in comparison with the native language and also with the written speech was made by Professor V. A. Artemov of the Maurice Thorez Foreign Language State Institute, Moscow. He pointed out that oral speech in the native language is acquired and mastered by children before they start school, whereas oral speech in a foreign language develops on the basis of the lexical and grammatical knowledge acquired in school. Professor B. A. Benediktov dealt with the study of the psychological features of mastering oral speech in a foreign language. His main conclusion is that in the process of its development, oral speech in a foreign language passes through two stages: (a) the indirect or translation stage; and (b) the direct, or non translation stage. Instant thinking in a foreign language, such as many linguists desire, cannot be achieved at the beginning of a course if only because of this psychological aspect. It is possible that the student may not be consciously aware of an inner translation process from cues taking place in his mind while developing and forming new verbal responses in a foreign language. Subconscious translation process, a functional result of the Pavlovian second signalling system, cannot be avoided. Comparative studies of higher nervous and psychic activity between the thought processes of pre-school children and students aged from six to ten are clearly indicative of the two stages of learning stated by B. A. Benediktov. More psychological data can be found in the research of I. V. Karpov (3) which is devoted to the psychological analysis of the process by which pupils gain an understanding of foreign texts. As a result of this analysis, he came to the conclusion that in this process four stages are revealed: (a) preliminary understanding achieved with the aid of the native language and expressed in the form of translation, i.e., loose translation; (b) an analytical study of the text, with subsequent literal translation; (c) the formulation of an adequate literal translation; (d) a second reading of the text, understanding without the translation.

HYPNOPAEDIA ENTERING INTO THE ACQUISITION OF FOREIGN LANGUAGES

Hypnopaedia as an adjunctive technique of memorisation assists greatly in the cognitive and reproductive faculty of a foreign language, which during the study course should be followed by the productive part of learning, i.e., by the construction of new sentences in the foreign language. Hypnopaedic vocabulary for learning foreign languages is recorded bi-lingually, with the mother tongue acting as a stimulus cue for triggering the recall of foreign expressions. My view is that it is quite unnecessary for linguists to feel anxious because students undergoing hypnopaedic courses will depend upon the use of their mother tongue as an interpretive thought resource. Studies conducted to investigate the development of speech in an evolutionary sequence generally conclude that the human semantic faculty has developed, physiologically, from peculiarities of the higher nervous activities of animals, which react not only to the immediate physical properties of things or phenomena, but also to their perceptive qualities.

Perceptive qualities and conditions are important in considering and assessing cerebral dynamics taking place during the learning process. The psychological conditions of the semantic learning period are not identical for pre-school children and for adults. However, scientists of the Russian school, investigating the Pavlovian equivalent, paradoxical and ultra-paradoxical phases of the C.N.S. with its behavioural concomitants, conclude that the aforesaid stages can reverse to a certain extent the functional and quantitative conditions of perception, cognition and memorisation. In practice this means the reproduction of certain mental states similar to those that have occurred also during early stages of learning.

The beginning stages of learning one's native language have the character of conditioned reflex behaviour, but very soon the process becomes one of imitation, invention and imagination. Generally speaking, this is the process of the basic discovery of the significance of speech signals in the given language. This was well understood by Pavlov, who considered the complex nervous activities involved in speech to be founded on the basis of conditioned reflex connections formed at the very beginning of the mastering of the native tongue. This may be the moment when speech signals begin representing reality and consciousness enters into the human relationship.

The purpose of hypnopaedia is to combine subconscious-conscious memorisation of rote material (lexical means) and phonetico-melodical patterns of speech with its conscious and productive application in speaking, writing and reading. Sharp distinction should be made between language and speech: language is a means of communication; speech is a process of communication. During infancy, humans learn to speak (verbal behaviour) but this learning is lacking the motivation of acquiring a foreign language.

The effectiveness of hypnopaedia rests on its dynamic qualities of memorisation occurring during an increased sensitivity of the paradoxical phases as defined by Pavlov and explained further by the Russian school of his followers.

Psycho-linguistic points of internal speech and external speech are also linked with the subconscious source of information. Internal speech, for instance, is characterised not only by internal speaking, but also by internal hearing, which process is animated by the stimulus coming from the internal environment (engram or memory trace), involving the memory of construction that was presented and assimilated during a hypnopaedic session. Linguists are undoubtedly right when they say that the characteristic of the oral expression of thoughts or speech is to be found in the subconscious use of the medium of language, which is aided by the automatic habits of oral speech. Here the writer agrees with the two basic ways of mastering a foreign language, namely: (a) the conscious discursive or logical method; and (b) the unconscious direct or intuitive, which are clearly revealed in all forms and process of speech activity. Accordingly, it is necessary to classify the conscious-discursive method as analytic and the direct-intuitive as synthetic.

From a linguistic and psychological angle the subconscious use of the medium of language can be greatly stimulated by hypnopaedia, applying it to occupational and professional need and personality factors. The analytical trait suits translators and philologists, and the synthetical appeals to those occupations where performance in a foreign language requires fluency and smooth talking.

A major project, the construction of a hypnopaedagogic language course, will need the skill of linguists and hypnopaedists based on continuous research concerning the structure, presentation and teaching of such a course.

SOURCES

Artemov, V. A. *The Psychology of Speech and Instruction in Speaking a Foreign Language*. SCR Education and Psychology Bulletin, **8**, No. 3–4, 1961.

Benediktov, B. A. *Features of the Mastery of Oral Speech in the Process of Learning a Foreign Language*. LNGPIFL, 1957, No. 5.

Karpov, I. V. *Psychological Foundations of Method of Developing the Speech of Students*. MS, published by RSPSR APN, 1950.

II

HYPNOPAEDIA AND LANGUAGE LEARNING

Brian Dutton, M.A., PH.D.
Birbeck College, University of London

THIS brief note is more concerned with the data presented to the learner than with the hypnopaedic method itself. There are many opinions ranging from naïve enthusiasm to utter disbelief concerning the effectiveness of sleep-learning. I do not intend to consider either view here, but merely to act on the assumption that the reports of experiments done in this field in the USSR have been validly reported (see Villen Lustiberg, 'New Education' V, p. 6 ff.).

Much attention appears to have been paid to the development of the methods of hypnopaedia, but not quite so much attention appears to have been paid to the actual language teaching material presented. It therefore seems timely for some comments to be made from the point of view of linguistics and programmed learning. I have seen only some material prepared in English by Cenek Heinz and Josef Vesely (Liberec—Most—Usti nad Labem—Czechoslovakia, 1965), but if these are typical it would seem that the application of some elementary linguistics would greatly improve the materials available.

Language contains three basic levels, which we shall refer to as sound, structure and roots (or message-factors) in order to avoid technical terms. If we imagine a statement as being a series of factors linked by value-symbols, as in

$$\mathrm{a} + \mathrm{b} = \mathrm{c}^2$$

then we can establish a whole series of permutations of (a) factors and (b) equations. The sort of linguistic structure represented by this equation could be

a and *b* are *c*'s

and just as we can replace the letters with numbers, provided we follow certain mathematical/meaningful rules, so we can replace the letters in the linguistic structure with 'words' or concrete roots as opposed to particles.

——— and	——— are	———s
Red	blue	colour
Coal	oil	fuel
Cheese	meat	food

This could be $9 + 7 = 4^2$ in mathematical terms.
Just as we can say that $\mathrm{a}^2 + \mathrm{b}^2 = \mathrm{c}^2$, so we can say

———s and	———s are	———s
Pig	cow	animal
Rose	violet	flower etc.

We can change the factors so that in the first structure *c* becomes *d* and in the realised statements the nouns are replaced by adjectives, producing such statements are *Cheese and meat are nutritious; Coal and oil are scarce; Roses and violets are beautiful,* etc. This high degree of permutation in linguistic structures, and in the factors that may be inserted into the structures, gives language its high degree of flexibility and expressivity.

If, then, we consider these two elements, we can arrive at a system of drill construction that will (a) present constantly recurring roots in a variety of structures and (b) a constantly recurring structure with a variety of roots. In many cases the possible series of statements using a given structure will be almost infinite. Here is an example which uses the only two 'words' in each structure, but any word from column 1 can be paired with any word from column 2 within the structure:

	1		2
	leave		here
I'd	like	it	now
	bring		at once
	use		tomorrow
	send		there

Here, one structure and ten words give twenty-five possible statements. Hence, if the material is presented as a series of structures containing words or roots, then the possibility of permutations enables the learner to make far more statements than he has actually heard. (Five structures and three groups of twenty words each, given probability of meaningfulness, give 40,000 statements!)

Next comes the problems of how to associate these structures. Perhaps the most effective way is a sort of stimulus/response pairing of question/answer, statement/comment, etc. Here is an example of the technique that can be applied to this sort of drill pattern.

When will he ———?	He'll be ———ing next week.
come	come
go	
leave	
start	
finish	
etc.	

The problem is not so much one of drill/pattern construction as of preliminary analysis. The structures that contain the most frequent particles in their most permutable combinations have to be identified, and also the roots or words that fit these structures have to be selected and used in recurring progression throughout the sequence of drills. There is also the problem of irregularities (e.g., Can you *sign* now? I've already *signed* is a structure into which, for sound only, *pay* would fit, but *write* would not). This, however, can be tackled by grouping irregular forms that form sub-systems in a given structure (e.g. past participle in -n for see, be, know, etc.) just as the regular /t/, /d/ and /ed/ past participles are in English. Another way is to use a common irregular (such as *see/saw* or *go/went*) as a constantly recurring particle in a given structure.

The presentation of meaning via hypnopaedia is clearly restricted to sound in our present state of knowledge. It is therefore probable that the best method would be to present the roots or words to be used in a given sequence first with their native equivalents. Next the meaning of the structure could be presented in the native language, and then the two integrated, possibly with the structure and root meanings also integrated and presented via the native equivalent. These brief ideas are simply presented as tentative considerations which would require further experimental validation. However, since it does not seem that the materials previously used do work, any rationalisation of the materials, via linguistic analysis, can only make them more effective.

Finally, a note on the third, and so far unmentioned element, 'sound.' The work of F. Rand Morton in the United States indicates that the learner of a foreign language requires a clear, distinctive acoustic image of the foreign sound before he can hope to utter it correctly. An approach to this problem could be to present series of words in which the same environment surrounds varying phonemes (as in pi*n*, pi*t*, pi*ll*, pi*g*, pi*ck*, pi*tch*, etc.).

For effective language learning, by whatever method, these three levels have to be learned: sounds, structures, roots (or message-factors). A rational analysis of these three levels, together with their progressive integration and the permutation of the members at each level seems to be as possible for hypnopaedic methods as for any other, and the basic ideas presented here, it is hoped, will be of some value to those applying the methods of hypnopaedia to language learning.

III

THE GERMAN EXPERIMENT

(*Report of a test carried out at the sleep-learning dormitory in London.*—
Journal of the Sleep-Learning Association, *July*, 1965)

On April 27, 1965, the German experiment started in the Sleep-Learning Dormitory of the Sleep-Learning Association, 14 Belsize Crescent, Hampstead, London, N.W.3.

The object of the experiment was to show that it is possible to learn material during apparent sleep without the use of visual aid.

Mrs. Phyllis Pilgrim, a teacher aged twenty-six, and Miss Kirsteen Clark, a student aged eighteen, settled down to sleep. Dunlopillo mattresses were used, with soft feather pillows. A pillow speaker (designed and manufactured by the Association) was pressed down into the top surface of each pillow, under the pillow-case.

The wires from the two pillow speakers ran to a single plug fitted to a Telefunken Magnetophon 55 Tape Recorder on which a Conditioning Tape (prepared by the Association) was placed in the usual playback position. In the wakeful state both subjects heard the Conditioning Tape which ran for approximately 40 minutes. This was done in order that they should know consciously what they were going to hear during the night.

The volume was set at 4. The tape was then rewound and reset to begin again at midnight.

Mrs. Pilgrim fell asleep at 12.10 a.m. and 'slept peacefully.' Her reaction to the conditioning was that she felt drowsy while hearing the tape, and fell asleep soon after hearing it the second time. She slept well. She had a feeling that she heard a little of the tape during sleep, after the initial ten minutes.

Miss Clark fell asleep at 1.15 a.m., some time after the Conditioning Tape had finished for the second time. She 'became restless'. On being questioned in the morning she said that she felt alerted by the experience, more mentally active than when she had gone to bed, and that she was unable to sleep.

On the second night the procedure was repeated, the Conditioning Tape being set for the second time for a replay at 11.30 p.m. Mrs.

Pilgrim fell asleep at 11.45 p.m. and slept peacefully. In the morning she reported that she had slept well and went to sleep comfortably while the tape was still playing.

Miss Clark fell asleep at approximately 12.5 a.m. and reported being more relaxed. In the morning she said that she had responded better, feeling a little more relaxed but still apprehensive. She went to sleep before the tape concluded.

On the third night the procedure was repeated. Starting at 11.30 p.m. the tape was played only once. Mrs. Pilgrim fell asleep immediately, in the morning reporting that she slept well. Miss Clark went to sleep at midnight, reporting in the morning that she had experienced more relaxed sleep than on previous nights.

On the fourth night the tape started at 11.30 p.m. Mrs. Pilgrim fell asleep at 11.45 p.m. and slept soundly throughout the night, hearing only a small portion of the Conditioning Tape. Miss Clark fell asleep as the tape ended at 12.15 a.m. In the morning she stated that she might have dozed off once or twice while the tape was playing. She remembered the tape switching off when it reached the end. Then presumably she went to sleep.

On the fifth night the tape was started at 11.45 p.m. Mrs. Pilgrim fell asleep at 12 midnight hearing some of the tape during her sleep, but not really awakening. Miss Clark fell asleep just before 12 midnight. In the morning she stated she had slept well, hearing only the beginning of the tape.

For the remaining two nights of the first week of conditioning both subjects went to sleep almost immediately, did not hear the tape at all, awakened in the morning feeling refreshed.

For the second week of the test, the second side of the conditioning tape was used, relayed from the master control room in a different part of the building. It was arranged by automatic control from a Sangamo Domestic Time Switch, for the tape to commence at 12 midnight each night, shortly after the estimated time of sleep of the two subjects (time taken from the previous week's statistics). The tape was heard once each night by both subjects, although neither heard the tape at any time in full. Although the content of the tape was now different it did not arouse their attention or interest; nor did it consciously produce relaxation and a feeling of well being. *Both subjects slept each night in the normal way* without giving very much attention to the experiment at all.

On the third week, the German Language Tape was relayed from the master control room from a UHER 5000 Universal Tape Recorder, utilising the automatic rewind and playback mechanism to allow the twenty minute tape to repeat German phrases approximately twelve times each night. Controlled for three periods by the Sangamo Domestic Time Switch, the periods of learning were: 12.15 a.m. to 1.45 a.m., 2.45 a.m. to 4 a.m., 6.30 a.m. to 7.54 a.m.

Thus, for fourteen nights the two subjects heard during their sleep twelve repetitions of the twenty minute tape containing 185 German words and 219 German phrases. These phrases were recorded in a triad pattern—German-English-German with a pause between each triad.

On June 9th, Mrs. Pilgrim was examined by a Board of invigilators including a representative from London University College, with Mr. Alan Mayne, M.A., B.SC., and Mr. Geoffrey Stocker, President of the Association. The examination was based on a marking system of one mark for a completely correct answer and half a mark for an incorrect answer which showed a grasp of the meaning of the phrase.

The examination was carried out at 9 p.m. and Mrs. Pilgrim, on this occasion, showed some signs of tiredness. She achieved 70 per cent accurate recall.

Miss Clark was examined at 9 p.m. on June 30th. The delay in examining her was due to the fact that she was taking other examinations at the time and we did not wish to disturb her programme. On this occasion the Editor and Mrs. Phyllis Wadsworth were also present. Using the same system of marking, Miss Kirsteen Clark attained 93·5 per cent recall. The marks were gained from a direct question and answer technique, allowing the subject to hear the English phrase from a tape, and then the invigilators awaited her recall in German. Both subjects were questioned in German by Mr. Alan Mayne and the Editor, when it became apparent they both had a comprehensive grasp of the German phrases.

Questioned before the experiment on what they thought of sleep-learning, Mrs. Pilgrim replied: 'I'm not sure whether it's likely to work.' Miss Clark said: 'It seems a good idea.' When asked if she thought she would learn in this way, Miss Clark said: 'We shall see.'

After the experiment the same questions were put to them and Mrs. Pilgrim replied: 'It certainly is an aid to learning.' Miss Clark said, with very much enthusiasm: 'Sleep learning is a marvellous way to learn.'

No visual aids were used in this experiment. The subjects did not refer to any written work relating to German during the period of four weeks, nor did they see the script at any time.

Neither subject knew any German before they started on the experiment, other than an odd word or two which we are all likely to know. Mrs. Pilgrim, on the whole, was a somewhat restful sleeper, whereas Miss Clark, according to Mrs. Pilgrim's report, tossed and turned in her sleep, frequently arching up in bed and putting her head under the pillow. Neither subject drank alcohol nor had stimulants before going to bed. Both had moderate living habits, working during the day, with social functions in the evenings, going to bed at regular hours, approximately at 12 midnight, sleeping until 8 a.m.

The experiment confirmed that it is possible to learn during the hours of sleep, that is, between the time of apparently falling asleep and waking in the morning.

It also showed that the degree of success is not always predictable; but that sleep-learning with the correct instruction and conditioning is a practical possibility for all people in general good health, with average intelligence and good hearing, who have no undue resistances.

The start of the experiment was witnessed by members of the Press, including Miss Ann Buchanan of the *Daily Sketch,* and by Mr. Torrie Pilgrim, who attended to wish his wife success.

[Editor's note: Sleep was not monitored by the EEG, therefore the depth of sleep could not be established physiologically.]

25

ELECTRICAL ACTIVITY OF THE BRAIN AND ITS PRESUMPTIVE LINK WITH HYPNOPAEDIA

The study of the electrical changes taking place in the cortex and subcortex is contributing more and more—as techniques of recording become more refined—to the understanding of the complex activities and events taking place within them. It has been seen already during experiments that acoustic signals from click stimuli, pure tone and multi-frequency sounds can cause change in the EEG until the stimulation is terminated either in waking or sleeping persons. Experiments conducted in the Walter Reed Army Institute of Research, Washington, in Australia (H. C. Beh and P. E. Barratt at the University of New England, Armidale, N.S.W.), and Russia resulted in discriminative responses to acoustic signals during sleep, and, finally, B. W. Levinson (see chapter 17, page 194), reports changes in the EEG of anaesthetised patients upon the fluctuation of environmental noise in the operating theatre. The assimilation of speech during behaviour, EEG sleep or anaesthesia activates corresponding areas of the cortex, subcortex and cortico-thalamical sections causing simultaneous and synchronised excitatory and inhibitory functions in the brain cells.

Whether or not the Pavlovian 'alert points' have an actual topographical location, their real importance rests in functional changes involving multi levels of excitation and inhibition of sensory, associative and motor neurons. The bio-electrical activity of brain cells corresponds with their excited or inhibited state and, therefore, there is a possibility of co-ordinating the function of 'alert points in action or being dormant' with further electro-physiological research. Electro-physiological reactions occurring during learning processes have not been investigated in an exposed human brain—to the writer's knowledge.

In following a sequence from animal experiments to a presumptive examination of human learning during behavioural or EEG sleep (and in the waking state as well), the Editor presents here some interesting material from experiments conducted on cats, with the object of observing cerebro-electrical activities taking place during the animals' learning processes by auditory stimulation. As the basic functions of learning in a purely experimental physio-psychological sense are similar in mammals and humans, and it does not alter much during different levels of consciousness, the following material will provide valuable information for research to be conducted in the future.

EEG AND LEARNING

Some of the electrical correlates of conditioning are of great interest and open the way to more revealing experimental analysis of the learning process. For example, if a cat is trained or conditioned to jump on the table for food in response to one type of conditioning stimulus, and conditioned to remain on the floor in response to another type, we find that these auditory stimuli have a definite effect on the EEG as recorded over the Rolandic somaesthetic area; the positive stimulus, i.e., the one that tells the cat to jump on the table, causes a blocking of the spontaneous rhythmic discharge, while the negative stimulus augments it. Thus, because of the presumable 'shunting' of the auditory stimuli, the cortex is prepared for motor activity or inactivity, a blockage of the EEG (the appearance of high-frequency low-voltage waves) being the manifestation of 'arousal', with the accentuation of the spontaneous rhythm (high voltage alpha waves) reflecting presumably an inhibited state.

EVOKED RESPONSES

Again, once the conditioned responses have been established, the conditioned stimulus, for example, the sound of the bell, will give and evoke responses on the surface of the cortex corresponding to the region of both the unconditioned and conditioned analysers. Thus, if the sound of the bell is the conditioned stimulus for jumping to obtain food, it evokes responses not only in the primary auditory receiving area, but also in the Rolandic somatomotor cortex.

With a speculative manipulation of changing expressions, the dynamics of the above may also apply hypothetically to humans, who are, in the case of hypnopaedia, doing associative learning.

Therefore, if a person is trained or conditioned to assimilate verbal texts in response to one type of special stimulus (which is the voice of the hypnopaedic instructor) and not assimilate speech in response to another type (incidental speech), then it is likely that these acoustic signals will have an effect on the EEG generally or on records taken from specific areas. The positive stimulus, i.e., the one that tells or instructs the persons to memorise the text, causes a blockage of the actual spontaneous discharge whilst the psychologically negative stimulus augments this. Thus, because of the presumably sub-cortical 'shunting' of the acoustic signals, the cortex is probably prepared for speech associative-memorisation activity or inactivity. The presumptive blockage of the EEG, i.e., the appearance of K-complex followed by altered wave patterns as being the manifestation of the activation of the 'alert points', should reflect its preceding passive state.

Again, once the conditioned response has been established, the conditioned circumstantial stimulus (which is the voice of the hypnopaedic speaker at a certain time) will give and evoke responses in the cortex corresponding to the region of both the unconditioned and conditioned analysers. If the sound of the speaker at a specific time is the conditioning stimulus for assimilating texts, it evokes responses not only in the primary auditory receiving area, but also in the secondary. EEG signs of arousal rhythms did not wake the subjects participating in Russian experiments (Svyadoshch, Zuchar), as their external behaviour and subjective experiences during the experiments continued as that of sleeping persons. An auditory stimulus can block the preceding rhythms in a human subject, i.e., the EEG record becomes desynchronised and shows only rapid small oscillation of potential. If this stimulus is repeated regularly, however (as it is done during hypnopaedic sessions by the repetitive occurrence of multi-frequency acoustic signals), there is a habituation occurring, so that the blockage is eventually inhibited or, put in other words, the stimulus fails to 'arouse' or wake.

LIMITS OF INFORMATION TRANSMISSIONS DURING SLEEP

It will be recalled that in the relaxed waking subject the characteristic response to visual and auditory stimulus is a blocking of the alpha rhythm; in the sleeping subject a click stimulus (or a similar sound effect) not loud enough to waken the subject, has a characteristic effect, most prominent in the 'C' or fourth stage of sleep. This was called by Loomis, Harvey and Hobart (1938) the K-complex, consisting of a large delta wave on which is superimposed a complex of rapid 14/cps waves.

Experiments (Fishgold and Schwartz, 1961) ascertained that it was at stage 'C' that obedience to instructions begins to dissolve and disappear completely. Thus, although there were some signs in the EEG record of an effect of the stimulus, the link between auditory sensory information and motor response had been broken. It is likely that when the auditory stimulation through multi-frequency sounds continues, and its volume is not loud enough to waken the subject during hypnopaedic session, the appearing K-complex may be followed by an altering wave pattern, and rapid oscillation with occasional alpha type bursts may dominate the EEG. [Simon and Emmons (1954, 1955, 1956) interrupted the presentation of speech signals at this stage during their experiments—contrary to the Russians. American experiments were discontinued while the Russians tried to assess also the acoustic parameters for the correct intonation of hypnopaedic speech (L. A. Bliznitchenko, 1965, 1966).]

If this happens, the depth of sleep decreases with the effect of continuous auditory stimulation and, by establishing a link between associative memorisation and sensory information process, the perception and assimilation of hypnopaedic speech can occur. H. L. Williams reports (1963, Walter Reed Army Inst. of Research) that behavioural response thresholds appear to be as high in the high-voltage, low-frequency stages of sleep, as they are in high-frequency lower-voltage stages. It remains to be seen, however, whether response thresholds become lower during deeper stages, when stimuli with immediate and significant consequences are used. Results of experiments showed that accurate discriminative responses can occur in any stage of sleep.

If the pattern and meaning of auditory signals can be recognised by sleeping subjects, how are we to define sleep? If sleep is not a silent state, what limit does the sleeping state impose on the organisation of behaviour and mental activity? This question may be answered shortly also by hypnopaedia. Finally, another significant fact taken from EEG records: which is the occurrence of high frequency oscillations in the psychologically active REM phase of sleep, waking state, hypnosis and hypnopaedic state of assimilation.

Perceptual conditions during the various stages of sleep, hypnosis and chemically induced anaesthesia should be investigated more thoroughly in the future, with attention to the circumstances of recall, as the latter was not analysed explicitly enough in the data published by several authors. The Editor suggests that the EEG activity of children be examined especially during the period when they acquire their native tongue (as an evolutional aspect of learning) and compared with the EEG of sustained phasic states (occurring in hypnosis, sleep and during hypnopaedic lessons) of normal adults. This would involve an analysis of *dominating* EEG patterns of children aged six months to three years, using a diurnal circle as a basis in comparison with dominating EEG patterns occurring during hypnosis and hypnopaedic sessions. Although no special studies or investigations were conducted in this particular field to gain any assessment fitting into this subject, Dr. Grey Walter's views on the EEG are quite interesting to consider. He states: '. . . The sequence of dominant EEG rhythms during the first three years begins with the domination of delta waves which are gradually taken over by irregular beta spindles followed by alpha bursts, etc. The dominant EEG rhythms involving the periodicity of *years* occur in the same patterns during the *daily* periodicity of sleep-wakefulness of normal adults.'

Is it perhaps possible to reconstruct and sustain similar brain physiological conditions during hypnopaedia (and hypnosis) to those of the early stages of learning? Further research on the bio-electrical and biochemical aspects of memorisation and learning may clarify this question. Recent reports on the controversy over the electrical and chemical functions of memorising process may indicate some interesting points on why, for instance, sleep has a beneficial effect on long-term memory. According to one theory, long-term memory (which occurs in hypnopaedia) takes a physical form in the brain much less evanescent than an electric current.

SOURCES

Starling and Lowatt Evans, *Learning, Memory, Sleep and Personality,* Chapter 53. Principles of Human Physiology, J. & A. Churchill.

H. L. Williams, H. C. Morlock, Jr., J. V. Morlock, *Discriminative Responses to Auditory Signals During Sleep,* Paper presented at APA Convention, Philadelphia, 31 Aug., 1963.

B. W. Levinson, States of Awareness During General Anaesthesia, (Preliminary Communication) *British Journal of Anaesthesia,* 1965, **37**, 544.

H. C. Beh and P. E. H. Barratt, Discrimination and Conditioning During Sleep as Indicated by the Electroencephalogram, *Science,* 1965, **147**.

H. Davies, P. A. Davies, A. L. Loomis, E. N. Harvey and G. Hobart, Electrical Reactions of the Human Brain to Auditory Stimulation During Sleep, *Journal of Neurophysiology*, 1939, **2**, 500–514.

Dr. W. Grey Walter, *The Living Brain,* Penguin Books, 1965.

26

SELECTIVE CONTACT WITH THE EXTERNAL ENVIRONMENT DURING SLEEP

'SENTRY POSTS' OF THE BRAIN

THE 'Sentry Posts' (Pavlovian term used in describing partial sleep and rapport in hypnosis) are wakeful sections of the brain functioning during sleep to establish and maintain contact with the external environment. Sleeping humans and animals can be alerted also by specific types of noises or sounds. The development of such special nervous functions which play an important role in the preservation of life, served for the protection of both humans and animals in their primitive and civilised environment. It has been found that by an increased sensitivity, conditioned to selected types of signals associated with threats of danger, the response of humans and animals was their partial or complete arousal from sleep. It was also observed that the 'sentry posts' receive and transmit only those important particular signals to which they are tuned. Man therefore has a biologically inherent ability to establish and maintain contact with his surroundings during different stages of sleep, and this originates from evolutionary adaptation of the orientation reflex.

'SENTRY POSTS' HAVE A SELECTIVE FUNCTION

The Editor can cite several examples of natural sleep with the 'sentry posts' in action and selecting certain but important signals only; this explains how a tired mother sleeps—loud noises may not wake her, but the faintest sound made by *her* baby arouses her immediately. [Oswald, Taylor and Treisman (1960) in well controlled experiments reported that during sleep a subject tends to respond selectively to his name. The review of the behavioural evidence led Deutsch and Deutsch (1963) to the probable conclusion that a message will reach the same perceptual and discriminatory mechanism whether attention is paid or not; and such information is then grouped or segregated by these mechanisms.]

Other examples of sleep with 'sentry posts' on duty are: the muscular automatism of water fowl paddling on the water with one leg in order to keep their balance. As soon as the waves become bigger or there is a splash, the birds wake up. Monkeys or apes living on trees are alerted by a special sound signal produced by the sentry animal if danger approaches them, but they are not alerted or awakened from their sleep if a noisy herd of elephants passes by under their trees.

The sleeping man is more easily awakened by sound, touch or changing temperature than by visual, olfactory or gustatory irritants (N. Kleitman, 1963); therefore his 'sentry posts' will be more sensitive in responding to auditory stimuli. The corresponding cortical areas of hearing could be conditioned to remain in a prolonged excited state after the onset of behavioural sleep.

'SENTRY POSTS' TRANSFORMING INTO ACOUSTIC CONTACT ZONE

By knowing that the sound of the hypnopaedic instructor is not a signal associated with danger or threat but one providing benefit of importance, the 'sentry posts' will transform into a conditioned *acoustic contact zone* (Editor's own term) acting as a 'receiving station', transmitting and assimilating selected auditory information during certain stages of sleep without the conscious participation of the sleeper. The development of the acoustic contact zone can be the result of the adaptive function of the brain, based upon the formerly emerging unconditioned and conditioned functions of the biological 'sentry posts'.

Helen C. Beh and P. E. H. Barratt write:

> 'Studies of humans alerted during sleep have suggested that certain critical stimuli have the power of evoking an alerting response as indicated by the EEG, whereas neutral stimuli do not. The results of our investigation confirm earlier findings that this stimulus significance may be experimentally built in by conditioning. Our results also extend earlier findings by indicating that the organism, even during low levels of vigilance such as sleep, is capable of responding to changes in stimulus significance brought about by conditioning.
>
> 'Our findings indicate that it is not only possible for the human organism to discriminate between stimuli during sleep on the

basis of their significance but that stimulus significance 'built-in' during sleep appears to carry over to the waking state. Thus, it would seem that, even during lowered levels of vigilance, some sort of scanning mechanism operates, sifting important from unimportant information as it impinges on the organism.'

PHYSIOLOGY AND HYPNOPAEDIA

Pavlov's followers, who were investigating the intricate functions of higher nervous activity of man, came to the conclusion (with their western contemporaries and followers) that a verbal stimulus may facilitate and even accelerate the formation of a newly conditioned response, if the name of the stimulus is known to the subject and added to the new conditioned stimulus. Thus, the word which signifies the name of a given object—and is a well-established naturally conditioned stimulus—may greatly reinforce the new conditioned response, which, in this case, is the word newly acquired during a hypnopaedic session.

Laboratory investigations, to assess more details on the functioning of hypnotic 'rapport zones' (K. I. Platonov, 1957), conclude that it is positively induced under the influence of the inhibitory state of the surroundings sections of the brain. The 'sentry posts' are in a state of increased excitability which ensures the maintenance of its connection with specific or selected signals from the external environment. As Pavlov observed: 'The waking state of higher organisms always includes a cerebral condition of partial sleep and precisely in the subtlest relation of the organism with the external environment; moreover, in the sleeping state there are always waking, active sections in the brain, which are, as it were, sentries on duty.'

Physiologists observed one more important phenomenon, namely that during the transition of the brain cells from an active state into the state of inhibition (sleep), the inhibition does not arise in them all at once, but gradually. Before the onset of complete inhibition (only occurring in very deep sleep), a number of intermediate (phasic) states are observed in the cells. This is also verified by the EEG stages of sleep. During the development of such transitory states between sleep and waking, changes were observed in the cortical cells, response to the conditioned stimuli depending on the degree of their inhibition. Whereas in the waking state, with normal tone of the cerebral cortex, the strength of the irradiative excitation of cortical cells corresponds to the strength of the stimulus (law of force relation), during the rise of the transitory states this law becomes violated. Thus, during the equalising phase, the weak and strong stimuli begin to provoke reactions of equal force. In the ensuing transitory phase, a weak stimulus provokes a strong response, while the strong stimulus produces a weak response. This is called the 'paradoxical phase' by the Pavlovian school, which is followed by the ultra-paradoxical phase, during which the negative-conditioned stimuli begin the provoke positive reactions in the cortical cells, while the positive stimuli provoke no reactions. Still deeper inhibition of the cortical cells gives rise to the appearance of the narcotic phase. Arising during the lapse into sleep, or at the other end, during awaking, the phasic states may be disrupted through the cerebral cortex unequally, by being localised first in one and then in the other section. Hyponopaedic phenomena rest upon the beforementioned cortical dynamics, as the periodicity of the phasic states suitable for assimilating information could be sustained. [Japanese EEG studies of Zen Buddhists (monks) have reportedly shown that the meditation state is a *sustained* period of alpha rhythm. Dr. J. Kamiya, at Langley Porter Institute in San Francisco, has used the EEG as a teaching instrument demonstrating that control of the alpha state can be learned with surprising rapidity.]

The existence of phasic states in man during sleep has also been proved by the method of conditioned reflexes in the studies of P. Povorinsky and N. Traugot, in a series of investigations conducted by N. Krasnogorsky (1951). It will be observed that, according to N. Krasnogorsky, the phasic states may be localised and sustained in various analysers (auditory analysers in the case of hypnopaedia) during the general optimal excitability of the cortex. Phenomena of suggestion and suggestibility, often appearing in the life of man, are closely connected with one of the phasic states of the cerebral cortex. The studies conducted by S. Levin (1934) with the method of observing conditioned reflexes during experiments which were carried out in N. Krasnogorsky's children's clinic can provide a remarkable illustration of the significance of the lowered tone of the cerebral cortex, a condition which aids in increasing response to induced verbal stimuli. A verbal suggestion of eating apples inducted during the drowsy state evoked the children to salivate two and a half to three times as much as the same verbal induction did in the complete waking state.

The phases of cerebral reactivity are an ever-moving dynamic feature of the different sections of the cortex creating a simultaneously changing picture of perceptual and associative co-ordination bombarded by internal and external stimulation. The complex functioning of the brain does not come to a state of inertia during natural sleep which explains the phenomenon of sleep-learning amongst many others. This functioning of the brain is called the wakeful subconscious mind and is responsible for continuous autonomic functions, etc.

The scientific aspects of hypnopaedia are firmly set on the dynamics of higher nervous activity whose pioneer, I. P. Pavlov, laid down the fundamentals by his observations of unconditioned and conditioned reflexes as the basic mechanism of learning. (Many lay authors have credited to the subconscious, with being responsible for the possibility of sleep-learning, but no further speculation or investigations were made by those who put their comments to this subject without any scientific background.)

THE CONDITIONED 'ACOUSTIC CONTACT ZONE' IN HYPNOPAEDIA

In hypnosis and sleep-learning the phylogenetically evolved 'sentry post' function of the brain is superimposed by a rapport or acoustic contact zone for transmitting specific signals to the first and secondary auditory centres. It is produced by the sleeper's motivation functioning as a more or less confined centre of concentrated excitation, isolated from the remaining regions of the brain by negative induction. For this reason the coupling functions of the brain-cells of the corresponding parts of the 'acoustic contact zone' sharply increase. The continuous and sustained function of the acoustic contact zone provides the possibility not only of retaining the contact towards the specific signals from the hypnopaedic speaker, but of increasing effectuation. The subject, under these conditions, receives and retains the text without actually disturbing his sleep from a behaviour angle.

INCIDENTAL SLEEP-LEARNING

One subject of the Research Department at Charkov Paedagogical Institute of Higher Nervous Activity, Mr. V. K., aged fifty-three (reported by K. I. Platonov, 1957), attracted the attention of scientists to the following phenomenon quite frequently observed: he often fell asleep surrounded by his family, as his wife was reading stories to the children. Taking little apparent interest in the reading he always fell asleep at the beginning of the reading and usually slept, snoring, for thirty to forty minutes. If the reading continued during his sleep (which was not monitored by the EEG), he could recall all that was read. There are reasons to believe that in this case a conditioned reflex bond was formed while the cortex was in an intermediate phase between wakefulness and sleep and the 'acoustic contact zone' had been activated for keeping the contact with the voice of the story-reading person. This type of phenomenon should not be overlooked, because it shows that sleeping persons are not devoid of the faculty of speech-perception during apparent sleep.

N. Krasnogorsky furthermore observed that in cases of examining conditioned reflex bonds, he finds that they can be deeper induced during certain phases of sleep than in the waking state. Therefore, new conditioned reflex bonds may be elaborated successfully by *all* the cells of the cortex under wakeful conditions. Y. Povorinsky observed that certain conditioned reflex bonds, reinforced by verbal stimuli, are formed faster during hypnosis and sleep than in the waking state. All this has been confirmed in its time by physiological research. Thus, in studying the activity of the brains of children and adolescents, N. Krasnogorsky (1939) came to the following conclusions: 'In the cerebral cortex, which is in a state of inhibition or sleep, extremely deeply seated and stable reflexes may form in its wakeful zones'—and these conclusions are also referable to the 'auditory contact zones', responsible for the occurrence of hypnopaedic phenomena. Hypnopaedic speech as a stimulus, effectuated by its frequent repetition presented during the suitable stages of sleep, could be also retained as neurograms, engrames or memory traces without the participation of the subject's consciousness. The activated auditory analysers of the brain will not terminate sleep by arousing the whole organism. Hypnopaedia as an aid to conventional study shows ample evidence of eliminating pro and retroactive inhibition (as stated by A. R. Luria, Professor of Psychology, Moscow University, in a letter written to the Editor) and other traumatising effects of the external and internal environment.

HISTORICITY OF THE NERVOUS SYSTEM

By carrying out analytical and synthetising activities, the cerebral cortex fixes the temporal succession of all the processes occurring in it and retains the possibility of subsequently reproducing them under corresponding conditions.

It is well known that precisely this dynamism of the brain underlies the function of memory, i.e., the process of memorising and recalling that which occurred significantly in the past in its direct successions and connections. This property of the cortex testifies to the fact that the entire nervous activity is permeated with the principle of historicity which is also the basic feature of hypnopaedic memorisation. By means of speech, presented during the lighter stages of sleep, study material will act as an accumulated past experience registered by the brain. This seems also to be quite feasible by reason of the historicity of the nervous system. The functional state of the cerebral cortex represents a mosaic picture of excited (alert) and inhibited (dormant) sections, dynamic structures which are in a state of greater or lesser activity during sleep and wakefulness. Under these conditions any stimulation of the cortex, combining with the traces of former stimulation (memories of sleep-learning sessions), will revive the complex of chain responses with which it was linked in the past. It is precisely the verbal stimulus which may be particularly active in this respect, and which can call to life the most diverse and complicated reactions.

On the basis of these considerations and experimental data presented in this symposium, it is concluded that man has the possibility of specially directing the activity of his faculties for memorising and reviving those impulses which were presented to him during the lighter stages of sleep.

SOURCES

I. P. Pavlov, *Lectures on Conditioned Reflexes,* Lawrence and Wishart, Ltd., London, 1941.

K. I. Platonov, *The Word as a Physiological and Therapeutical Factor,* Medgiz, 1957, Moscow.

H. C. Beh and P. E. H. Barratt, *Discrimination and Conditioning During Sleep as indicated by the Electroencephalogram,* Science, 1965, **174**.

N. Kleitman, *Sleep and Wakefulness,* Chicago University Press, 1963.

Current Research on Sleep and Dreams, published by U.S. Dept. of Health, Education and Welfare, Washington.

27

HYPNOPAEDIA—A TECHNIQUE OF SUBLIMINAL STIMULATION?

Seldom has anything in psychology caused such an immediate and widespread stir as the recent claim that the presentation of certain stimuli below the level of conscious awareness can influence people's behaviour in a significant way. The assimilation and memorisation of speech during different stages of natural sleep belongs, from a psychological angle, to the technique of subliminal stimulation.

In the following, the Editor wishes to co-ordinate some results of special data on subliminal perception and stimulation with hypnopaedia. Two major criteria are to be considered when we speak of subliminal stimulation itself and of whether it occurs in hypnopaedia or not. *They are the two factor determiners, namely, the internal state of the organism and, externally, the physical properties of the stimulus related to the state of the organism.*

RESEARCH ON BEHAVIOUR WITHOUT AWARENESS

In the hope of providing a more substantial foundation upon which to base judgments of the validity of sleep-learning claims for subliminal stimulation, a systematic review of relevant scientific work was undertaken. From several examples of experiments, I will cite from those cases, which again support incidentally the psychological foundations of perceiving and memorising speech during the hypnogogic reverie state and light stages of sleep. The records collected by J. V. McConnell, R. L. Cutler and E. B. McNeil, University of Michigan, provide evidence for the increasing interest in establishing a scientific foundation for hypnopaedia. Although the following material was taken from cases (i.e., respondings) occurring in the waking state, their psychological significance for hypnopaedia cannot be ignored.

EFFECTS OF INNER STATES UPON THRESHOLDS

Whatever the possibility that subliminal stimulation may significantly alter behaviour there is excellent evidence that certain inner states of the organism, as well as externally induced conditions, may significantly alter the recognition threshold of the individual. This, of course, has important implications for the susceptibility of the individual to the effects of subliminal stimulation. It is well known that physiological factors, such as fatigue, visual acuity, or satiation, may change the threshold of an individual for various kinds of stimuli.

Recent evidence has accumulated to show that, in addition to these physiological factors, certain psychological states, such as psychological need, value, conflict and defence, may also significantly influence thresholds, as well as other aspects of the perceptual process. (Stroh, Shaw and Washburn found evidence for subliminal stimulation when auditory stimuli whispers were presented at such a distance that the subjects were not consciously aware that they were hearing anything, which is a similar situation when recalling 'never heard', i.e., hypnopaedically memorised words.) *Newhall and Sears in* 1933 *have attempted to show that it is possible to condition subiects to subliminary stimuli, as was done during sleep-learning experiments conducted in Russia and in the dormitories of the S.L.A. in London.* This suggests that subjects may either (a) 'learn' certain subliminally presented stimuli (whispering voice during sleep) or (b) make use of subliminal reinforcers either to learn or strengthen previously learned responses.

While a complete review of the experimental work on perceptual defence and selective vigilance would take us too far afield, it seems wise to indicate, by example, some of the inner state factors which allegedly produce variations in recognition thresholds. Brunner, Postman and Goodman were able to show that such factors as symbolic value, need, tension and tension release, and emotional selectivity were important in the perceptual process. More specifically related to the issue of altered recognition thresholds is a study by McGinnies in which he demonstrated that emotionally toned words had generally higher thresholds than neutral words. (This conclusion was drawn from experiments during the waking state, but it can be the opposite during sleep, as is thought by L. A. Bliznitchenko.) Lazarus, Ericksen and Fonda have shown that personality factors are at least in part determiners of the recognition threshold for classes of auditory stimuli. Reece showed that the association of shock with certain stimuli had the effect of raising the recognition threshold for those stimuli. This is a basic fundamental used in certain types of sleep-learning experiments when electrical shocks were applied.

UNANSWERED METHODOLOGICAL QUESTIONS

Having now concluded that, under certain conditions (the waking state, and also in sleep and anaesthesia), the phenomenon of subliminal perception does occur, we turn our attention next to the many unanswered questions which this conclusion raises. For example, what kinds of behaviour can be influenced by subliminal stimulation?—(Learning). What types of stimuli operate best at sub-threshold intensities?—(Auditory). Do all subliminal stimuli operate at the same level of unconsciousness? Or do different stimuli (or modes of stimulation) affect different levels of unconsiousness (or sleep in hypnopaedia)? What characteristics of the perceiver help determine the effectiveness of subliminary stimulation (or hypnopaedia session)?

A few words of caution concerning the word 'subliminal' seem in order, however. It must be remembered that the psychological limen is a statistical concept, a fact overlooked by far too many current textbook writers. The common definition of the limen is: that stimulus value which gives a response exactly half the time. One of the difficulties in analysing the many studies on subliminal perception is the fact that many experimenters have assumed that, because the stimuli which they employed were below the statistical limen for a given subject, the stimuli were therefore never consciously perceivable by the subject. This is, of course, not true. Thresholds vary from situation to situation, as well as from day to day and from moment to moment. The writer simply wishes to make the point that the range of stimulus intensities which are in fact subliminal may be smaller than many experimenters in the past have assumed. It has been commonly assumed that the several methods of producing subliminal stimuli, i.e., reducing intensity, duration, size, or clarity, are logically and methodologically equivalent. While this may be true, it remains to be demonstrated conclusively.

It may seem fairly clear that learning can take place when the stimuli to which the organism must respond are presented or received subliminally, and hypnopaedia in this case is no exception.

LEVELS OF UNCONSCIOUSNESS AFFECTED BY SUBLIMINAL STIMULATION

We must now differentiate between stimuli which a subject cannot bring to awareness under any conditions (completely subliminal stimuli) and those stimuli of which he is merely not aware at the moment but could be made aware of should his set be changed. (The latter refers to hypnopaedia.) At any given moment a vast conflux of stimuli impinges upon the subject's receptors, during wakefulness and sleep as well. Few of the sensations arising from this stimulation ever enter the focus of attention. A great many experimenters have demonstrated that subjects could make use of stimuli well above the threshold of awareness but which could not be reported on. Thus, in one phase of the experiment, Perky raised the intensity of the visual stimuli she was using to such a level, that other psychologists who had not participated in the study apparently refused to believe that the subjects had not been aware of the stimuli. Perky's subjects, however, operating under a set to call up images of the stimuli presented, did not notice even relatively intense stimuli. Correspondingly, Newhall and Dodge presented visual stimuli first at below-threshold intensities, then increased the intensities so slowly that the subjects were not aware of them even when they were well above threshold. When the stimuli were turned off suddenly, however, the subjects experienced after-images. Thus certain stimuli may be well above threshold and yet be subliminal in the sense that they cannot be reported on under certain experimental conditions.

The above mentioned part serves an analogous link between hypnopaedic experiments and those mentioned previously in connection with the recall of images and hypnopaedic speech, as the subjects were not aware of the stimuli in both cases.

There are other levels of unconsciousness which are deserving of our attention, however. Much work has been done at the animal level in which conditioning has been attempted upon animals with various parts of the brain removed. The same is true of animals and humans under various types of anaesthesia. Miller, in summarising the experimental data dealing with conditioning and consciousness, concludes that:

(a) Conditioning can take place in other parts of the nervous system than the cortex—even in the spinal cord.

(b) If conditioned responses are evidence of consciousness, then consciousness is not mediated solely by the cortex.

(c) It may be possible to develop conditioning . . . at more than one level of the nervous system at the same time.

(d) Animals (and humans as well) are conditionable even when anaesthetised.

The nervous system has many levels of anatomical integration. Should we be surprised to discover that incoming stimuli may have an effect on the lower level and not on a higher and that under certain conditions this effect can later be demonstrated in terms of behavioural changes? We shall not be able to speak clearly of the effects of subliminal stimulation upon the various levels of consciousness until we have some better method of specifying exactly what these levels are and by what part of the nervous system they are mediated. Experimentation is badly needed in this area.

Education with hypnopaedia is triggered off by the first use of subliminal techniques. Psychologists, liking or disliking this idea, shall be aware that a great deal of our normal perception occurs on the fringe of conscious awareness, and subliminal events are no more effective than weak conscious stimuli.

Rarely does a day pass without a statement in the press somewhere mentioning hypnopaedia and relating it to the Utopian promise or the 1984 technique of learning. Subliminal perception and stimulation opens up the way of influencing the subconscious, but this instrument is a two-pronged weapon which can be used as a voluntarily selected technique or storing information, or by psychological manipulation to alter behaviour patterns.

SOURCES

Munn, Norman L. *The Fundamentals of Human Adjustment, 4th Edition,* pp. 576 ff, George G. Harrap & Co., London, Bombay, Wellington Sydney, 1961.

McConnell, J. V., Cutler, R. L. and McNeil, E. B. *Subliminal Stimulation, An Overview*, American Psychologist, 1958, **13**, 229–242.

PART III

28

SOME PROBLEMS AND PARAMETERS OF SLEEP LEARNING

Martin Lee Coyne

PREFACE

The writer wishes to acknowledge the assistance of Noah Rosenzweig and Konstantine Kulesha for their tireless efforts in the running of this experiment, and to the twenty-eight subjects who co-operated so fully. The author is further indebted to Professor Joseph J. Greenbaum, without whose suggestions, advice and constant inspiration this work could never have been accomplished.

I PURPOSE OF STUDY AND HISTORICAL BACKGROUND

Almost one-third of our life is spent in sleep. In spite of the obvious importance of this phenomenon, relatively little is known about its nature. We do know, if only phenomenologically, that sleep is effective in restoring body energy, in 'rebuilding' our bodies after activity, and seemingly is necessary for the continuance of life.

We know also something of the physiological and neural changes that occur, and a few facts on the psychological processes that may transpire during sleep. In addition, some facts are known about the individual differences among sleepers. Of course, considering the practical difficulties involved in studying sleep, this knowledge is not inconsiderable, nor easily come by. When we consider though that a college sophomore of twenty years of age, if he fulfils his life expectancy, will spend 16 of his next 48 years literally asleep, we can appreciate the practical importance of obtaining much greater information on sleep and at least investigating the possibility of a more fruitful use of this time.

One such possibility is learning during sleep. The feasability of such learning has long been prevalent in folk-lore. There are many curious tales of mothers tiptoeing into the rooms of their sleeping children and repeating in soft whispers to their unsuspecting charges the local mores, in the hope of painlessly effecting the socialisation process. Science fiction and fantasy writers too have been fascinated with the possibility of acquisition occurring during sleep. Witness Huxley's *Brave New World* (10), where the main moral and social learnings of man are accomplished by hypnopaedia (i.e., sleep-learning).

Few people though have actually attempted serious scientific investigation of this problem. *The Psychological Abstracts,* a compilation of articles published in the psychological journals throughout the world, report only four such investigations in the past 20 years.

LeShan (15), about ten years ago, was the first to attack in any systematic manner the possibility of sleep-learning. At a summer camp he picked forty children who, by inspection, were found to be habitual nail-biters. He divided these 40 subjects into two equal groups, a control group and an experimental group. To one group, the experimental, LeShan played a phonograph record containing the words, 'my fingernatils taste terribly bitter'. The record was played six times a night for 54 successive nights. He made certain the subjects were asleep by direct observation. The control group, of course, received no sleep instructions. During the courses of the experiment, which lasted almost two months, both the experimental and control groups were subject to frequent examination of their nails to determine if any change in the subjects' nail-biting behaviour was occurring. For the first few weeks there were no apparent results, but as the weeks went on the examinations began to reveal some changes. By the final examination all twenty subjects of the control group were still classified as habitual nail-biters. In the experimental group, however, only twelve of the twenty subjects could still be so classified. Thus the experimental group showed a drop of 40 per cent in nail-biting behaviour, while the control group remained the same.

Leuba and Bateman (16) found a subject who claimed that she was able to remember events which presumably occurred while she was asleep, although she was not aware of them going on at the time. To test the accuracy of her claim five phonograph records, containing songs with which she had no previous experience, were played to the subject during her sleep. The next morning she was able to recall the words to the songs with only a few small errors. Her husband reported that the subject slept essentially the same way that night as she usually did. This incidentally is the only report in the literature of accurate free recall of material presented during sleep.

Recently Fox and Robbin (3) have carried out a fairly well-designed investigation of sleep-learning. Thirty subjects were matched on their ability to learn the English equivalents of 15 Chinese words, and then were divided into three groups of ten each. One group, the facilitation group, heard a different list of 25 Chinese words and their correct equivalents repeated during the night for one-half hour (15 times). A control group listened to music for this same half hour period. The third group, the interference group, heard the same 25 Chinese words as did the facilitation group, but this time the words were paired with incorrect English equivalents. The next morning the three groups were tested on the number of trials required to learn the list of 25 English-Chinese paired associates. The average number of trials required by the facilitation group was 5·6; for the control group 7·7; and for the interference group 11·1. These different were all statistically significant, i.e., such differences would occur by chance only 5 times in one hundred. While these results strongly suggest that learning during sleep occurred, there are some weaknesses in the Fox-Robbin experiment. One difficulty, and probably the major weakness of the experiment, was the failure to observe the subjects during sleep. It is possible that some of the subjects might have heard the words during the night and awoken without remembering this experience the next day, in which case learning could not have been said to have occurred during sleep.

Though there is a paucity of data available on sleep-learning, the results that have been obtained are certainly challenging enough to warrant further investigation. The unsolved problems connected with learning during sleep are obviously many. It is the purpose of this study to explore these problems and attempt, at least, some tentative experimental answers to them, within the limits imposed by such practical considerations as time, money and subjects.

More specifically, this study is concerned with:

(1) *The demonstration of acquisition during sleep;*

(2) *Ascertaining if traditional day-time learning phenomena hold for sleep-learning;*

(3) *The investigation of certain parameters of sleep-learning, such as time of presentation, method of presentation, length of presentation, etc.*

If positive results are obtained from our study, such findings will bear on such important psychological problems as the consciousness-unconsciousness dichotomy, incidental learning and reinforcement theories of learning. There is also the possibility of inducing attitude formation and attitude change during sleep. If people can be taught Chinese words, or poems, or not to bite their nails, why can they not be taught political beliefs, hates, and loves? One may shudder at the potential ethical consequences of this technique, but the challenge and possibility are still there. Many other practical and significant uses of sleep-learning could be suggested, specifically those having to do with psychotherapy and teaching techniques; suffice it to say though that both the pragmatic and theoretical consequences of acquisition during sleep are many and are extremely important.

II WHAT IS SLEEP?

Before proceeding to the actual experiment, it would perhaps be helpful to present some theories as to why we sleep, how we sleep, and what goes on while we sleep. There is some experimental evidence available on the physiology of sleep which enables us to see it in relation to the knowledge we have of the normal waking person.

Five main answers have been offered to the question of why we sleep. First, there is the circulatory theory which explains sleep by the brain being deprived of its normal blood supply and thereby causing a loss of consciousness. Second, the neurological theorists maintain that during the awaking hours certain cell structures undergo great changes and thus sleep is necessary in order for the body to repair the neurological lines which have been damaged. Third, the chemical theory of sleep is merely that of an exhaustion of oxygen causing a subsequent loss of consciousness. Fourth, there is the biological theory which points out that all nature moves in specific rhythms and cycles, and man as a part of the scheme of nature has sleep as one of the principle rhythms. A fifth theory is that of the notion of a cortical sleep centre whose activity affects other neural processes in the cortex and by shutting them off brings on sleep. The main trouble with this cortical theory of sleep is that it has been demonstrated that totally decorticated animals do sleep.

It is quite clear that we still do not know why we sleep, or for that matter why we stay awake. However, there is some rather good evidence on what happens while we sleep. For one thing, our body is at its lowest point of activity as measured by oxygen taken in and carbon dioxide released. For another, the absolute stimulation thresholds of the various reflexes are raised. Further, there is an apparent loss of some consciousness, or better, a loss of some awareness of the environment. This loss, however, is seldom complete. A sleeping subject is often seen to brush a fly from his face, rearrange the covers on his bed, or react to noise made by a passing car. Strong sensory stimulation, however, is capable of arousing a sleeping individual to full awareness.

A study at Colgate University by Laird and Muller (14) has added some further facts to our knowledge of sleep. These experimenters found, using college students, that upon falling asleep we first lose the power to make conscious movements; the last thing we lose is the ability to hear noises. But upon awakening, the reverse is true: first we regain the ability to hear noises, and last we regain the ability to make conscious movements. Laird and Muller also found that right after going to sleep their subjects' muscle tension, which uses up much energy, was lessening rapidly but the energy consumption of the person as a whole increased rapidly for about an hour. After four hours of sleep, however, the level of energy consumption falls so low that it can barely maintain the blood pump.

Nathaniel Kleitman (12, 13), long interested in the phenomenon of sleep, has more than anyone else added to our data on the physiology of sleep. He found that characteristic of the somatic activity of the individual during sleep are the relaxation of the muscles and the closing of the eyes. The autonomic activity of the individual gives us some important differences between the waking and the sleeping states. Kleitman has demonstrated that during sleep the heart rate is reduced, the blood pressure goes down, the respiration and circulation of the body are slowed and the body temperature shows a marked decrease. These physiological facts seem to indicate that nothing is really going on that you would not expect to find in a completely inactive, mentally and physically, *waking* subject.

Kleitman is primarily responsible for the most widely accepted theory of sleep today. It is based upon the experimentally supported assumption of the existence of a sleep-centre in the hypothalmic-mesencephalic region of the brain. Ranson and his associates (22) found that if they produced lesions in that general area in animals, the resultant effect was one of sleepiness. Perhaps it is better to call the centre a wakefulness centre, as it is the destruction of it which causes sleep and therefore its activity which is responsible for wakefulness. Kleitman maintains that the activity of the wakefulness centre is necessary for the functioning of the higher integrative processes of the brain concerned with adjustment to the external world. The sense organs continuously send in millions of nerve impulses to this centre which causes its activity. The most important of these impulses are the ones from the muscles. Continued activity of the muscles causes them to fatigue and thus to relax. As a result of this the nerve impulses sent to the wakefulness centre are greatly reduced in number. After this happens, the wakefulness centre with its connecting fibres to the thalamus and cortex causes a reduced activity level there. Thus when activity in the wakefulness centre is reduced, so also is that of the cortex and its responses to incoming stimuli. The result of this overall cortical inactivity is sleep. This theory of sleep by Kleitman seems far and away the closest to the experimental data which are available on sleep.

The measurement of the electrical activity of the brain yields data which suggest a real difference between brain activity of a sleeping and waking subject. Kleitman, by means of electroencephlograph, has demonstrated that the normal alpha waves (8–12 per second) are replaced during sleep by a mixture of spindle waves (14 per second) and slow random delta waves (4–5 per second), the latter being characteristic of deep sleep. Evidence shows us that we do not go from a light sleep into a deeper and deeper sleep as the night progresses. Rather, EEG studies indicate that sleep is a cyclical phenomenon, with the depth of sleep constantly varying during the night. One hour it may be light, the next hour deep, and then the next hour light again.

All these data seem to indicate that sleep may well be defined in the context of the levels of consciousness-unconsciousness. A reasonable assumption can be made that consciousness-unconsciousness are not really separate phenomena, but rather should be considered as a continuum. Therefore, each part of normal activity of the individual could be placed on this continuum in relation to its being at a higher level or lower level of consciousness than another activity. By this method we would avoid the confusion raised by calling sleep an unconscious phenomenon and could classify it in accordance with the subject's other activities. This would also allow us to put difficult parts of the sleep pattern on different parts of the continuum rather than lumping all sleep activity under one ruberic.

III PLAN OF REMAINING SECTIONS AND OVERALL EXPERIMENTAL DESIGN

In order to investigate the problem of sleep-learning, several small independent experiments were carried out. The next seven sections will deal with each of these experiments considered as a separate unit. Thus each section will cover the history, procedure, experimental design, and results of each individual experiment. Following these sections will be a discussion of some of the practical problems which had to be faced in the study as a whole. Then will come a discussion and comparison of the overall results which we can report on the basis of the separate experiments which were done. The final two sections will be devoted to some implications of our work and suggestions for further experimentation, and a short summary of the paper.

Before reporting on the individual experiments, it would be best to give an overall description of the experimental set-up.

The experiment was carried on at Foss House, an old wooden three-story building on the Wesleyan campus. One large dormitory room was cleaned out and equipped with five single beds in which the subjects slept. This room was approximately 10 ft. wide and 30 ft. long. An adjoining room was set aside for the experimenters to work and sleep. It also housed all the mechanical equipment necessary for the experiment. A third room, located directly opposite the room the subjects slept in, was used to observe the subjects during sleep by means of an observation panel, and also as a testing room. (See Appendix 28.1 for diagram of the layout of these rooms.)

The equipment consisted of a Multi-Speed Pentron Tape Recorder, five Telex pillow speakers, and a multi-coloured light panel located in the experimenters' room and operated by pushbuttons at the head of each subject's bed.

The tape recorder was in the experimenters' room and wires from it led to the speakers located under the pillow of each bed. A control switch panel enabled the experimenters to turn any of the individual loudspeakers either on or off without affecting the speakers of the other subjects. The purpose of the light panel was to enable the subjects to inform the experimenters at the exact time that they were woken by any noise. For instance, if when the tape recorder started to play one of the subjects awoke, he would push the button next to his bed which in turn would light one of the bulbs on the light panel. The experimenter was thus informed of which subject had awoken and was then able separately to turn off that subject's speaker by means of the control switch panel. An exact record of the times at which each subject awoke and when each subject's speaker was turned off or was thus able to be compiled.

The subjects for this experiment were all members of the Sophomore Class at Wesleyan University. Their ages ranged from 18 to 20. All subjects were paid volunteers who served for two consecutive experimental nights. Each subject served in one and only one of the experiments conducted. Usually, five subjects were experimented with at a time, but occasionally only four subjects were used. A total of twenty-eight subjects took part in the experiments.

The subjects were required to arrive at Foss House at about 11.00 p.m. with their sheets, pillows, and blankets. After they had made their beds, they were given any tests which were necessary for that particular experiment. The subjects were informed of the seriousness and importance of the study and were asked for their full co-operation in taking the tests and in doing what was asked of them. After the testing was completed, the subjects were sent to bed, which was usually by midnight depending upon the length of the testing. They were all informed of what to do in case they awoke during the night and were told of the importance of letting the experimenter know as soon as they woke up. It was also suggested that the noise from the tape recorder would not be sufficient to awaken them. During the night the appropriate material was played to them and a record was kept of which subjects awoke. At 7.00 a.m. all the subjects were awakened and asked to refrain from all conversation until they were tested. They all washed their faces and were given coffee in order to facilitate their awakening. This process necessarily had to be speeded up because of their classroom obligations. At approximately 7.30 a.m. the subjects were again tested on the appropriate task for that experiment. An attempt was made to test all the subjects at the same time on any particular task, but because the subjects outnumbered the experimenters this was not possible. However, there was never more than a 20-minute gap between the first and last subjects tested. Upon completing the tests, the subjects were free to leave and were requested not to talk about the experiment to anyone. Fortunately, the co-operation of the subjects in carrying out all requests was far better than had been expected.

With this overall experimental design in mind, let us proceed to a discussion of the first experiment performed: The investigation of retroactive inhibition during sleep.

IV AN EXPERIMENT ON RETROACTIVE INHIBITION DURING SLEEP

History

In the study of retention probably one of the most thoroughly investigated and experimentally well-established phenomena is retroactive inhibition. Essentially, retroactive inhibition represents a negative transfer in which the learning of some new material impairs the ability to retain previously learned material. Paradigmatically this can be represented as follows:

Group I (Control)	Learn A	Rest	Test A
Group II (Experimental)	Learn A	Learn B	Test A

Depending on the nature of the interpolated material, it is usual to find that Group I better retains the A material than does Group II. This difference in retention is taken as the operational definition of retroactive inhibition. The smaller retention of Group II is attributed to the interpolation of interfering material between the original learning and retesting.

It is not pertinent to the major problem of this paper to survey the large experimental and theoretical literature on the problem of retroactive inhibition. The following facts seem most relevant to our problem. It has been hypothesised by Skaggs and Robinson (23) that the degree of similarity between the originally learned and the interpolated material will affect the amount of retroactive inhibition that will occur. The Skaggs-Robinson hypothesis can be formally stated as follows: 'As similarity between interpolation and original memorisation is reduced from near identity, retention falls away to a minimum and then rises again, but with decreasing similarity it never reaches the level obtaining with maximum similarity.' (24). Thus two almost identical lists will cause little retroactive inhibition, two similar but distinct lists will cause maximum inhibition, while two dissimilar lists according to the hypothesis will result in only a small amount of retroactive inhibition. In general, experimental evidence supports the first half of the Skaggs-Robinson hypothesis, but the second part is less well-established.

As we have already indicated, most retroactive inhibition experiments compare retention after an interval of non-learning activity with retention after an interval of learning activity. The problem of what activity should constitute the non-learning interval has undergone much investigation. Perhaps the most relevant factor to be considered in the light of the present experiment is the difference between sleep and normal waking activity as methods of filling this interval. Jenkins and Dallenbach (11) and Van Ormer (29) have arrived at the general conclusion that any way in which the interval is filled during waking will cause greater interference than if the interval had been occupied by sleep. It has been shown that if 8 normal waking hours intervene between original learning and retesting, almost 90 per cent of a list of 10 nonsense syllables will be forgotten. However, if after learning the same list the subjects go immediately to sleep, then the retention after 8 hours of sleeping is over 50 per cent. Again an experimental support of the hypothesis that one of the major causes of forgetting is interference. Incidentally, this experiment demonstrated also that time in itself is not a sufficient explanation of forgetting. Jenkins and Dallenbach also found that the greatest decrement in retention occurred during the first two hours of sleep, after which retention stays relatively constant throughout the remaining 6 hours of sleep.

Because the experimental findings on retroactive inhibition are so strongly established, we decided to use this phenomenon both as an instrument to demonstrate the possible occurrence of acquisition during sleep, and as a method of evaluating whether sleep-learning follows the same principles as does normal learning and retention.

Experimental Design

Fig. 28.1 presents an outline of the design of the present experiment. On the first evening of testing the subjects of Group A learned a list of 12 adjectives to one perfect trial (List I). The list was learned by the method of anticipation, i.e., the experimenter would read the list of adjectives once slowly; then the subject was asked to repeat the list in the same order in which it was read to him. If the subject gave a wrong word or misplaced a word, he was told what the correct word was. If, however, ten seconds after giving the previous word the subject made no response, he was told what the next word was. This process was continued until the subject repeated the list perfectly in correct sequence. There was a 15-second

	EVENING	NIGHT (During Sleep)	MORNING (Testing)	AFTERNOON
DAY I	*Group A* Adjective List I *Group B* Adjective List III	*Group A* Adjective List II *Group B* Concept Formation Problem Solution	*Group A* Adjective List I *Group B* Adjective List III	*Group A* Adjective List II
DAY II	*Group A* Adjective List III *Group B* Adjective List I	*Group A* Concept Formation Problem Solution *Group B* Adjective List II	*Group A* Adjective List III *Group B* Adjective List I	*Group B* Adjective List II

Fig. 28.1. Experimental design of retroactive inhibition experiment.

inter-trial rest. This same procedure was followed in the learning and relearning of all other lists for both groups. The adjectives for various lists were drawn from a table containing the average similarity ratings between two syllable adjectives as standardised on a college population (6). Lists I and II were considered of high similarity. For example, List I contained words such as 'perfect,' 'noonday', 'exact'; the synonyms of which could be found in List II, i.e., 'faultless', 'midday', 'precise', etc. List III was dissimilar from List I and II, containing such words as 'alien', 'fated', 'crafty', and the like. (See Appendix 28.2 for complete word lists used.)

After learning List I, Group A then was given a conception formation problem, which will be discussed in Section VII. That night during their sleep, from 4.00–5.00 a.m. a list of 12 similar adjectives (List II) was played to the subjects. The next morning the subjects were again required to learn List I, this relearning serving as a test of retention. That same afternoon the subjects were asked to learn List II, the list with which they had no previous experience, except for its presentation during sleep. The second evening the same five subjects of Group A returned and were presented adjective List III to learn. That night during their sleep the subjects were played, again between 4.00 and 5.00 a.m., the correct instructions to a concept formation problem that they would have to solve the next morning. That morning the subjects were tested on their retention of List III. Group A had now completed their part in the study. The following night another group of five subjects, Group B, was put through the same procedure. However, in their case the experimental sequence was reversed. Thus, Group B received List III on the first evening and the solution to the concept formation problem during the first night. On the second evening they learned List I and were played List II in their sleep. This counterbalance of test order was done to control for the possible effect of list sequence on the results. It was possible, for example, the one list might be more favoured than the other, i.e., more easily learned because it was presented first or last. Both groups were also tested in the afternoon on their learning of List II. Before proceeding to the results, it should be remembered that the testing and retesting on all of the lists followed exactly the same procedure and was carried to the same criterion as described above for Group A.

Results

Because of the design of the experiment, it was possible to test if any learning occurred at all during sleep. This could be done by comparing the learning of List II (the list presented to both groups during their sleep) with the learning of Lists I and III. By chance,

Table 1
Comparison of the Mean Percentage Increase in Facility of Learning Adjective List II (as compared to average learning of Lists I and III) between Those Who Slept and Those Who Awoke.

Groups compared	*Mean difference*	*Standard error of mean*	*t*	*Degrees of freedom*	*P**
Sleepers (5) v. Non-sleepers (5) .	35·8%	15·45%	2·317	8	Below 2½%

* One-tail curve.

exactly one-half of our subjects awoke during the night and thus had their speakers disconnected. Four of these subjects were from Group B and the remaining one from Group A. This gave us the opportunity to compare those subjects who awoke and therefore received no material during their sleep with those five subjects who did hear List II during the night on their speed of learning List II. Table 1 shows the difference in the learning of List II between the sleepers and the non-sleepers. The statistic used in this comparison measures the percentage increase in facility of learning List II for any subject as compared to his average learning of Lists I and III; i.e., for each subject the following statistic was calculated

$$\frac{\left(\frac{\mathrm{I} + \mathrm{III}}{2}\right) - \mathrm{II}}{\frac{\mathrm{I} + \mathrm{III}}{2}}$$

The number of trials necessary to learn List II were subtracted from the average number of trials to learn Lists I and III, and then divided again by the average number of trials to learn Lists I and III. Thus each subject served as his own control. As can be seen from Table 1, the mean difference in this 'facility savings score' between the two groups was substantial and is significant beyond the 1 per cent level of confidence using a one-tail test of significance. These results are highly indicative of the fact that some learning did occur during sleep. It should be pointed out that no direct recall was possible of the material presented during the night, but the increase in the facility of learning that material shows that some acquisition did occur.

In order to test for retroactive inhibition effects, the subjects were tested on the relearning of Lists I and III; that is, a test of retention of the lists they had learned the previous evenings. As will be remembered, the interpolated material between the learning and relearning of List I was a similar list of adjectives. The interpolated material between the learning and relearning of List III was completely dissimilar material, namely the concept formation solutions. On the basis of day-time retroactive inhibition data, we hypothesised that the relearning of List I would be more difficult than that of List III, because of the greater interference effect of List II on List I (the Skaggs-Robinsons hypothesis). In other words, there should be

Table 2

Comparison of the Mean No. of Errors per Trial to Relearn List I as Compared with List III (Non-sleepers excluded).

Groups compared	*Mean difference*	*Standard error of mean*	*t*	*Degrees of freedom*	*P**
Mean errors per trial to relearn List I v. List III	0·9	0·38	2·37	4	Below 4%

* One-tail curve.

a larger mean error per trial total for List I than for List III. Table 2 shows such a comparison for sleepers only. The results bear out this hypothesis. The mean difference between the mean errors per trial of the two lists is 0·9 with a standard error of 0·38. The *t* of 2·37 is significant at below the 1 per cent level with a one-tail curve. The results suggest that retroactive inhibition can function during sleep. Of course, this fact also makes the case for at least the occurrence of some acquisition during sleep stronger. The interpolated material was obviously absorbed and the similarity of the material presented resulted in enough interference to cause a decrement in the learning of List I. It should be noted that not just any interference, e.g., concept formation instructions, but specific material, similar to the original, causes negative interference and hence greater retroactive inhibition. This is a confirmation of the Skaggs-Robinson hypothesis for sleep-learning.

In order to check further our results, it was felt that a comparison of the non-sleep subjects on the relearning of Lists I and III was necessary. These subjects received no interpolated material; therefore it was to be expected that their performances in the relearning of the lists would show no difference. Again a comparison was made between the mean number of errors per trial to relearn List I v. List III, but this time only the non-sleep subjects were included. As was hypothesised, no difference occurred. In fact the mean difference between the two lists turned out to be exactly zero.

Another test for retroactive inhibition effects is to compare the mean errors on the first relearning trials of Lists I and III. Table 3 shows the results of such a comparison. It should be predicted,

Table 3

Comparison of Number of Errors on First Relearning Trial of Lists I and III (Non-sleepers excluded).

Groups compared	*Mean difference*	*Standard error of mean*	*t*	*Degrees of freedom*	P*
No. of errors on 1st relearning trial of List I v. List III . .	1·00	0·71	1·41	4	Below 12% Below 2%

* One-tail curve.

according to the retroactive inhibition hypothesis, that in the relearning of List III less errors will be made on the first trial than on List I. The non-sleepers were excluded from the results. This prediction is supported by our analysis and is shown to be significant, again by a one-tail curve, at somewhere below the 1 per cent and above the 2 per cent levels. This result reaffirms our earlier conclusion that retroactive inhibition did occur.

Again a similar comparison was made, but this time for the non-sleep subjects. The same statistical method was employed, i.e., the number of errors on the first relearning trial of Lists I and III. Table 4 shows the results of this analysis. We hypothesised that for

Table 4

Comparison of Number of Errors on First Relearning Trial of Lists I and III (Sleepers Excluded)

Groups compared	*Mean difference*	*Standard error of mean*	*t*	*Degrees of freedom*	P
No. of errors on 1st relearning trial of List I v. List III . .	−0·20	0·49	0·41	4	Insignificant

the non-sleep subjects there should be no difference between the number of errors on the first relearning trial of Lists I and III. The results support this prediction and even indicate that perhaps List III was inherently more difficult than List I, thus making our previous findings even more convincing. The results presented in Table 4 preclude the argument that our positive findings are to be accounted for by the fact that List I was somehow inherently more difficult to learn than List III. These data suggest just the opposite, although not significantly. Furthermore, the initial learning, both by trials and errors, of Lists I and III show no significant differences.

The final method for testing for retroactive inhibition was the savings method, and as can be seen in Table 5, the results were not too encouraging. The savings method is based upon the subject

Table 5

Comparison of Savings (in Percentage) in Relearning List v. List III (Non-sleepers Excluded)

Groups compared	*Mean difference*	*Standard error of mean*	*t*	*Degrees of freedom*	*P*
% savings in relearning List I v. List III .	5·2%	22·09%	0·23	4	Insignificant

relearning material he has previously learned; the measure of savings is obtained by comparing the relearning with the original learning in terms of the number of trials to learn and relearn the material; thus:

$$\frac{O - RL}{O} \times 100\%$$

This method was used to compare the savings in relearning List I with that for List III. The non-sleepers were again excluded. It was hypothesised that the relearning of List III should show a greater savings percentage than List I because the latter list was interfered with by the interpolated material presented during sleep. This hypothesis, while not yielding a significant difference, was borne out in that the mean difference obtained was in the expected direction.

In this experiment we have tried to investigate the possibility of the occurrence of retroactive inhibition during sleep. The results indicate that retroactive inhibitory effects can occur during sleep as well as during waking. This application of a simple day-time learning phenomenon to sleep is to our knowledge the first of its kind. The clear-cut results which were obtained gave further impetus to our desire to test still another well-established day-time learning phenomenon to see if it too would occur during sleep; namely massed v. distributed learning, the subject of the following section.

V AN EXPERIMENT ON THE METHOD OF MASSED v. DISTRIBUTED LEARNING DURING SLEEP

History of problem

The relative merits of massed as compared to distributed learning have long been of concern to psychology. But unfortunately neither one nor the other can be said to be a superior method in every case. However, much work has been done to investigate the conditions under which either massed or distributed learning is found to be advantageous. The overall conclusion seems to be that distributed is favoured over massed in the majority of cases.

Carl Hovland, in the recent *Handbook of Experimental Psychology* (8), gives a short summary of the work that has been done in this area up to the present time. Ebbinghaus (2) can be considered the pioneer in this field of research and he early demonstrated in the learning of nonsense syllables that dividing practice over three days resulted in better learning than if the practice were massed into one long sitting. Since Ebbinghaus' time, much experimentation has been carried out concerning massed v. distributed practice in motor skills and other non-verbal areas, but we will limit our discussion to the verbal area, as it is most relevant to the present experiment.

In the specific field of verbal learning, the advantage of distributed practice seems to be most clear-cut. A recent, well-controlled experiment by Bumstead (1) demonstrates that the longer the time interval between readings of prose and poetry, the more rapid is the learning. But there are certain times when massing is favoured over distributing. When a warm-up period is necessary for the learning to begin, then the advantages of distributed practice are decreased because a warm-up will be required at the start of each unit of practice. In this situation, massing thus will be better because only one general warm-up period is required. An additional factor favouring massed practice is that when the interval between practice units is too long, forgetting may set in so that each new practice unit will require the learner to start from scratch.

On the other hand, many factors favour distributed practice. One obvious factor is that too much practice at a certain task will cause fatigue and thereby a decrement in learning ability. Further, a protracted period of practice will invariably lead to a loss of motivation to learn the material and thus again an impairment of learning ability. Some alternation of work and rest seems to be the best method of learning verbal material.

Certain factors seem to increase the advantage of distribution. One of the main factors is the amount of material involved. Lyon (18) and Hovland (7) have shown that an increase in the length of the material to be learned leads to an increase in intra-serial interferences and these interferences are best reduced by distributed practice.

One of the major obstacles which is faced when experimenting upon the effects of massed v. distributed practice is the control of the activity during the rest periods. McGeoch (19), in discussing this problem, comes to the conclusion that the type of activity engaged in during these rest periods have important and varying influences on the data of massed v. distributed practice. The main theoretical explanation of the apparent advantage of distributed practice centres around the fatigue effects of massed practice. Thus it is believed that the fatigue caused by massed practice has a decremental effect upon subsequent performance. Distributed practice eliminates this fatigue factor to a great extent by introducing frequent rest intervals between the practice periods. Of course, the ideal situation would be one in which there was no activity during the rest periods. But this situation is rather impractical in normal waking experimentation. However, we believe that the present experiment might help to throw some light on this problem by providing a situation wherein all subjects were engaged in the same interpolated activity or non-activity, sleep.

Experimental design

It was our object to see if the same findings which are obtained during the waking state, in regard to massed v. distributed learning, would also hold for sleep-learning. Fig. 28.2 gives an outline of the experimental design and it will be further explained here.

Five subjects were brought to Foss House and were not subjected to any testing in the evening, except for questioning on their sleeping habits and day-time activities. This information, incidentally, was compiled for each subject who participated in any of the

	Group A	*Group B*
NIGHT I	20 paired associates (List I) presented in one period of 24 massed trials	20 paired associates (List I) presented in 4 units of 6 trials each
NIGHT II	20 paired associates (List II) presented in 4 units of 6 trials each	20 paired associates (List II) presented in one period of 24 massed trials.

Fig. 28.2. Experimental design of massed v. distributed experiment.

experiments. The subjects were all asleep by about 12.00 p.m. Arbitrarily three of the subjects were put into one group, the massed group, and the other two subjects were put in the distributed group. The next night the groups were reversed, the massed group became the distributed group, and vice versa. Thus each subject served under both massed and distributed conditions.

A list of twenty paired number-word associates was presented to the subjects during sleep. On each night a different list of such paired associates was used. Examples of the associates used are: 34-light, 29-get, 13-terrace, etc. (List I); and 75-central, 52-season, 51-visual, etc. (List II). (A complete list of paired associates may be found in Appendix 28.3.)

For the massed group, the twenty paired associates were repeated twenty-four times consecutively. There was a two-second time interval between each paired number-word, and a fifteen second interval between each repetition of the list. For the distributed group, there were four presentations of six repetitions each for the presentation separated by about an hour. The interval between the presentation of each paired associate was two seconds, the same as

Massed Group	*Distributed Group*
24 repetitions from 3.05–3.47 a.m.	6 repetitions from 1.30–1.52 a.m. 6 repetitions from 2.40–3.02 a.m. 6 repetitions from 3.50–4.12 a.m. 6 repetitions from 5.00–5.22 a.m.

Fig. 28.3. Times of presentation of material during sleep.

for the massed group. However, the interval between each repetition of the list was two minutes as opposed to the fifteen seconds for the massed group. Fig. 28.3 shows the times during the night at which each of the groups received the list of paired associates.

Testing

The subjects were awoken at about 7.00 in the morning and the testing was begun at 7.30. The testing followed exactly the same procedure on both mornings. The testing procedure was complicated and perhaps detrimental to our results. We felt, however, that we should try and 'squeeze' as much information out of our experiment as was possible.

All the subjects were seated as a group in the large room (see Appendix 28.1) facing the tape recorder. They were told simply to listen to what was to be played on the machine. The section of tape played to them first contained a list of thirty number-word associates, including the twenty which were played during the sleep and ten new ones with which they had no previous experience. The sequence arrangement of these associates was completely random. (See Appendix 28.3 for the complete lists of paired associates played on both mornings.) After the tape was played through once, the subjects were instructed to write down all the words they could remember and then to try and match them with the appropriate numbers. A new section of the tape was then played, but this time the numbers were omitted and the words were repeated at a greatly increased speed so that they could not be distinctly heard. As a word was about to be played on the tape, the experimenter read its number and the subjects were asked to write down the word they thought they heard at the faster speed. This process was repeated three times. Following this, the subjects were again asked to write down all the words they could remember from the first tape and then appropriate numbers. It should be noted that both the first tape and the speeded-up tape contained the same words in the same order.

After the masking tape, the first tape was again played to the subjects and they were asked to listen carefully to what was on it. Upon completion of the tape, a sentence was read to the subjects containing five words. All the words in this sentence were from the original list of twenty paired associates presented during sleep. The subjects were told to write down the sentence and substitute the appropriate numbers for the words. Then they were given an additional sentence, a non-sleep sentence that contained only words that were not presented during the sleep but which they had heard previously during the testing on tape I. At the end of this number-substitution task the subjects were again asked to write down all the words and numbers that they could remember. The first tape was played through again, and the subjects once more had to substitute numbers for words for a sleep sentence and for a non-sleep sentence. Then they were asked to write down all the words they could remember and the appropriate numbers. The tape was played through a third time and now the subjects were instructed to substitute the numbers for the words in one long 10-word sleep sentence. Thus each of the thirty words of tape I was contained in sentences for which the subjects were asked to substitute numbers; twenty of the words were sleep words and ten non-sleep words. (A copy of the sentences which the subjects received may be found in Appendix 28.4.) Again after this was completed, the subjects were instructed to write down as many words as they could remember along with the appropriate numbers.

The rationale behind this particular complicated testing procedure was that we needed a method of testing for the learning of the paired associates which would not involve in the very testing itself a massing effect and thus perhaps wash out any sleep-learning effects which might have been obtained. By our procedure a total of five test trials were introduced in such a way that in spite of their frequent repetition little massed learning was likely to occur. In addition the activities between the five learning trials were exactly the same for all subjects, so the problem of rehearsal can be assumed to be constant for each of the subjects.

Results

As a result of adding ten new paired associates to the list of twenty paired associates presented during sleep, we were able to arrive at a measure of the subjects' learning of the sleep words compared to the non-sleep words. The data from both nights were combined giving a total of forty possible correct sleep-word responses and twenty non-sleep word responses. Table 6 shows the comparison of each subject on his retention of sleep words v. the non-sleep words. This measure represents the subject's performance on the first trial, that is the first time that they were asked to write down all the words that they could remember (after hearing the tape once).

Table 6

Comparison of Each Subject on the Percentage of Sleep Words Correct and Non-Sleep Words Correct on First Trial

Subject	*Sleep words*	*Non-sleep words*
A*	35	35
B†	18	15
C	15	10
D	20	15
E	45	25

* Subject A woke up the night he was in the massed group and missed about 1/2 of the presentation.

† Subject B woke up during the night he was in the distributed group and missed about 1/4 of the presentation.

As an example of how Table 6 is arrived at, we can look at the performance of any subject, say Subject C. Out of the forty possible sleep words which he could have got correct on the first trial (counting both mornings), he actually received six, or 15 per cent. Out of the twenty possible non-sleep words (those words which were added to the original list of paired associates) he had two correct, or 10 per cent. We find that in every case but one, more sleep words (in percentage) were remembered than non-sleep words, and that the one exception, Subject A, showed no difference in his two performances. (He also awoke during massed instructions.) Table 7 shows the results of a t test performed between the percentages of sleep words correct v. the percentages of non-sleep words correct for each subject. The mean difference of 6·6 per cent with a standard error of 3·47 yields a t of 1·90 which is significant at between the 1 per cent and 2 per cent level using a one-tail curve.

Thus it is clear that the words from the lists played during sleep were more easily learned than those words which the subjects had never 'heard' before. This is a further example of the fact that the presentation of material during sleep facilitates the subjects' subsequent learning of that material. This appears to be the most reasonable explanation for the fact that the non-sleep words were not retained as well as the sleep words.

Table 7

Comparison of Percentage of Sleep Words Correct v. Non-Sleep Words Correct for Each Subject

Groups compared	*Mean difference*	*Standard error of mean*	*t*	*Degrees of freedom*	P*
Percentage of sleep words correct v. non-sleep words correct . .	6·6	3·47	1·90	4	Below 6½% Above 1%

* One-tail curve.

To return to the main purpose behind this particular experiment, the investigation of the relative effect of massed v. distributed practice, we find further encouraging results. As will be remembered from the experimental procedure, all the subjects served one night under massed learning conditions and another under distributed learning conditions. Thus in comparing massed v. distributed conditions, we do not have to worry about individual differences, because each group is made up of the same subjects. As will also be remembered, all the subjects were required five times during the morning testing to write down all the words they could remember. We were thus able to find out if the Distributed group differed from the Massed group in total correct responses on each of the five trials and on the total of the five trials.

We hypothesised that on each of the five trials and on the total number of trials there should be better retention under distributed conditions than under massed conditions. This hypothesis was made on the basis of daytime learning data in which the learning of such lists is favoured by distributed practice. Our method of testing this was to compute the number of errors (i.e., words not recalled) made by each subject on each of the five trials under these two conditions. (Of course, only sleep words were counted, so there was a maximum possibility of twenty errors per trial for each subject in the massed group, and the same for the distributed group). Table 8 shows the mean number of errors made on each trial for the subjects under massed conditions and for the same subjects under distributed conditions. As can be seen, for each trial the distributed group

Table 8
Mean number of errors on Each of the Five Trials under Massed and Distributed Conditions

Trial No.	*Massed*	*Distributed*
1	16	15·2
2	14	12·4
3	10·6	8·6
4	8	7·4
5	7·4	5·4

made fewer errors than did the massed group. Graphically this is represented in Fig. 28.4. Here we have plotted the cumulative mean error scores for each trial under the massed and distributed conditions. In other words, under massed conditions the mean cumulative error score (i.e., words omitted) on trial I was 16 and on trial II it was 14. Thus on the cumulative mean error score graph, a score of

Table 9
Statistical Summary of Results Obtained by Comparing the Mean Number of Errors under Massed v. Distributed Conditions

Trial	*Mean difference*	*Standard error of mean*	*t*	*Degrees of freedom*	*P**
1	0·80	1·31	0·61	4	Insignificant
2	1·60	0·68	2·35	4	Significant below 5% level
3	2·00	1·30	1·54	4	Significant below 10% level
4	0·80	1·65	0·48	4	Insignificant
5	2·00	1·65	1·21	4	Significant below 13% level
Total	1·44	0·47	3·07	4	Significant below 2% level

* One-tail curve.

16 would be plotted for trial I, and total of 16 plus 14, or 30, would be plotted for trial II. We can test the significance of these results by doing a simple *t* test between the mean number of errors for massed and distributed groups for each trial and for the total trials. Table 9

gives a summary of the statistical findings of such comparisons. It is quite apparent that employment of massed v. distributed practice in sleep-learning leads to differential effects upon subsequent performance.

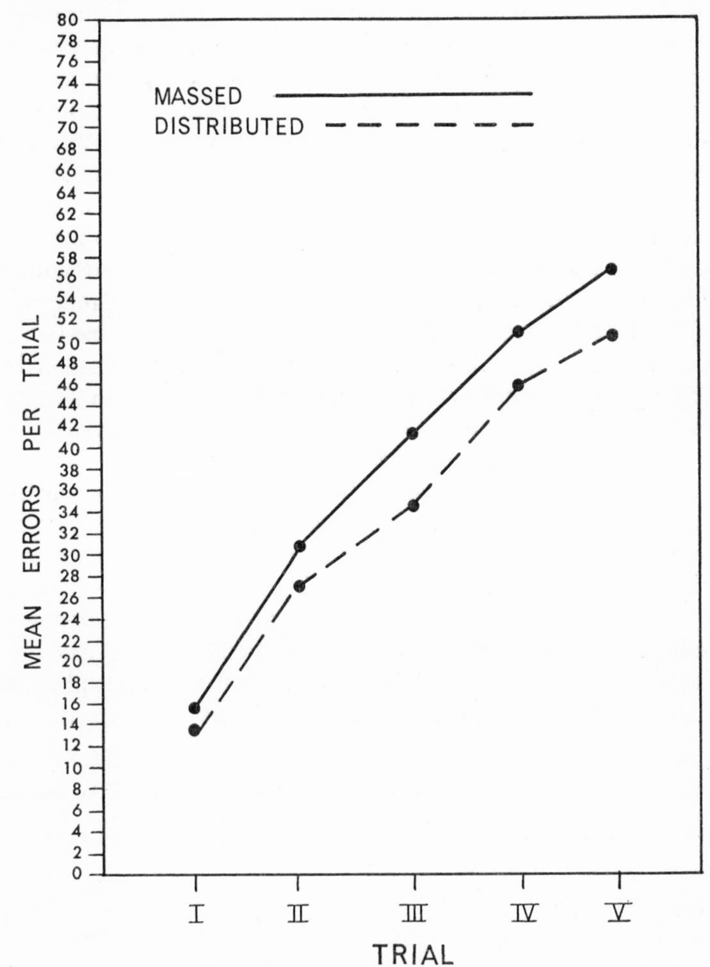

As can be seen, all results are in the expected direction. The overall difference between massed v. distributed learning is significant and three out of the five trials also yield significantly reliable differences. It would appear that distributed practice during sleep is more favourable to retention and learning than is massed practice.

Many other data were compiled during testing but analyses of these data are somewhat discouraging. However, many vitiating factors were present during testing and may account for our failures. An attempt to analyse subjects' responses to the words played to them at rapid speed was fruitless. We had hoped that we would be able to ascertain whether the subjects could distinguish more of the speeded-up sleep words than the non-sleep words. However, we found that there was such a great discrepancy in the inherent recognizability of the speeded-up words, that it was impossible correctly and fairly to analyse the data. On relistening to the words which were played at fast speed, we found that some words could be clearly distinguished (such as attractive, recognition, evolution, etc.), while other words were completely indistinguishable (such as dance, bright, get, etc.). We feel that if we could have matched the words on their auditory clearness, we may have been able to obtain some valuable data. But with the great variability of the words we did use, our data cannot be properly interpreted.

Also our attempt to analyse the subjects ability to substitute numbers for words in the sentences we gave them brought no clear results. Whether this was due to this particular tasks place in the testing procedure (immediately following the speeded-up words), or due to the fact that there was too much interference among the numbers, or perhapas the task was too difficult to allow true differences to manifest themselves is unclear. Whatever the explanation, our results were negative. Table 10 presents the percentage of

Table 10

Comparison of Percentage Correct Number-Word Substitutions between 'Sleep' and 'Non-Sleep' Sentences.

Subject	*Sleep*		*Non-sleep*	
	Trial I (%)	*Trial II* (%)	*Trial I* (%)	*Trial II* (%)
A	25	45	0	22·5
B	60	80	80	60
C	10	10	10	12·5
D	55	52·5	30	87·5
E	30	42·5	50	65

correct numbers substituted for words in the sleep v. non-sleep sentences for massed and distributed conditions combined. It will be remembered that there were ten words to be substituted for sleep sentences and a like number for non-sleep sentences on the two trials. As an example, Subject B correctly substituted numbers for 6 out of the 10 words in the first sleep sentence, thus obtaining a score of 60 per cent. On the first non-sleep sentence Subject B substituted 8 out of 10 words correctly, thus obtaining a score of 80 per cent. Simple inspection of the table shows that no possible conclusion can be drawn one way or the other. The same type of analysis was attempted to determine whether the number substitution task would be better carried out if the paired number-word code were learned under distributed rather than massed conditions. The results of this investigation are as indecisive as the previous one.

So far we have found that two major day-time learning phenomena are also upheld in the sleep. The next section will deal with an experiment on a third learning phenomenon, that of frequency of presentation.

VI AN EXPERIMENT ON THE EFFECTS OF THE FREQUENCY OF MATERIAL PRESENTED DURING SLEEP

History of Problem

The effect of frequency on learning is an old and well studied problem in psychology. In spite of the long concern with this question, it is still not possible to give any single law relating frequency to learning. Practice, in short, does not always make for perfection. The term 'frequency' will be used here to refer to the total number of trials or repetitions used in the learning of some response. Frequency is the common variable against which improvement is plotted on learning curves. McGeoch and Irion (20), summarising probably the most commonly held view in learning theory today, write: 'When a stimulating situation is frequently presented with no specifications of the responses and no formal knowledge of results or effect, behaviour does not change in the direction of the experimenter's criterion, although it may change toward some standard adopted by the subject. Responses which are frequent early in practice do not gain as a result of their initial frequency.'

McGeoch and Irion continue by stating: '. . . in the absence of consequences or reinforcement, there is little learning and withdrawal of the reinforcement tends to cause the dropping out of the response . . . Frequency of reinforced or rewarded situation response connections is productive of large amounts of improvement, other factors being equal.' (21)

According to this argument, repetition is only effective when it leads to reinforcement of some need satisfaction. Of course, we see numerous instances of increased performance following increased frequency of practice, but it is maintained that it is not frequency *per se* which is the cause, but rather allowing certain other factors, e.g., reward, vividness, belongingness and the like to operate, that is responsible for the increased acquisition. While these are exceptions, it is generally true that repetition (frequency) helps acquisition; though to be sure frequency *per se* may neither be a sufficient or even a necessary factor in order for learning to occur.

Experimental Design

The purpose of this experiment was to assay the effect of differential frequency of instruction on sleep-learning. Would any difference in learning rates result if one group of subjects had a list of 12 adjectives repeated to them during their sleep for four hours as compared to another group who only heard the adjectives for one hour?

Eight subjects were used in this experiment. The subjects were assigned to groups in such a manner that each subject received material for four hours on one night and one hour on the other night. Fig. 28.5 is an outline of the experimental design. (The nature and purpose of the perceptual problem solutions will be discussed in Section IX.)

Four subjects were used at a time, two of them in the four-hour group and two in the one-hour group. The next night the two groups were reversed. An additional group of four subjects followed the same procedure and were run on the two succeeding nights. Subjects received no testing in the evening and were all in bed by about midnight. At 1.00 a.m. the tape was turned on for the four-hour group. The tape contained a list of twelve adjectives similar to those used for the retroactive inhibition experiment. (See Appendix 28.5 for copy of Lists I and II.) At 2.00 a.m. the speakers of the one-hour group were cut in and were left on for one hour. The

	Group A	*Group B*
NIGHT I	List I presented from 1.00–5.00 a.m. Perceptual problem solution presented from 5.00–6.00 a.m.	List I presented from 2.00–3.00 a.m. Perceptual problem solution presented from 5.00–6.00 a.m.
NIGHT II	List II presented from 2.00–3.00 a.m. Perceptual problem solution presented from 5.00–6.00 a.m.	List II presented from 1.00–5.00 a.m. Perceptual problem solution presented from 5.00–6.00 a.m.

Fig. 28.5. Experimental design of frequency of presentation experiment.

remaining subjects had the tape played to them until 5.00 a.m. That morning all subjects were tested on their learning of the list presented during sleep (List I). The next night a different tape, containing List II, was played to the subjects; those subjects who heard List I for one hour the previous night now heard List II for four hours, and vice versa.

The following morning the subjects were first tested on the Perceptual Problems (see Section IX), and then were required to learn List II. The procedure for the subjects' learning of the adjective lists was exactly the same as that employed in the retroactive inhibition experiment; that is, the oral method of anticipation continued until one perfect trial is achieved.

Results

Of the eight subjects in the experiment two of them had to be dropped. One, because he woke during both nights when the recorder was playing and thus did not hear any of the material; and the other, because it was found that his speaker was not properly connected. Our hypothesis that the 4-hour group would learn better than the 1-hour group was not substantiated. However, from the point of view of the frequency theories presented earlier in the chapter, we really did not have too firm a stand on which to base our hypothesis. Table 11 shows the results of a comparison between the total number of trials required by each of the subjects to learn the adjective lists after 1- and 4-hour presentations of those lists

Table 11
Total Number of Trials to Learn Adjectives Lists of Each Subject After 4-Hour and 1-Hour Presentations

Subject	*4-hour*	*D*	*1-hour*
A	14	+1	15
B	9	+7	16
C	7	+4	11
D	10	+1	11
E	5	−1	4
F	11	−4	7

during sleep. As can be seen, the variability among subjects is great, but the results tend in the direction of favouring the 4-hour presentation. However, in a comparison of the number of errors made on the first learning trial under each of these two conditions, it was found that the 1-hour group is favoured. Neither this result nor the previous one approach significance, and from the data it appears that no case can be made for either favouring the 4-hour presentation or the 1-hour presentation. For that matter, we have no indication if any sleep-learning actually occurred at all during this experiment.

The question of the effect of frequency on sleep-learning is still very much unanswered. It is possible the one-hour practice is too much, and the ceiling of acquisition for a simple adjective list is reached before this; thus four hours add nothing or at best very little. It is also possible that over-practice, again on such a simple list, may lead to some fatigue or interference effects, thus explaining our two reversals. A reverse argument may also be made to the effect that practice during sleep follows a steep negative growth function such that many more trials than is possible in four hours are needed in order for practice effects to be manifested. In any case, certainly further experimentation is needed on the problem of frequency.

VII AN EXPERIMENT ON GIVING SOLUTIONS TO CONCEPT FORMATION PROBLEMS TO SUBJECTS DURING SLEEP

Because of the great expenditure both in manpower hours and money that experimentation on sleep involves, we found it necessary to combine several experiments in one night. This compounding of experimental procedure was risky, but we felt it necessary so as to maximise the value of each experimental hour and dollar invested in the study. Thus, in conjunction with the experiment on retroactive inhibition (see Section IV), we tried to ascertain if we could teach subjects the solutions to certain concept formation problems during sleep.

Experimental Design

A group of sixty-four 4 x 5 cards were used on which were printed two symbols in several colours. The two symbols used were 'X' and 'Z' and the colours were red and blue. Each card contained two symbols, either an 'X' and a 'Z', or two 'Xs', or two 'Zs'. The symbols were either drawn in red or in blue and the card could either contain one red and one blue symbol, or two red symbols, or two blue symbols. In addition to colour and symbol, cards were varied in terms of which symbol was on the left or right. Thus an 'X' or 'Z' or a 'red' or 'blue' could appear on either the left or right side of the card. There were then sixteen possible combinations in all, so that in the set of sixty-four cards each possible combination appeared four times. The serial order of the pack of cards was arranged in a completely random manner.

A subject was seated at a table with the cards in front of him and was instructed to try and find the concept that ran through all the cards. The subjects were told that the experimenter had one solution in mind, such as, 'Any card with an "X" on it is correct', and the subjects had to figure out what the correct solution was. The experimenter turned over one card at a time and the subject guessed whether the card was 'right' or 'wrong'. If the subject responded correctly, the experimenter said 'correct', if incorrectly, the experimenter said 'incorrect'. Thus the subject had to figure out from the experimenter's responses to his guesses what the solution was.

Fig. 28.6 shows the experimental design of this study. (It should be remembered that the solution given in the sleep was considered the dissimilar material as previously explained in the retroactive inhibition experiment.) On the first evening of the experiment both Groups A and B were given a practice Concept Formation Problem I to solve. The solution to this problem was: 'A red Z with any X'. This practice problem was given to make certain that all the subjects understood fully what was required of them. Both groups also received the solution to Concept Formation Problem III presented

	EVENING (Testing)	NIGHT (During Sleep)	MORNING (Testing)
DAY I	*Group A* C.P.I. *Group B* C.P. I	*Group A* — *Group B* C.P. III	*Group A* C.P. II *Group B* C.P. III
DAY II	*Group A* — *Group B* —	*Group A* C.P. III *Group B* —	*Group A* C.P. III *Group B* C.P. II

Fig. 28.6. Experimental design for concept formation problem experiment.

during their sleep for one hour, from 4.00–5.00 a.m. The next morning they were presented with this problem and instructed to find the right concept. The correct solution and thus the words they heard in their sleep, was, 'any card with a blue X on it is correct'. The groups differed in the procedure only in that Group A received Concept Formation Problem II on the first morning and Group B received it on the second morning. Also, they received the intructions on different nights. The solution to Concept Formation Problem II (C.P. II) was: 'Any red symbol on the left side of the card'. (The Concept Formation Problem will from here on be symbolised by 'C.P.'). The experimental design of the retroactive inhibition experiment necessitated Group A receiving C.P. II before C.P. III and Group B having Problem II after Problem III. However, we felt that all the subjects sufficiently understood the mechanics of the problems after the practice problem (Problem I); thus any possible benefit which Group A may have received from solving C.P. II *before* C.P. III was negligible.

The crucial comparison, of course, is between each subject's performance on C.P. II and C.P. III, since C.P. I was used only to equate for practice and understanding. The method of scoring each subject's responses was a bit complicated. The experimenter had before him a sheet with sixty-four blanks representing each of the sixty-four cards. After each of the subjects' responses, the experimenter marked down in the appropriate blank either an 'O', a check, or a double check. The 'O' represented the subject's giving the wrong response. A single check stood for the case in which the subject said 'wrong' to a card (that is, the card did *not* contain the specific requirement for that problem, e.g., a blue X) and he was correct. A double check meant that the subject had responded 'right' to a card (that is, the card *did* contain the specific requirements for that problem, e.g., a blue X) and he was correct.

It was our hypothesis that the subjects would arrive at the correct concept for C.P. III (the one to which the solution was played during their sleep) more quickly than they would for C.P. II. The results are somewhat confusing, but in general they tend to uphold the hypothesis.

Results

The first comparison made was between the number of double checks (or right-rights) obtained by subjects on C.P. II and C.P. III. That is, the total number of cards which the subject spotted as containing the correct solution. This number was then divided by the total number of possible correct responses. Thus if a subject had sixteen double checks on C.P. II, he received a score of 50 per cent, as there were thirty-two possible correct solutions. On C.P. III there were only twenty-eight possible correct responses, but by using a percentage score a comparison could be made between the two Concept Formation Problems. The results of this comparison, including all ten subjects, showed a mean difference of 6·6 per cent in favour of C.P. III, as predicted. This difference yields a t of 1·06, which is significant at the 20 per cent level of confidence (again using a one-tail curve). After dropping the three subjects who awoke during the presentation, we find that the mean difference increases to 10·5 per cent but the level of significance drops only slightly.

A comparison was also made between the total number of correct responses (that is, single checks and double checks) made between C.P. II and C.P. III. The three subjects who awoke were dropped. There was a maximum possibility of 64 correct responses for each of the two Concept Formation Problems. The results show that on C.P. III a mean of 3·7 more correct responses were given than on C.P. II. Once more, this is in line with our prediction. However the mean difference gives a t of only 0·86 which is statistically insignificant reaching only about the 25 per cent level of confidence.

Although these results are not conclusive, they do suggest that some benefit was gained by the presentation of the correct solution to the subjects during their sleep.

While it would not be fair to call the material used in this experiment exactly meaningful, it was certainly more meaningful than the simple lists of adjectives. There are some indications then that meaningful material can be learned during sleep. The problem of the differential effects of learning meaningful v. meaningless material during sleep, however, still remains to be studied.

VIII AN EXPERIMENT TO DETERMINE THE BEST TIME FOR THE PRESENTATION OF MATERIAL DURING SLEEP

In the various experiments we changed the time of night at which we played the to-be-learned material. However, we were never able to estimate confidently which time during the night was best for sleep-learning, or for that matter whether there were any differences. Each time seemed to have its own particular advantages and disadvantages. If the material was presented very early, say from 1.00–2.00 a.m., the number of subjects who awoke was usually small. Based upon the amount of noise required to wake an individual at this hour, the time between 1.00 and 2.00 a.m. seems to be the time of deepest sleep. But it is possible that depth of sleep might be negatively correlated with the effectiveness of sleep-learning. Playing the material at a very late hour, say between 5.00 and 7.00 a.m., had the disadvantage of causing many subjects to awaken. But it also had the advantage of being close (in terms of time) to the hour when the subjects were tested. Thus the possible advantageous effect of recency may operate when material is played close to waking time. The presentation of material during the middle hours, 3.00–5.00 a.m., seemed to combine the advantages and disadvantages of the two extremes plus introducing possible interference effects.

With these conjectures and observations in mind, we decided to devote an experiment to evaluating whether there was a 'best' time for presenting material during sleep. We thought that if we could establish whether there is a best time, and just what that time is, our subsequent experiments could be more efficiently carried out. Only five subjects took part in this particular experiment, as time and money prohibited further experimentation. Fig. 28.7 shows the design of this experiment. (The Perceptual Set part of the experiment was not varied according to time and will be discussed independently in Section IX.)

	EVENING (Testing)	NIGHT (During Sleep)	MORNING (Testing)
DAY I	N.S. I List A	* N.S. II at 2.00 a.m. * List B at 5.00 a.m. * P.S. (1) at 3.30 a.m.	N.S. II List B P.S. (1)
DAY II	N.S. III List C	N.S. IV at 5.00 a.m. List D at 2.00 a.m. P.S. (2) at 3.30 a.m.	N.S. IV List D P.S. (2)

* N.S.—Nonsense syllable list
List —Word list
P.S. —Perceptual set solution

Fig. 28.7. Experimental design for time of presentation experiment.

Four lists of ten nonsense syllables each were compiled and matched on their association value as measured by Glaze (4). (A copy of the four nonsense syllable lists and of the four word lists may be found in Appendix 28.6.) Also four lists of twelve words each were compiled and matched on the basis of the Thorndike-Lorge word count (27). This technique rates words according to the frequency of their occurrence in the English language.

Experimental Design

The subjects arrived at the laboratory at 11.00 p.m. and were individually tested on two tasks. The first was learning a list of 10 nonsense syllables (N.S. I), and the second was learning a list of 12 words (Word List I). The procedure used in learning these lists was exactly the same as that used for the experiment on retroactive inhibition, i.e., the anticipation method to a criterion of one perfect trial. After learning these two lists, the subjects were sent to sleep. That night at 2.00 a.m., N.S. II, equivalent to N.S. I in association value, was played to the subjects while they slept for one hour. Then Word List B, equivalent to World List A in frequency of usage, was played to the subjects at 5.00 a.m. also for one hour. At 3.30 a.m. the subjects received instructions for a Perceptual Problem which they were to experience the next morning. In the morning they were tested on: (1) Perceptual Problem; (2) N.S. II; (3) Word

List B (for all three of which they had received material during the night).

The following evening the five subjects had to learn N.S. III and Word List C to the same criterion as usual. At 2.00 a.m. that night Word List D, equivalent to C, was presented to them over the tape recorder. At 3.30 a.m. they received instructions to another Perceptual Problem, and at 5.00 a.m., N.S. IV, equivalent to N.S. III, was played. Thus on one of the two nights the word list was played at 2.00 a.m. and the nonsense syllables at 5.00 a.m. and on the other night the word list (a different one) was played at 5.00 a.m. and a nonsense syllable list at 2.00 a.m.

We therefore had an opportunity to make several comparisons not only between the relative merits of the 2.00 a.m. and 5.00 a.m. presentations, but also on straight learning. For if the lists were properly matched, we should expect the learning of the lists in the morning following sleep to be easier than the learning of the lists in the evening with which the subjects had no previous experience. We therefore first tried to determine if any sleep-learning had occurred. We hypothesised that: (1) the performance on N.S. II would be better than on N.S. I; (2) N.S. IV would be better than N.S. III; (3) Word List B would be better than Word List A; and (4) Word List D would be better than Word List C.

Results

The results in general tend to support our hypotheses, although in some places the results are confusing and not in line with expectations. In the comparison of the number of trials to learn N. S. II v. N.S. I we found that, as expected, N.S. II was better. The mean difference between the two is 1·4, which yields a t of 1·2069, significant at the 15 per cent level using a one-tail curve. However, if these two lists are compared on the number of errors made on the first trial, we find that there were less first trial errors on N.S. I, which is the reverse of our prediction. The explanation for this result is not apparent and must be left for further investigation.

The comparison between N.S. IV and N.S. III on number of trials to learn also yields significant differences. As predicted N.S. IV required fewer number of trials, the mean difference being 2·4, which is significant at below the 15 per cent level of confidence using a one-tail curve. We again compared the two lists on the number of errors on the first trial, and this time the predicted result was arrived at. The mean difference of number of errors on the first trial was 1·25, which yielded a *t* of 1·67, significant at below the 9 per cent level of confidence using a one-tail curve.

Let us now consider comparisons between the word lists. Although the lists were matched in terms of frequency, we discovered during experimentation that the lists contained many surprising intra-serial associate values. Further, these intra-list associations varied among subjects so greatly that not too much confidence can be placed in the obtained results. By comparing Word List B with Word List A on the number of trials to learn, we find that Word List B required more trials than List A, although the difference is not significant. However, when we compared the two lists on the number of errors made on the first trial, we find that Word List B is significantly better. The mean difference is 2·2 with a *t* score of 2·29, which is significant at between the 4 per cent and 5 per cent levels with a one-tail curve. Again, a comparison between Word Lists D and C on number of trials to learn yields no significant results, but the differences go in the expected direction, i.e., Word List D was learned more rapidly. The comparison on number of errors made on the first trial also yields results that tend in the expected direction, but are not statistically significant.

These somewhat confusing results may be explained in part by the different times of presentation which were involved. With these results let us turn our attention now to an investigation of the relative merits of the 2.00 a.m. and 5.00 a.m. presentations, the main purpose of this particular experiment.

Unfortunately no conclusions can be drawn which favour one presentation time over the other. The design of the experiment does not allow a lumping together of the nonsense syllable lists and the word litsts to arrive at an absolute score for particular time presentations. We found that the two word lists and the two nonsense syllable lists presented during sleep did not appear to be equally difficult. Thus it was not fair to assume that Word List D, presented at 2.00 a.m., was learned faster than Word List B presented the next night at 5.00 a.m., because the difference might well have been caused by the differential difficulty rather than the different times of their presentation. We honestly cannot present good evidence which favours either the 2.00 a.m. or the 5.00 a.m. presentation. However, we do feel that the 2.00 a.m. presentation has been more favourable in our experiment. The main reason for this assumption is the fact that no subjects awoke during that time, while a number of subjects awoke during the later presentation. Unless real evidence is uncovered that the subjects absorb the material best at some particular hour, we feel that the advantage of having few subjects awaken at the 2.00 a.m. presentation makes this time most favourable. Of course, further investigation of this problem is necessary for an improvement in the technique of sleep-learning.

IX AN EXPERIMENT ATTEMPTING TO ESTABLISH A PERCEPTUAL SET IN SUBJECTS DURING SLEEP

In conjunction with the experiments on frequency and time of presentation we attempted to establish a perceptual set in our subjects during sleep. This was done in the following manner:

Experimental Design

Two groups of subjects participated in the experiment, one group of five and another group of four. Both groups had somewhat different instructions, so it would be best to discuss them separately. Group A, the five subject group, which also took part in the Time of Presentation experiment, had certain material presented to them during their sleep from 3.30–4.30 a.m. On each of the two nights they served in the experiment they had different material presented. The material on Night I was: 'in the first picture I show you tomorrow morning you will see a group of six students sitting around a table drinking cokes. In the background is a lone figure watching the group'. On Night II the material presented was: 'in the first picture I show you tomorrow morning you will see a man in his shirtsleeves working at his desk. In the background, his wife and daughter are standing looking at him'.

On following mornings, after the subjects had received perceptual-set material in their sleep, a slide projector and screen were set up in the sleeping room (see Appendix I). The subjects sat facing the screen and were supplied with a pencil, paper and writing surface. The subjects were instructed that a slide would be shown on the screen which would be completely out of focus, and that they should write down what they thought they saw in the picture. Even if they could distinguish nothing, they were told to make a guess as to what was being shown. Then the focus was slightly improved and the subjects again had to guess as to the contents of the picture. It was stressed to the subjects that they should write down something after each presentation, even if it were only a guess. The experimenter working the machine moved the lens one step nearer to focus every thirty seconds. The focusing device on the machine enabled the focus to run from extremely vague setting of '1' to a sharp in-focus setting of '10'. On Morning I Group A was first shown the picture of the six students sitting around a table, the picture described to them during their sleep. They were then shown a picture of a man working at his desk with a clock on a steeple in the background which read ten after six. The same instructions as mentioned above were given to the subjects for both pictures. On Morning II the first picture shown was again the one described in the sleep the previous night, i.e., a man working at his desk with his wife and daughter in the background. Again, a second picture was presented to the subjects. This one of a secretary handing some papers to a business executive sitting behind a desk. The four pictures chosen for presentation to this group were selected on the basis of a pre-testing as to their differential visual acuity at the various focusing levels.

Results

It was our hope that the subjects would more easily identify the two pictures for which they had been prepared in their sleep than the other two control pictures. It should be kept in mind that the subjects were really given a quite difficult task. For not until the 8th or 9th presentation were the details of the pictures clear enough to be accurately seen. Thus we really were requiring our subjects to recognise or even recall what was presented to them during sleep and we have not been able to obtain such retention in any of our other experiments. And, as was feared, no positive results were obtained. The control pictures were recognised with as much ease or difficulty as were the experimental (sleep pictures).

With Group B, the four subjects who participated in the frequency experiment, we tried a somewhat different approach to the perceptual set problem. This time the focus extremes were limited from 5 to 10; i.e., from fairly vague and out-of-focus to very sharp focus, as compared to our previous settings which began completely out of focus. Also, we decided to give the subjects a choice of five possible correct solutions to the picture. Group B received the same two presentations which Group A had received during their sleep.

They also were presented with the same two control pictures. The projector was turned on at the 5th focus point and the subjects were first asked to guess what they saw, and then they were given five choices, including the correct one. (A list of the choices given for the four pictures may be found in Appendix 28.7.)

We hypothesised that the subjects would pick the correct choice for the 'sleep' pictures more often than for the non-sleep pictures. But as before our hypothesis was not supported. The individual variability was great and those subjects who early chose the correct solution of the 'sleep' pictures also did so for the 'non-sleep' pictures. In fact, there was no difference in the overall facility in arriving at the solution for the 'sleep' v. 'non-sleep' pictures.

We can only conjecture on the possible reasons for not obtaining positive results. One explanation might be that the pictures used were not really equally matched. Some of the pictures were perhaps more easily recognisable than were others—in spite of an attempt to pre-test them. Another explanation might be that sleep-learning is not favourable to the teaching of meaningful material, or at least that more instruction is required for such material. However, our results in the Concept Formation Problem Experiment, which involved a type of meaningful presentation, did indicate that the possibility of teaching meaningful material is not hopeless. The third, and most logical explanation for our failure in this particular experiment, is that the stimulus was presented verbally during the sleep and visually in the testing the following morning. That is, perhaps the visual stimulus was not strong enough to call up the appropriate material which was presented to the subjects verbally. What may be needed is an auditory test situation. Another explanation might be that the problem was too difficult for any set established during sleep to be effective, especially if the set were weakly established.

The present experiment is somewhat related to the possible establishment of attitudes, their formation and change. Certainly the results we have obtained are not encouraging, but with equal certainty we can say that they are far from conclusive. Further, careful, systematically varied experimentation needs to be done in this area.

X A DISCUSSION OF SOME PRACTICAL PROBLEMS INVOLVED IN OUR STUDY OF SLEEP-LEARNING

One of the first and most obvious criticisms of the present experiments is the small number of subjects involved. Experimentation in a field as complex as sleep-learning requires, if anything, more than the average number of subjects. We were fully aware of the dangers inherent in small sampling, but because of the practical limitations of time and money we could not afford additional subjects. While it is true that we might have concentrated our subject strength on one particular experiment, we felt that we would rather map out, if perhaps somewhat hazily, the broader terrain of sleep-learning than restrict ourselves to just one problem. Therefore the decision was to explore and to try a series of 'pilot' investigations. What was wanted was only a rough map of the territory, the careful surveying to be left for later study when we could be more certain that there was some land actually to survey.

Even in these preliminary investigations the experimenters faced many serious problems. A realisation of these problems by the reader will result in a greater appreciation of the positive results which have been obtained and a better understanding of some possible reasons for the negative findings presented in the paper.

First, it was necessary for the subjects to adapt themselves very quickly to a new environment. The locale of the experiment, Foss House, was certainly not the ideal site for our work. It is an old, dilapidated, creaky and somewhat eerie residence. The subjects had no time in which to adjust to these strange surroundings. At $2.50 per night, per subject, we could not afford the luxury of allowing them to adjust. Thus, the subjects were asked to sleep soundly in this strange environment which was not entirely conducive to such sleep.

Because of the nature of this experiment, we were dependent on volunteer subjects. Our group, therefore, was not entirely a random one. We used only college sophomores, for there are important data on individual differences, e.g., intelligence, rigidity, suggestibility available on these subjects. Further, the apparatus which was available was not of the highest quality and, therefore, its reliability and efficiency left much to be desired. The tape recorder was a relatively inexpensive one and gave much trouble. Breakdowns of the apparatus were common, and the overall running efficiency of the machine was low. The tonal quality was also poor. In addition, the Telex pillow speakers which were used gave a very tinny tone to the material presented over them. The voice of the speaker could certainly have been much sharper and more distinct. In connection with this, we also ran into the problem of differential auditory thresholds among the subjects. The equipment did not allow each individual's speaker to be played at different volume levels, so that all subjects received the material at the same volume (one-third of full volume). Possibly those subjects with higher auditory thresholds than others did not hear the material clearly enough. This, of course, would handicap us and tend to yield negative results, where possibly positive ones might be forthcoming with better equipment. The sleeping habits of the individuals also quite possibly had some effect upon the subject's performances. Some subjects undoubtedly slept with their heads off the pillow or with their heads resting on their arms. With the speaker located directly under the pillow, the movements of the subjects assuredly resulted in varying amounts of actual reception time amongst the subjects.

All testing on the subjects' ability to learn material previously presented in sleep took place within one hour after the subjects awoke. There is experimental evidence (30) which demonstrates a decrement in learning which takes place immediately after sleep. Thus the subjects' performances could be expected to have been even better if the testing had taken place at a later time. But being students, the subjects had classroom obligations which had to be met, and thus the testing had to be carried out as quickly as possible. To this end the subjects had to be woken before their normal waking hour, and were usually quite tired at the time of the testing. This fact undoubtedly caused a decrement in their learning rates.

The improvements which could be made in the set-up of our experiment are fairly obvious and will be discussed in part in section XII. However, we believe that when one considers all the practical problems that plagued this study, the results obtained become even more convincing. We cannot believe that these 'faults' of the experiment contributed favourably to our findings, but rather that their elimination would have made our data even more conclusive.

XI A DISCUSSION OF THE RESULTS OF THE SLEEP-LEARNING EXPERIMENT IN THE LIGHT OF CURRENT LEARNING THEORY

The establishment of learning during sleep as a real phenomenon can be quite important in the light of current learning theory. The issues of reinforcement, motivation, retroactive inhibition, massed v. distributed practice, and the like are all still open to new interpretations and redefinitions. It is not the object of this paper to formulate a new learning theory or rewrite old ones, as a result of the present experiments. However, it is felt that these experiments can possibly suggest new areas of investigation by learning theorists.

The issue of reinforcement as a necessary condition for learning is under much dispute in learning theory today. On the one side are those who believe that learning necessitates there being some kind of motivating state followed by some kind of reinforcing (goal) situation. The most recent outstanding proponent of this argument has been Hull (9), but many others share his ideas on this subject (17, 25, 26). On the other side we have a group of theorists who do not believe that motivation and reinforcement are prerequisites of learning. Rather, they maintain that mere sequence in experience (or association by contiguity) is the main factor which governs learning. Guthrie (5) and Tolman (28) are the main proponents of this view.

The data obtained from this experiment suggest that the latter view is more probably the correct one. Motivation and reinforcement certainly do not appear to be active forces in the process of sleep-learning. It is rather difficult to imagine that our subjects were motivated to learn while they slept and there was certainly no reinforcing situation. Superficially it appears that the subjects were able to absorb in some way material presented to them in their sleep and as a result were able to show an increment in learning performance on subsequent testing. However, the possibility of some unconscious motivation is not too far-fetched. Certainly the gathering of more data on the physiological as well as psychological processes involved in sleep-learning will help to throw more light on this problem.

Another issue upon which sleep-learning throws some light is that of retroactive inhibition. The basis for retroactive inhibition is the interference effects caused by some interpolated material between original learning and relearning of a specific task. It is the nature of these interference effects which have been the cause of some controversy among learning theorists. The main question seemed to centre around the problem of whether it was mere interference that was the cause of retroactive inhibition, or whether it was a specific type of interference. The Skaggs-Robinson hypothesis, discussed earlier, supports the latter view. The hypothesis maintains that it is the similarity of the interpolated material which results in retroactive inhibition. Our experiment seems to support this hypothesis for sleep-learning. For we found that it was not the presentation of just any material during sleep (between original and relearning) that caused a decrement in the relearning, but more specifically the presentation of material similar to that of the original learning caused the decrement to occur. This is in agreement with the Skaggs-Robinson hypothesis, and perhaps helps to clear up some existing confusion in interference theory.

A further issue to be considered is that of the relative effects of massed v. distributed practice. One of the major explanations offered for the advantage of distributed practice is the decremental effect of fatigue on massed practice. It is maintained that the rest periods involved in distributed practice allow for the elimination of any fatigue produced, and thus greater performance follows. The experiment reported in this chapter provided an ideal set-up in which to examine this problem. The activity of the groups learning under massed and distributed conditions was exactly the same: sleep. Thus the possible fatigue effects produced by massed practice were minimised and the activity between practice periods was constant for both groups. Our results quite clearly support the advantage of distributed practice for sleep-learning. But whether we fully succeeded in eliminating the fatigue effects of massed practice, we cannot be sure. Physiological investigation of the sleep-learning process may show that learning during sleep does have a fatiguing effect. Thus, we cannot yet make a definite assertion as to the effects of fatigue on massed and distributed practice.

We have tried to give some suggestions as to the possible effects of sleep-learning data on current learning theory. We believe that an increasing body of data on sleep-learning will result in not only some changes in present day learning theory, but also a better and more comprehensive understanding of the whole learning process.

XII SOME IMPLICATIONS OF SLEEP-LEARNING AND SOME SUGGESTIONS FOR FURTHER EXPERIMENTATION

Questions which might well be asked upon the completion of the reading of this Chapter are: Just what purpose can sleep-learning serve? Can it add anything to our lives? We believe that these questions can be very simply answered. The implications of sleep-learning can be discussed under three main headings: educational; social psychological; and theoretical.

The implications which sleep-learning might have for education are rather obvious, for our experiments surely show that learning can be eased by previous presentations during sleep. With the greater knowledge of sleep-learning that we hope will be forthcoming soon, the possibility of certain educational methods being used in conjunction with sleep looms as a reality. The aid to the student which sleep-learning offers cannot be overlooked. We suggested that sleep-learning can greatly help the learning of foreign languages, poetry, vocabulary etc. Further, sleep-learning may possibly become a great aid to the education of young children in such fields as spelling, multiplication tables and the like. Essentially the evidence suggests that the greatest help from sleep-learning will be with simple types of learning tasks. It is very doubtful whether reading a book to a person during his sleep will have any effect upon that person, for sleep-learning seems to have very definite limitations. The mere presentation of material during sleep does not insure its absorption and subsequent aid to the individual. But our results do indicate that the presentation of certain material can greatly improve the subject's ability to master that material later.

The implications of sleep-learning for social psychology are also quite important, primarily in the fields of attitude formation and change. We saw the first evidences of this in the LeShan experiment discussed previously in which some children were convinced by sleep-learning that they should stop biting their nails. Of course, this is attitude change on a very small scale. However, the possibility of attitude change and formation on a broader scale is not too bizarre. If children can be taught to stop biting their nails, why can't adults be taught to love, hate, kill or the like by sleep-learning? When material is presented to subjects during their sleep, they have little choice but to 'listen'. But the problem arises as to whether the subjects can actually choose what they want to learn during sleep. That is, can they discard that material which goes against their own desires, motives and opinions? If they cannot, the possibilities of attitude formation and change are wide indeed. There is no reason to assume either that the subjects can or cannot selectively choose to absorb the material presented to them. Therefore, at least an attempt to delve into this problem seems a worthwhile investigation. The knowledge that people's attitudes, opinions, sets, beliefs, loves, hates, etc., may possibly be influenced by sleep-learning techniques makes this investigation a challenging and vastly important area of study.

Finally, the study of sleep-learning holds many theoretical implications. Perhaps the major theoretical importance of a thorough knowledge of sleep-learning is that it will lead to a fuller and more comprehensive psychology. Practically our whole psychology is built upon data gathered from normal waking individuals. The activity and behaviour of sleeping individuals certainly should hold a more important place in psychology than it does at the present time. Take for example the problem of fatigue. Much speculation has occurred on the effects of fatigue upon learning, the generalisation being that it is decremental. Also, the reverse is considered to be true, i.e., that too much learning causes fatigue. Sleep-learning can certainly throw light on these areas. Can sleep-learning be accomplished as well on a fatigued individual as on a rested individual? Will a large amount of sleep-learning cause an individual to become fatigued? These questions need to be answered for a fuller comprehension of the whole problem of fatigue.

A further theoretical implication suggested by sleep-learning is in the problem of the levels of consciousness. The question of whether there is a dichotomy between consciousness and unconsciousness, or whether there is merely a continuum has long remained unanswered. Sleep has often been thought of as an unconscious state, but the fact of sleep-learning indicates that perhaps sleep is merely a low level of consciousness. For it is not a very convincing assumption that learning can occur at a completely unconscious level. Or if it does, then we need a new rewording of the definitions of consciousness and unconsciousness.

Theoretically, sleep-learning offers many implications for psychotherapy. The possibility exists that sleep-learning can 'penetrate into the unconscious' of the individual and perhaps bring certain problems out into consciousness where the individual can best deal with them. This is somewhat related by hypnosis and suggestibility in that the individual is not able to offer much resistance to the suggestions of the therapist during sleep. Thus sleep-learning may offer a means of suggesting to an individual the solutions to certain problems, anxieties, tensions and the like which may exist within him.

Before any of these implications can be realised, much work needs still be done in the field of sleep-learning. We hope the present experiments have served as a starting point for such further experimentation, for we have surely done no more than scratch the surface of this field. What needs to be done is rather obvious. How it is to be done is the crucial point.

We feel that the mechanical apparatus necessary for the proper carrying out of this type of experiment needs to be of a high quality. There are enough variables and problems to worry about without taking into account the defects of the mechanical equipment. An expensive and smooth running tape recorder; a speaker which can be plainly heard no matter where the subject has his head; an individually controlled volume range for each subject's speaker; a reliable instrument for measuring the subject's brain waves while asleep (in order to find out the depth of sleep and the change in brain wave patterns that may occur during sleep-learning); a method of obtaining running body temperature records (also a technique for measuring depth of sleep); a restful and comfortable environment; these are just some of the requirements which can and should be met in making further sleep-learning experiments.

An ideal set-up would involve being able to obtain subjects willing to serve great lengths of time. This would enable the experimenter to ascertain the affects of prolonged presentation over a series of nights on the subject's subsequent performances. We only presented the material for one night, while perhaps twenty nights of presentation of the same material would have resulted in greatly increased performance ability for the subjects.

A great variety of experiments which need to be carried out are suggested by this study. There is no reason to believe that any of a great number of experiments already performed on waking subjects should not be similarly attempted on sleeping subjects. These include experiments on such basic learning phenomena as whole v. part method of learning, meaningful v. meaningless material and further work on the phenomena tested in this paper (retroactive inhibition, massed v. distributed practice, frequency).

In addition to these fundamental learning principles many problems of sleep-learning need to be investigated. These include the determining of the best volume to play the recorder at, finding whether the bass or treble tone is more effective, seeing if a loud-speaker system is better than the present pillow speaker system, determining what kind of voice is best suited for the presentation of the material (e.g., male or female). All these problems and many more are capable of being solved and their solution is necessary to a better understanding of the phenomenon of sleep-learning.

XIII SUMMARY OF CHAPTER 28

An attempt was made to investigate some of the problems and parameters of sleep-learning. Several exploratory, independent experiments were carried out to solve these problems. Day-time learning phenomena were tested on sleeping subjects to ascertain if they would hold equally as well for sleep-learning as they do for normal day-learning. It was found that:

(1) Acquisition does occur during sleep.

(2) The interpolation of similar material during sleep had a decremental effect upon the relearning of a list of adjectives which subjects had learned the previous evening. The interpolation of dissimilar material did not have a decremental effect upon the relearning.

(3) The presentation of paired associates during sleep by the distributed method was found to be significantly better than the same presentation by the massed method.

(4) There was no significant difference between the presentation of material for a 4-hour period and for a 1-hour period.

Other experiments dealt with:

(1) The presentation of solutions to concept formation problems to subjects while they slept;

(2) An attempt to produce perceptual sets in sleeping subjects;

(3) An attempt to ascertain the best time of presentation of material during sleep.

The results on this latter group of experiments were not too conclusive but added to the support of the earlier experiments showing that sleep-learning is a real phenomenon.

Some problems which were raised by this experiment were discussed and suggestions for further experimentation were made. Possible redefinitions of some facets of learning theory in the light of our experiment were suggested along with some implications of sleep-learning on our lives in general.

XIV APPENDICES

APPENDIX 28.1

Plan of location of experiments

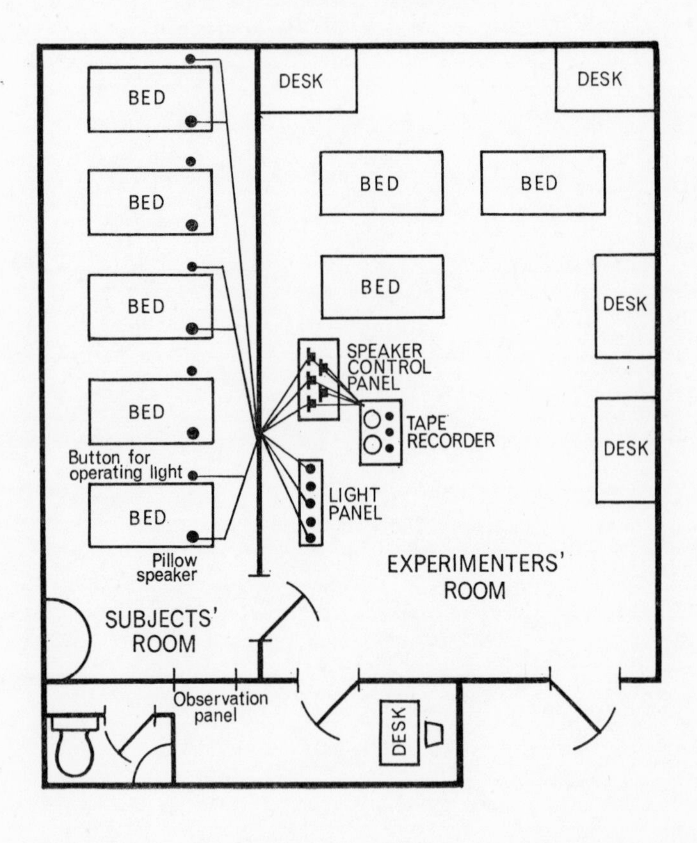

APPENDIX 28.2

List I	List II	List III
PERFECT	FAULTLESS	ALIEN
NOONDAY	MIDDAY	FATED
EXACT	PRECISE	CRAFTY
BOASTFUL	BRAGGING	ABSORBED
FATAL	DEADLY	LAWFUL
READY	PREPARED	AWARE
FOREMOST	LEADING	OPEN
TOTAL	ENTIRE	FAMOUS
EMPTY	VACANT	COMIC
AWKWARD	CLUMSY	ROCKY
USELESS	FUTILE	HAPPY
BAFFLING	PUZZLING	TEPID

APPENDIX 28.3

Lists Of Paired Associates For Massed v. Distributed Experiment

1. Paired Associates Presented On Night I

34	LIGHT
29	GET
13	TERRACE
18	PARADE
26	MAKING
19	FROM
33	BRAVE
25	THROUGH
31	DANCE
27	CITATIONS
35	DOWN
14	MARBLE
10	HALL
22	SOLDIERS
17	REVEALING
23	COUPLE
38	SHONE
30	STREET
32	LOVE
21	HORSES

2. Paired Associates Presented on Morning I

(Including 20 sleep words and 10 non-sleep words)

12 JUNGLE
18 PARADE
23 COUPLE
28 YELLOW
33 BRAVE
25 THROUGH
20 SUNSHINE
38 SHONE
24 DENSE
30 STREET
22 SOLDIERS
32 LOVE
10 HALL
34 LIGHT
14 MARBLE
39 TOMORROW
35 DOWN
15 ROAM
27 CITATIONS
21 HORSES
17 REVEALING
16 ARE
31 DANCE
26 MAKING
29 GET
11 ATTRACTIVE
19 FROM
37 FLOWERS
36 TIGERS
13 TERRACE

3. Paired Associates Presented On Night II

75 CENTRAL
52 SEASON
51 VISUAL
66 INDICATE
55 DATA
76 ENRICHMENT
80 SPRING
58 RECOGNITION
56 TRAINING

79 DIFFERENCES
61 CERTAIN
74 EDUCATION
62 RESTRICTED
68 PRELIMINARY
78 SOUL
65 BASEBALL
77 RECENT
64 PARTS
73 PURPOSE
67 FIELD

4. Paired Associates Presented on Morning II
(Including 20 sleep words and 10 non-sleep words)

53 EVOLUTION
74 EDUCATION
78 SOUL
64 PARTS
73 PURPOSE
55 DATA
80 SPRING
75 CENTRAL
63 MAN
65 BASEBALL
77 RECENT
50 CONCERN
79 DIFFERENCES
76 ENRICHMENT
57 FILING
62 RESTRICTED
52 SEASON
54 EFFICIENT
51 VISUAL
70 CABINETS
59 DEVELOPMENT
67 FIELD
72 ESSENTIAL
60 PRINCIPLE
58 RECOGNITION
71 MANAGEMENT
66 INDICATE
68 PRELIMINARY
61 CERTAIN
56 TRAINING

APPENDIX 28.4

Sentences for Number-Word Substitution Test

1. *Sentences For Morning I*

   'Brave soldiers get citations.' (*Sleep*)
   'Yellow flowers are attractive.' (*Non-Sleep*)
   'Tigers roam the dense jungle.' (*Non-Sleep*)
   'Horses parade through the street.' (*Sleep*)
   'The light from the dance hall shone down revealing the couple making love on the marble terrace.' (*Sleep*)

2. *Sentences For Morning II*

   'The principal concern of evolution is the development of man.' (*Non-Sleep*)
   'The central purpose of education is the enrichment of the soul.' (*Sleep*)
   'Spring training is preliminary to the baseball season.' (*Sleep*)
   'Filing cabinets are essential to efficient management.' (*Non-Sleep*)
   'Recent data indicate that recognition differences are restricted to certain parts of the visual field.' (*Sleep*)

APPENDIX 28.5

Lists For Frequency Experiment

List I	List II
PERFECT	ALIEN
FATED	NOONDAY
BOASTFUL	BAFFLING
ROCKY	EMPTY
FOREMOST	LAWFUL
TEPID	AWARE
ABSORBED	OPEN
USELESS	TOTAL
READY	COMIC
FAMOUS	FATAL
AWKWARD	CRAFTY
EXACT	HAPPY

APPENDIX 28.6

Lists For Time Of Presentation Experiment

1. Nonsense Syllable Lists

N.S. I	N.S. II	N.S. III	N.S. IV
BEK	BUP	ZUG	VOD
GEZ	NOY	YAF	YIT
DAF	ZIM	NOL	HEB
KAM	CAX	RUK	ZAN
YOB	YUK	GIZ	DIB
BIV	MOF	DUP	WEG
NAL	VEK	PUV	KUV
ZUN	BOZ	CAJ	ZUL
HUZ	NID	ROF	FOV
WEM	MIP	PIV	WAP

2. Word Lists

Word List I	Word List II	Word List III	Word List IV
ABOUT	ABOVE	MILK	MARK
MADE	MAKE	AFTER	AGAIN
SHALL	SIGHT	CITY	CASE
HARD	HAND	GAVE	GOLD
BIRD	BODY	SHORT	SERVE
COLD	CALL	DEAR	DARK
PAPER	POINT	PLACE	PLANT
GIRL	GIVE	LEAVE	LARGE
DOOR	DEAD	FEET	FILL
FALL	FIVE	ROUND	READY
LAUGH	LEARN	HAIR	HELP
RIGHT	REACH	BANK	BOOK

APPENDIX 28.7

Choices For Perceptual Set Problem: Pictures

1. *Choices for Test Picture*

   A. View of the Grand Canyon from the top.
   *B. Six students sitting around a table with a lone figure in the background.
   C. Some cars in a parking space.
   D. View of the New York coastline, including the Statue of Liberty.
   E. A baseball game at Ebbets Field.

2. *Choices of Control Picture*
   A. Man and woman putting flowers on a grave.
   B. Group of mechanics working on a large machine.
   C. Woman kissing husband goodbye in the morning.
   *D. Man working at his desk with clock steeple in background.
   E. Two men playing golf with a caddie standing nearby.

* Correct choices

REFERENCES

1. A. P. Bumstead, Finding the best method for memorizing. *J. educ. Psychol.*, **34**, 110–114.
2. H. Ebbinghaus, Über das Gedächtnis: Untersuchungen zus experimentellen Psychologie. (Leipzig: Duncker and Humbolt, 1885). [Translated as *Memory: A contribution to experimental psychology,* by H. A. Ruger and C. E. Bussenius. Columbia Univ. Coll. Educ. Reprints, No. 3. New York: Teachers College, Columbia University, 1913.]
3. B. H. Fox and J. S. Robbins, The retention of material presented during sleep. *J. exp. Psychol.*, 1952, **43**, 75–79.
4. J. A. Glaze, The association value of nonsense syllables. *J. genet. Psychol.*, 1928, **35**, 255–267.
5. E. R. Guthrie, *The Psychology of Learning* (New York: Harper, 1935).
6. E. R. Hilgard, Methods and Procedures in the Study of Learning, *Handbook of Experimental Psychology,* ed. by S. S. Stevens (New York: John Wiley and Sons, Inc., 1951), 548–552.
7. C. I. Hovland, Experimental studies in rote-learning theory. VI. Comparison of retention following learning to same criterion by massed and distributed practice. *J. exp. Psychol.*, 1940, **26**, 568–587.
8. C. I. Hovland, Human Learning and Retention, *Handbook of Experimental Psychology,* ed. by S. S. Stevens (New York: John Wiley and Sons, Inc., 1951), 613–689.
9. C. T. Hull, *Principles of Behavior.* (New York: Appleton-Century-Crafts, 1943).
10. A. L. Huxley, *Brave New World* (London: Chatto & Windus, 1932).
11. J. G. Jenkins and K. M. Dallenbach, Obliviscence during sleeping and waking, *Amer. J. Psychol.*, 1924, **35**, 605–612.
12. N. Kleitman, *Sleep and Wakefulness* (Chicago: Univ. Chicago Press, 1939).
13. N. Kleitman, The Sleep-Wakefulness Cycle, *Problems of Consciousness.* Transactions of the First Conference March 20–21, 1950, New York (New York: Corlies, Macy and Co., Inc., 1950), 15–61.
14. D. A. Laird and C. G. Muller, *Sleep* (London: Williams and Norgate Ltd.), 1930.
15. L. LeShan, The breaking of habit by suggestion during sleep. *J. abnorm. soc. Psychol.*, 1942, **37**, 406–408.
16. C. Leuba and D. Bateman, Learning during sleep. *Amer. J. Psychol.*, 1952, **65**, 301–302.

17. K. Lewin, Field theory and learning. In National Society for the Study of Education, *The forty-first yearbook,* Bloomington, Ill.: Public School Publishing Co., 1942.
18. D. O. Lyon, The relation of length of material to time taken for learning and the optimum distribution of time. *J. educ. Psychol.,* 1914, **5**, 1–9, 85–91, 155–163.
19. J. A. McGeogh and A. I. Irion, *The Psychology of Human Learning* (New York: Longmans, Green and Co., 1952), 138–193.
20. *ibid.,* 278–298.
21. *ibid.,* 295–296.
22. S. W. Ranson, Somnolence caused by hypnothalmic lesions in the monkey. *Arch. neurol. Psychiat.,* **41**, 1–23.
23. E. S. Robinson, The 'similarity' factor in retroaction. *Amer. J. Psychol.,* 1927, **39**, 297–312.
24. *ibid.,* 298–299.
25. B. F. Skinner, *The Behaviour of Organisms* (New York: Appleton-Century-Crofts), 1938.
26. E. L. Thorndike, *et al. The Fundamentals of Learning* (New York: Teachers College, Columbia University, 1932).
27. E. L. Thorndike and I. Lorge, *The Teacher's Word Book of* 30,000 *Words* (New York: Teachers College, Columbia University, 1944).
28. E. C. Tolman, The acquisition of string-pulling by rats—conditioned response or sign—Gestalt? *Psychol. Rev.,* 1937, **44**, 195–211.
29. E. B. Van Ormer, Retention after intervals of sleep and of waking. *Arch. Psychol.,* N.Y., 1932, **21**, No. 137.
30. P. Worchel and M. H. Marks, The effect of sleep prior to learning. *J. exp. Psychol.,* 1951, **42**, 313–316.

APPENDIX I

Hypnosis and Hypnopaedia

Studies of sleep behaviour and neuro-physiology have begun to map out some of the possibilities and limits of sleep-learning and to illuminate how the sleeping brain reacts and what it is capable of doing. The data produced by various authors suggest that hypnopaedia has an intriguing possibility. The Russians have succeeded in teaching English at a fast rate in courses, in which hypnopaedic sessions were included but the Americans, so far as it is known, remain more sceptical. Many people, of course, assume that hypnopaedia is a slightly miraculous technique offering success in acquiring skills without effort.

Learning and performing under hypnosis have also received favourable experimental results, and the monographs listed at the end of this appendix give a comparison between learning in the hypnotic state and learning with hypnopaedic techniques. One of the main questions is: what personality factors are involved in applying successfully hypnotic or hypnopaedic teaching method? To provide some light on these lines, the two informative papers on learning in the state of hypnosis are given in Appendices II and III. One of them contradicts conventional beliefs in suggestibility of people.

Material designed for learning in hypnosis and hypnopaedia (visually or by audio methods) requires special pacing. It would seem that relationships can be imparted by presenting the related items—whether they are words or something else—close together in time. In human study somewhat analogous to the cat study, subjects discriminated between the significant (shock-paired) tone and a neutral tone by showing a particular brain wave formation whenever the meaningful tone was played during deep sleep (Beh and Barratt, 1965). These subjects had been given chloral hydrate to induce sleep and they showed no signs of shifting into the lighter stage of sleep. Tests given to the subjects later, during waking, showed that the significance that had been conditioned during sleep was carried over into the waking state. The importance of this recent work is precisely that sleep-conditioning did not arouse the subject and that it did carry over into waking. This study underscores one of the most mysterious aspects of recent studies of hypnopaedia and memory. Many investigators have emphasised the individual differences they have observed and the by-no-means uniform success in sleep-conditioning or hypnopaedia—except that of the Russians (e.g. Bliznitchenko), who created a successful technique of practical hypnopaedia by special intonation of hypnopaedic speech for collective instruction. Concerning the individual differences observed by other Russian scientists, they report more success in those who enjoy a prevailing mechanical memory, while people with a prevailing logical memory seem to be less successful in hypnopaedic learning.

Suggestible persons are also better subjects for hypnopaedic teaching, but increased suggestibility can be also acquired by interplaying circumstances and motivation (M. N. Pai, 1961).

Increase in suggestibility has so long been associated with hypnosis that such increase has commonly been considered to be defining characteristic in hypnosis.

It is well known, however, that responses to suggestions of a kind given within hypnosis may be obtained *outside* the hypnotic state; such suggestions are often called 'making suggestions,' a term of convenience that can be used without implying that hypnosis is a sleep state (Hilgard and Tart, 1966).

Studies of hypnotic and non-hypnotic subjects may help to reveal overlooked possibilities in sleep-learning. Efforts to find out what suggestibility means, and something about the hypnotic subject's memory process, may also indicate whether elaborate sleep-learning can be accomplished in the ordinary person. During a recent pilot study at the University of Pennsylvania, J. P. Brady and B. S. Rosner found that the hypnotic suggestion to dreams produces a trance state with a waking brain wave pattern accompanied by the rapid eye movements that are characteristic of the vivid dream phase. Dreams reported by these hypnotic subjects sounded almost indistinguishable from ordinary nightly dreams, but *unlike* night-time dreams that seem to evaporate from memory within seconds, these hypnotic dreams have been remembered ten minutes and longer in great detail. Is the suggestible or apparently non-suggestible person capable of using his brain, manipulating his state of consciousness? Is it possible to voluntarily 'turn on' brain states that we think of as involuntary? EEG studies may eventually begin to characterise the way in which the suggestible and apparently non-suggestible person functions by elucidating the brain activity in persons who seem especially receptive to instructions and capable of retention.

If it is possible to discover how the suggestible person uses his brain or, indeed, what brain mechanisms are called into play in acceding to a suggestion, it may also be possible to teach such internal manipulations to apparently non-suggestible persons. Such a possibility might open the door to unforeseen advantages in education. This knowledge is likely to take a long time in the gathering, and will probably attract attention long before the full evidence is obtained. This is one of the most promising aspects of the problem—the as yet apparently mystical question of learning less or more complicated material during behavioural sleep. A good deal of our insight may come from neuro-physiological studies where already, in far less sensational facets of hypnopaedia, we have observed one aspect that is exhibited by all normal people, which is the continuation of higher mental states during EEG sleep.

Voluntary control over sleep behaviour and, indeed, some facets of waking consciousness, have come into systematic investigation only recently. Only a bare beginning has been made in the study of sleep behaviour itself. Some people can respond to the outside world without showing apparent EEG changes in their sleep, yet others show rhythms resembling those we identify with waking. The behaviour of lying still with eyes closed is not enough to tell us that a person is asleep, and sleep-like brainwaves may be contradicted by apparently alert behaviour. Although the conditioning of brainwave sequences and the exploration of introspective development may seem Olympian and distant from practical application, such studies may ultimately offer powerful new techniques. We have discovered that people can discriminate between one phase of sleep and another, can accept and memorise information during sleep, and can communicate with the outside world. They can learn to control states of consciousness that they could not previously identify and for which they had no awareness. Most of the findings cannot be applied at once, but progress has been rapid, for the work described here has been accomplished largely in the last fifteen years.

Research is still in a beginning stage, but as it can be seen from the work already done, learning during sleep is not a miracle.

Conclusions drawn from the material published and presented in this symposium suggest that the total process of hypnopaedia consists briefly of the following: (1) short learning prior to sleep while awake (sleep has a beneficial effect upon memory); (2) learning during drowsiness and hypnagogic reverie state, lapsing into (3) the light stages of sleep, and (4) sustaining (2) and (3) until hypnopaedic session ends (maximum one hour and thirty minutes).

Hypnopaedic phenomena may also be reflected from the classic notion of conditioned reflexes. The unconditional stimulus in this case is a continuous acoustic signal (pure tone, noise and etc.) presented on a volume below the wakening threshold. The unconditioned response will be a change of the EEG pattern and a probable decreasing depth of sleep.

The conditioned stimulus will be the 'verbalization' of the acoustic signal changing into speech that can leave an engram or memory trace. The memorization of the contents of meaningful signal is the conditioned response during a decreased depth of sleep which could be reinforced by continuous stimulation and repetition of texts.

APPENDIX II

A Comparison of Hypnotic and Waking Learning of the International Morse Code

Alden B. Sears

After a survey of the literature in the field of hypnosis, no studies were found which were directly comparable to this particular experiment. Previous experiments differed in the following ways:

1. Much of the learning in previous experiments was done in the waking state and the amount of learning was determined by recall under hypnosis.
2. Some of the previous experiments were concerned with the learning of nonsense or meaningful material, but none were concerned with symbol learning.
3. Because of the nature of the material learned in previous experiments, the number of sessions varied for each person and the criterion for learning was one perfect performance. In this experiment time was kept constant and errors were recorded.
4. In previous experiments there was no practice to increase efficiency after the intial learning.

Clark L. Hull listed 102 outlines of experimental projects and procedures for examining hypnotic phenomena and included an outline of an experiment concerned with the question as to what extent, if any, positive suggestion can accelerate, and negative suggestion retard, the rate of learning. This study is concerned with the extent positive suggestion can accelerate the rate of symbol learning and increase efficiency in practice.

There are several experiments which have been written in the literature that are concerned with the effect of hypnosis on learning nonsense and meaningful material. Gray conducted an experiment to determine whether spelling can be taught more readily under the influence of hypnosis than in the waking state. A group of six who were known to be weak in spelling learned how to spell one list of words while in hypnosis and another list while in the waking state. This investigation found only a small improvement in hypnosis; the total difference in favour of hypnotic learning was 1·92 per cent. Weitzenhoffer says, 'There may, however, be some question of the general validity of his (Gray's) results since he used subjects who were known to be weak in spelling. Whether or not hypnosis could improve their spelling ability would depend, in part, upon what caused the weakness. This is particularly important in view of the small number of subjects that were used' (6, p. 166).

Huse performed an experiment on the recall of recently learned nonsense material and found that there was a slight mean tendency for recall twenty-four hours after learning to be better in the normal state than in the trance state, White, Fox, and Harris devised an experiment to test hypnotic hypermnesia for three types of recently learned material. These results confirmed those of Huse, and the investigators reported that 'Hypnosis conferred no benefit on the recall of paired nonsense associates learned the day before, but it created substantial hypermnesia for meaningful poetry and there was some evidence for a similar gain in the case of moving-picture scenes without captions or plot' (7, p. 102).

Cooper and Rodgin made a comparison of two methods of learning paired nonsense syllables. In one method, the subject copied the syllable 5 times while awake; in the other he hallucinated the writing of the syllable under conditions of time distortion in the hypnotic trance. After the subject had been hypnotised, his sense of time was altered and he printed the letters only in his imagination. Only five seconds were allowed for the trance study but, to the subject, the study period seemed to last four or five minutes. The results indicate that the study in the trance state in distorted time was more effective than that in the waking state. *Under hypnosis, the subject was able to master in only* 7·4 *seconds what it had taken him thirty-one seconds to learn while awake*. Tested after twenty-four hours, he had retained more of what he learned under *hypnosis* and could re-learn the forgotten material in less time. However, Cooper and Rodgin's investigation differs from the present one in the type of material learned and in the fact that the present instructions to the subjects included no suggestion of time distortion or an altered subjective sense of time. In Cooper and Tuthill's (2) experiment with time distortion in hypnosis and motor learning, the investigators state that there is no evidence which would indicate that the learning process itself is facilitated by such practice. The motor learning involved was the writing of words and sentences with the subordinate hand, and the practice was done under conditions of distorted time in the hypnotic trance.

As previously stated, no other studies were found which are directly comparable to the present one. In the majority of those studies which are related to this experiment, most of the evidence indicates there would be no improvement in learning and retention. Therefore, the Null Hypothesis was used, stated thus, 'The learning of the Morse Code will not be improved by the use of hypnosis.'

EXPERIMENTAL DESIGN

In order to test this hypothesis, it was determined to use two groups of subjects, individually matched on the basis of the Otis Quick Scoring Mental Abilities Tests, Gamma Test, Form D. The experimental group would consist of twenty-five good hypnotic subjects who had previously been trained to go into a medium trance state (according to The Davis and Husband Hypnotic Susceptibility Scale) on counting to ten. This group would memorise the characters of the Morse Code and practice receiving the code while hypnotised. A control group of twenty-five subjects, after having been individually matched with the experimental group on the basis of the Otis test results, would learn the code characters and practice receiving it while in the waking state. All subjects would be university students who had volunteered to participate in this study. Each person would be paid $1.00 per hour.

The materials to be used in this study are:

1. White 5 × 8 cards (for the initial memorisation of the code) on which were printed the alphabet, numbers, and common punctuation marks, each being followed by its appropriate code symbol.
2. An Instructograph, made by the Instructograph Company of Chicago, Illinois, equipped with an extension speaker which would be positioned above the practice table. Only tapes 1–5 would be used. The oscillator tone would be set on medium pitch, as this seems to be the most pleasing and easiest to read.
3. A stop watch to be used for timing the tests.

Each subject would spend thirty hours in Morse Code instruction. The time during which each subject would participate in the experiment would depend on his own schedule. Each week he would spend two or three hours learning and practicing the code, these hours to be arranged at his convenience. It was endeavoured to group from two to six subjects together at the same hour. Thus this would be classed as group practice rather than individual practice.

The first ten hours would ge spent in memorising the code symbols, which would be printed on a white 5 × 8 card, and in receiving the code to gain practice in speed. Each subject would be allowed as much time as he needed to memorise the code symbols, and he would not start receiving the code from the instructograph tape until he had completed the memorisation. During the remaining twenty hours in the experiment the subjects would receive the code from the instructograph tape at increasing rates of speed.

Proficiency in this type of learning can be tested, either for mistakes made in receiving transmitted signals at stated rates, or on speed of reception with no mistakes.

In this study it was determined to test all subjects at the end of each tenth period of instruction as follows: At the end of ten hours all subjects would be tested, in the waking state, at the speeds of five and seven and a half words per minute. (As is common practice in radio telegraphy, five characters constitute a word.) The mistakes would be noted and the two groups of matched subjects compared on their total mistakes. At the end of twenty hours all subjects would be tested again. This time the tests would be made at five, seven and a half, ten, and twelve and a half words per minute. The resulting mistakes would be grouped and compared as before. The final tests would be given at the end of thirty hours. At this time the subjects would be tested at five, seven and a half, ten, twelve and a half, and fifteen words per minute. The mistakes would be grouped and compared in the same manner. The subjects would always be tested on a section of the instructograph tape which they had not heard previously in practice.

In the final analysis, the '*t*' test for matched pairs would be used to determine the significance of the differences in total errors made by the two groups at the stated speeds in each test.

METHOD AND ANALYSIS

All subjects were university students between the ages of seventeen and twenty-nine. Each person volunteered to participate in this study and was paid $1.00 per hour.

The experimental group consisted of twenty-five good hypnotic subjects who had previously been trained to go into a medium trance state (according to the Davis and Husband Hypnotic Susceptibility Scale) on counting to ten. This group learned and practiced the Morse Code while hypnotised. The control group learned and practiced the code while in the waking state. This group was composed of twenty-five subjects who were individually matched with the experimental group on the basis of the Otis Quick Scoring Mental Abilities Tests, Gamma Test, Form D. The individuals were matched within one point on the test. I.Q.'s ranged between 112 and 136 with an average I.Q. of 124. Due to drop-outs, sickness, etc., twelve of the original twenty-five pairs of subjects did not complete the experiment. Consequently, the results given here are on the thirteen pairs (fourteen men and twelve women) that completed the full thirty hours of training. It is interesting to note that, of the drop-outs, eleven were in the control group and six in the experimental group.

Each subject spent two or three hours per week learning and practicing the code until he had completed thirty hours of instruction. The time during which the subject participated in the experiment depended on his own schedule, and hours were arranged at his convenience. Two to six subjects who had the same time available for the experiment were grouped together at the same hour.

At the beginning of each session the subjects in the experimental group seated themselves at a table and assumed a comfortable position. Then the experimenter suggested sleep and began counting from one to ten. Each person had previously been trained to go into a hypnotic trance by this procedure. After the group had been hypnotised, the experimenter suggested that the subject would learn the code easily and remember the symbols both in the waking and hypnotic states. He was then told he would open his eyes without awakening from the trance and begin learning or practicing the code. At the end of the session, the subjects were awakened with the suggestion that they would remember all that they had learned during that session. Because approximately five minutes of each hour of practice time in the experimental group was used for trance induction, this group actually had five minutes per hour, or a total of 150 minutes, less practice time than the control group.

The first hour for both groups was spent in memorising the code symbols which were printed on a white card. At the beginning of the second session, the subject wrote out in Morse Code the alphabet, numbers, and common punctuation marks that he had memorised the preceding session. He then concentrated on learning the remainder of the code symbols. At the beginning of the third hour, the subject again wrote out all of the code symbols that he could remember, and he spent the rest of the hour learning those symbols that he had not yet mastered. Each subject was allowed as much time as he needed for memorisation, and he did not begin to receive the code from the instructograph tape until he could write out the alphabet, numbers, and common punctuation marks with the appropriate code symbol.

An Instructograph with the oscillator tone set on medium pitch was equipped with an extension speaker positioned above the table at which the group practiced. Only tapes one to four were used for practice, and tape five was used for testing exclusively. It was endeavoured to keep the speed of the tape just beyond the level of proficiency of the group. Consequently, the tape was run progressively faster from session to session.

After completing each ten hours of instruction all subjects were tested in the waking state. The subjects were always tested on a section of a tape which they had not heard previously in practice. A stop watch was used for timing each test.

At the end of the first ten hours of instruction, all subjects were tested in the waking state at speeds of five and seven and a half words per minute. The number of errors made by each person was recorded, and the two groups were compared on their total number of mistakes. The subjects were again tested at the completion of twenty hours of practice. This time the tests were made at speeds of five, seven and a half, ten, and twelve and a half words per minute. The errors were grouped and compared as

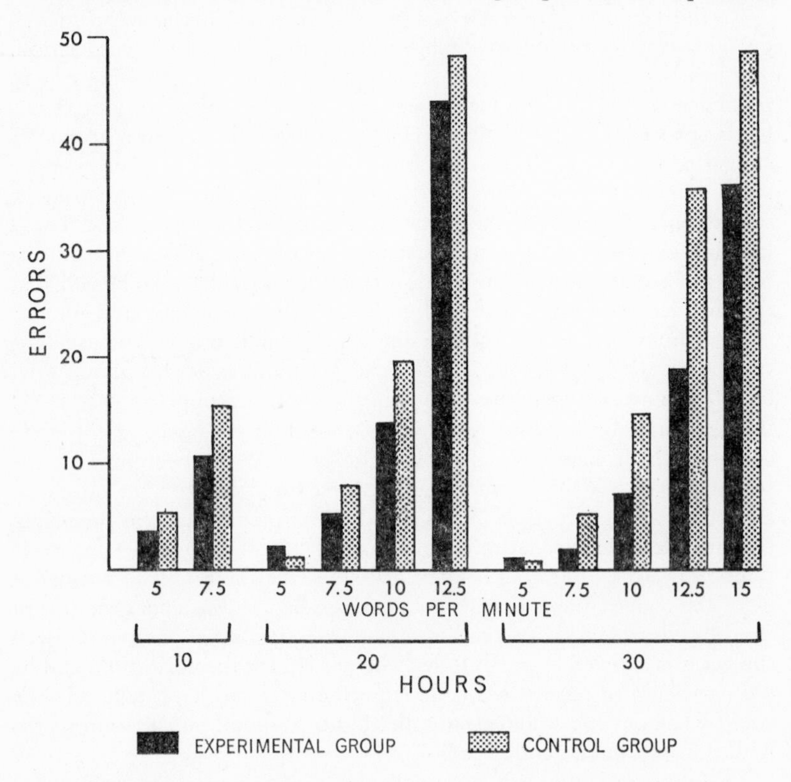

Fig. A2. Mean number of errors per minute made by each group

before. The final test was given at the end of thirty hours of instruction. Again the mistakes were grouped and compared. Fig. A2 shows the mean number of errors per minute made by each group at the stated rates of speed in each test.

In nine of the eleven tests, the mean number of errors made by the control group is greater than the mean number of errors made by the experimental group. There are two reversals of this general trend, one at twenty hours, five words per minute, and one at thirty hours, five words per minute. However, the differences in these two cases are not significant. In both instances one subject in the experimental group made a greater number of errors than any other subject; and thus, he raised the mean for the entire group. An analysis of Fig. A2 indicates that the differences in errors between the two groups became greater with an increased number of hours of practice. The *t* test for matched pairs was used to determine the significance of the differences in total errors made by the two groups at the stated rates of speed in each test. All significant differences were found in the thirty hour test, with the experimental group making significantly fewer mistakes than the control group. At seven and a half and fifteen words per minute, the differences were significant at the 5 per cent level of confidence; at ten and twelve and a half words per minute, the differences were significant at the 1 per cent level of confidence (Table I).

Table I

	w.p.m.	*Control group errors*	*Experimental group errors*	'*t*'	*level of significance*
10 hours	5	55	42	0·83	
	$7\frac{1}{2}$	187	130	1·48	
20 hours	5	9	16	−1·02	
	$7\frac{1}{2}$	101	59	1·43	
	10	242	172	1·08	
	$12\frac{1}{2}$	565	519	0·79	
30 hours	5	3	7	−0·63	
	$7\frac{1}{2}$	59	18	2·09	5%
	10	182	79	2·47	1%
	$12\frac{1}{2}$	451	244	3·67	1%
	15	615	457	1·85	5%

Another apparent difference between the two groups was in the general feeling of the subjects. The people in the control group seemed to lose interest and become bored with the practicing of the code; while the subjects in the experimental group seemed to maintain motivation and concentration throughout the experiment. After completion of the experiment, the subjects were questioned concerning their attitudes and general reaction to participating in this study. The control group complained of boredom and loss of interest, while the experimental group admitted they had no real goal in learning the code but were interested in knowing how well and how fast they could learn it. Thus, it appears that an artificial motivation may have been built in with the use of hypnosis although there were no direct suggestions given to this effect. Another fact which might substantiate this reported difference between the groups is that only six of the experimental group dropped out of the experiment as compared to eleven in the control group.

Therefore, on the basis of the results of this study, the Null Hypothesis, 'The learning of the Morse Code will not be improved by the use of hypnosis,' is refuted. It appears that the use of hypnosis does improve the learning of the Morse Code under these experimental conditions.

SUMMARY

This experiment was designed to test the hypothesis, 'The learning of the Morse Code will not be improved by the use of hypnosis'. There was an experimental group, who learned the Morse Code while in the hypnotic state, and a matched control group, who were not hypnotised during the course of the experiment. The subjects were tested at the end of ten, twenty, and thirty hours of learning and/or practice. All testing was carried out while the subjects were in the waking state. The differences in errors made by the two groups were greater as time of practice increased, becoming significant at the thirty hour test, with the experimental group making significantly fewer errors than the control group. Thus, the Null Hypothesis, 'The learning of the Morse Code will not be improved by the use of hypnosis', is refuted showing that learning of the Morse Code is improved under these conditions by the use of hypnosis.

It would be interesting to carry out another such study and extend the time to fifty or more hours to determine whether or not this trend of increasing difference continues. There is also the possibility that if both groups had been strongly motivated to learn the Morse Code the results would not have been the same. In this study neither group had any real desire to learn the code other than a willingness to participate in the experiment and earn the dollar an hour paid the subjects.

Editor's note: Hypnopaedically learned material without apparently induced hypnosis is similar in its achievement of higher scores of retention and recall, as it can be seen in the findings presented by A. B. Sears. This may be due to the similarity of cerebral states, characteristic of both the hypnopaedic phase and hypnotic state (experimentally induced before learning), which can also appear during sleep and be sustained until stimulation (by the voice of the hypnopaedic speaker) is terminated.

REFERENCES

Cooper, Linn F., and Rodgin, D. W. 'Time Distortion in Hypnosis and Nonmotor Learning,' *Science,* **115**, 1952, 500–502.

Cooper, L. F. and Tuthill, C. E. 'Time Distortion in Hypnosis and Motor Learning,' *Journal of Psychology,* **33–34**, 1952, 67–75.

Gray, W. H. 'Effect of Hypnosis on Learning to Spell,' *Journal of Educational Psychology,* **25**, 1934, 471–473.

Hull, Clark L. 'Quantitative Methods of Investigating Hypnotic Suggestion,' *Journal of Abnormal and Social Psychology,* **25**, 1930–31, 200–223, 390–417.

Huse, B. 'Does the Hypnotic Trance Favor the Recall of Faint Memories?' *Journal of Experimental Psychology,* **13**, 1930, 519–529.

Weitzenhoffer, Andre M. Hypnotism: *An Objective Study in Suggestibility,* New York, John Wiley & Sons, Inc., 1953.

White, Robert W., Fox, George F. and Harris, Walker W. 'Hypnotic Hypermnesia for Recently Learned Material,' *Journal of Abnormal and Social Psychology,* **35**, Jan.–Oct., 1940, 88–103.

APPENDIX III

More Hypnosis in the Unhypnotisable: effects of hypnosis and exhortation on rote learning

Perry London

Michael Conant and Gerald C. Davison

This study was conducted in the Laboratory of Human Development, Stanford University, Ernest Hilgard, Director, and was supported in part by United States Public Health Service Grants MH 03859 (*E.* R. *Hilgard, principal investigator*) *and MH* 08598 (*Perry London, principal investigator*).

In an experiment concerning the effects of hypnosis on the rote learning of nonsense syllables, Rosenhan and London (1963a) unexpectedly found that individuals who are very susceptible to hypnosis (*T*s) learn significantly more on base-rate trial conditions than do *S*s low in hypnotic susceptibility (*UT*s). More surprising still, they also found that when both groups were subjected to the same learning task while hypnotised, the effect was reversed significantly, so that *T*s tended to decline slightly in their retention of material while *UT*s improved rather dramatically. Since the authors did not anticipate these results in the first place, they were at some loss to explain them after the fact. They suggested, however, that the learning differences between susceptibility groups might rest in the degree of tension which characterised them at the start of the experiment. *T S*s might be optimally tense during base-rate trials, while *UT S*s might be too tense at first to perform optimally during these trials. If so, then it is plausible that if hypnosis has the effect of relaxing both groups, it might cause *T*s to relax *below* the optimal tension level for learning, while *UT*s would tend to descend *to* this optimal level.

Rosenhan and London's (1963a) results run counter to the results of most hypnosis and learning studies, but the latter have usually been obtained from studies of very susceptible *S*s only. More important, the results of Rosenhan and London seem to parallel Young's (1925) observation that relatively unsusceptible *S*s memorise nonsense syllables better than do very susceptible ones when both are subjected to a hypnotic induction; however, the results run counter to Schulman and London's

(1963) finding (in a study of acquisition rather than retention ability) that there are no differences at all in the base-rate learning abilities of *T* and *UT* female *S*s.

The present study was designed to resolve the two main problems posed by the Rosenhan and London (1963a) results:

(1) The base rate differences in retention between susceptibility groups were sufficiently unexpected to demand replication under more carefully controlled conditions.

(2) Alternative experimental conditions were required to test the relevance of hypnotic induction to the interaction effects of susceptibility and retention observed in their experiment.

METHOD

*S*s were 40 male undergraduates at Stanford University to whom the *Stanford Hypnotic Susceptibility Scale, Form A* (Weitzenhoffer & Hilgrad, 1959) had been administered several months before this experiment as part of the requirements in an introductory psychology course. By means of the scale, two categories of *S*s were selected: Tranceables (*T*s), i.e., those highly susceptible to hypnosis, and Untranceables (*UT*s), i.e., those relatively unsusceptible to hypnosis. To qualify as a *T*, it was necessary for an *S* to pass eight or more of the twelve items on the scale, including at least one of the most difficult ones (Nos. 4, 8, 10, or 12). To qualify as a *UT*, an *S* had to fail eight or more of the twelve items, including all of the most difficult ones. In this manner, twenty *T* and twenty *UT* *S*s were selected from scale profiles by a person not involved with the experiment.

*S*s were assigned to three experimental conditions: sixteen 'hypnotic' (eight *T*, eight *UT*), sixteen 'motivated,' i.e., exhorted (eight *T*, eight *UT*), and eight 'control' (four *T*, four *UT*). Two *E*s followed the procedures described below, sharing equally all possible combinations of *S*s and conditions. The *E*s were not informed of the susceptibility classification of any *S*s assigned them.

The stimuli used were two lists of ten consonant-vowel-consonant nonsense syllables of 53 per cent association value (Glaze, 1928), the same lists used by Rosenhan and London (1963a). Each trigram on the list was exposed to view in a memory-drum for one second, with two seconds between exposures. Each list was presented three times, in a different order each time, with an interval of five seconds between presentations. An *S*'s score was the number of syllables he could spell out loud correctly after all three presentations of the list were completed. Approximately thirty seconds were allowed to elapse after the *S* stopped spelling, and he was then asked once if he could recall any more syllables.

The order of presentation of the two lists was counterbalanced over all conditions. For each *S*, the base-rate level of learning was determined prior to any experimental (hypnotic or exhortative) manipulation. Following the establishment of the base rate, the second measure of learning was taken in accordance with the experimental or control condition to which *S*s had been assigned:

(1) *Hypnotic Condition:* Immediately after the base-rate task, *S*s assigned to the hypnotic group were given a six-minute hypnotic induction which was a modified version of *Form C* of the *Stanford Hypnotic Susceptibility Scale* (Weitzenhoffer & Hilgard, 1962). Instructions for the memory task were then repeated, after which *S*s were told to open their eyes and execute the task while remaining in the state they were in. Thus, both learning and recall took place under hypnosis; *S*s in this group were not exhorted to remember more syllables on the second list than they had remembered on the first.

(2) *Motivated Condition:* Since the motivating instructions were about four minutes shorter than the hypnotic induction, *S*s in this group were told to relax for a few minutes before the experiment proceeded.
The following instructions were then read to them:

> Now I'd like you to sit back in your chair, relax, and close your eyes. Just listen to what I'm going to tell you, but do not let yourself go into hypnosis. Remain relaxed, but alert and wide awake, with your eyes closed. I'm going to tell you a few things about what you're going to do next.
>
> There's a lot of evidence that people don't ordinarily use their capabilities to the fullest. You remember how apparently impossible a four-minute mile used to be considered—that is, until one man was able to do it. In the same way, the mind is capable of far more than we might think, if only we push ourselves to the utmost and really concentrate on what we're doing. I'm going to show you right now that your memory is far better than you've ever thought it to be.
>
> You remember the memory task that I gave you at the beginning of this session. Well, I have another list of words which I'm going to present to you in the same way on this apparatus. Even though you did well on that earlier list of words, I want you to attend even more closely to this list. Shut out all distracting thoughts and sounds, and concentrate only on this task. When you try harder, you will find that you will remember more of the words which I'm going to show you. I shall now repeat the instructions for the memory task.

The second list was then administered as the first had been.

(3) *Control Condition:* Five minutes elapsed before these *S*s were given the second list. The instructions for it were identical with those for the first list and were read to them while their eyes were closed.

RESULTS

The first hypothesis predicted, on the basis of Rosenhan and London's (1963a) results, that very susceptible *S*s learn nonsense syllables better than unsusceptible ones. Since two *E*s were used in the present study, it was possible also to ascertain whether differences between *S* groups were significantly influenced by *E* behaviour. For this purpose, the first (base-

Table 1

Mean base rate (first trial) memory scores by susceptibility status, experimental assignment, and experimenter

Experimenter	*Experimental assignment*	*Subject*	
		T	*UT*
M	Hypnosis	6·0	3·8
	Exhortation	6·5	4·8
	Control	4·0	8·5
J	Hypnosis	7·0	6·0
	Exhortation	6·5	4·2
	Control	7·5	5·0
Experimenters combined	Hypnosis	6·5	4·9
	Exhortation	6·5	4·5
	Control	5·8	6·8

rate) score of each *S* was used as the unit of measurement, and these scores, grouped by susceptibility status and by *E*, were subjected to a two-way analysis of variance (Table 1). Results of this analysis support the hypothesis; *T Ss* did learn nonsense syllables significantly better than *UT Ss* ($p < 0{\cdot}05$), the *E*s did not differ significantly from each other in their influence on *S*s' performance, and there is no significant interaction between *E* and *S* effects (Table 2).*

The present study extended the Rosenhan and London (1963a) study by proposing that differences in the performance of different susceptibility groups under base-rate and hypnotic conditions might result from *E* effects, from practice effects, or from some exhortative properties of hypnotic inductions which have nothing to do with hypnosis per se. The use of two 'blind' *E*s, of a control group which received no special instructions, and of a non-hypnotic verbal exhortation instruction permitted these respective alternatives to be tested.

For this purpose, a three-way analysis of variance was done, using the difference between each *S*'s scores (trial 2 minus trial 1) as the unit of measurement. Results of the analysis of all possible main effects, two-way interactions, and three-way interactions indicate that the main effect due to differences in the susceptibility of the *S*s is alone significant ($p > 0{\cdot}01$) (Table 3). The differences which Rosenhan and London (1963a) observed between the hypnotised and base-rate performances of different susceptibility groups are evidently reliable ones, but they do not seem to have anything to do with hypnosis as such. Mean-group scores for all conditions are presented in Table 4.

DISCUSSION

It is very clear that the results of the present study confirm those obtained by Rosenhan and London (1963a) and that they do so under conditions of control which make those surprising results seem much more capable of generalisation than was the case in the original study. Under the circumstances, the discrepancy between our findings and those of Schulman and London (1963) is even more puzzling than before. Since the latter study sampled females rather than males, it is possible, of course, to attribute its different results to a capacity or personality difference between the sexes. However, this explanation does not seem very tenable to us. In the first place, experimental research on hypnosis does not generally reveal sex differences. In the second, previous studies which have compared the performance differences of various susceptibility groups have sampled both sexes, and the differences between susceptibility groups have tended to be very consistent regardless of sex (London and Fuhrer, 1961; Rosenhan and London, 1963b; Slotnick and London, 1965). The very considerable procedural differences between the two

* Because of the limited numbers of *S*s assigned within *S* groups and among conditions and *Es*, a three-way analysis of the base scores was also conducted to determine whether or not some *S* bias had occurred despite random assignment. As in the previous analysis, only differences between susceptibility groups were significant.

Table 2

Analysis of variance for base-rate memory scores

Source	*df*	*MS*	*F*
Experimenter (*E*)	1	3·025	1·024
Subject (*S*) . .	1	15·625	5·291*
E x *S* . . .	1	3·025	1·024
Error (w) . .	36	2·953	

* $p < 0{\cdot}05$

Table 3

Analysis of variance of relative differences in memory scores (experimental–base-rate trial) by susceptibility, experimental condition, and experimenter

Source	*df*	*MS*	*F*
Experimenter (*E*)	1	9·025	3·293
Subject (*S*) . .	1	21·025	7·671*
Condition (C) .	2	2·374	0·866
E x *S* . . .	1	2·025	0·739
E x *C* . . .	2	6·519	2·378
S x *C* . . .	2	3·019	1·101
E x *S* x *C* . .	2	1·519	0·554
Error (w) . .	28	2·741	

* $p < 0{\cdot}01$

Table 4

Mean scores for memorization of nonsense syllables

Experimental assignment	*Susceptibility*			
	T		*UT*	
	Base score	*Experimental score*	*Base score*	*Experimental score*
Control . .	5·8	5·0	6·8	6·0
Hypnosis . .	6·5	5·5	4·9	5·4
Exhortation .	6·5	5·6	4·5	5·8

studies seem to offer a better basis for explaining their different results than do any differences between types of *S*s or samples. Schulman and London (1963) used a blind selection like ours, in which *S*s were classified by someone not involved in the experiment, and the experiment was administered by someone who did not know the classifications. In our experiment, however, as in Rosenhan and London (1963a) the *E* personally administered all instructions, *S*s went through the experimental tasks with their eyes open watching a memory drum, and the required performance of remembering the list began after all the presentations of stimuli had been completed. In Schulman and London's experiment, the *E* administered many of the instructions and all the stimuli by means of taped recordings to which *S*s listened with their eyes closed, and the required performance of *anticipating each nonsense syllable* on the recording was continuous with the presentation of the stimuli themselves. The relatively impersonal mode of stimulus presentation and the complex kind of attention it required of the *S*s seem much more plausible bases of difference between the two studies than do hypothetical sex differences.

Even more clear than the fact that the present results confirm the finding of Rosenhan and London is the fact that they confound its explanation. The hypothesis of optimal tension states differentially affected by *hypnosis* is clearly untenable in view of the fact that non-hypnotic motivating instructions produce the same effects as does hypnosis. The notion that *relaxation* of tension is a critical variable seems implausible in light of the fact that the nonhypnotic motivator was an *exhortation,* not an instruction to relax; like hypnosis itself, it very clearly facilitated the performance of the *UT* group and impaired that of the *T* group. Since the control groups responded with slight declines in performance from first to second session regardless of susceptibility, there seems no reasonable alternative to the assertion that the specialised instructions represented by hypnosis and exhortation elicited the peculiarly differing response patterns of *T* and *UT* groups.

All things considered, it seems reasonable to conclude from these results not only that there is some stable difference in personality, broadly conceived, between individuals of high and low susceptibility to hypnosis, but that the difference must be reflected somehow in characteristics other than susceptibility just as it is plainly manifested in performances which are dependent upon instructional sets other than hypnosis. In general, research on the personality correlates of hypnotic susceptibility has failed to reveal important trait differences between high and low susceptible groups. The results of this experiment suggest that the consistent differences in performance that have appeared between them in one experiment after another might somehow be related to different reactions which they manifest toward instructions per se, regardless of whether the instructional condition is explicitly related to hypnosis. If this is the case, then the underlying differences between these groups might be sought in the anticipatory sets or dispositions toward situations in which performance normally varies with different aspects of preparatory instructions, such as the manner in which they are given or the complexity of their content. Whether or not this is precisely the case, however, it is abundantly clear that the different learning performances which are elicited from *S*s of differing susceptibility do not depend on the presence or absence of hypnosis itself. The nature of those differences, moreover, makes it clear not only that hypnosis cannot be understood as a positively motivating state per se because of its differential effects on various groups, but that positively motivating instructions cannot themselves be understood as positive motivators except in relation to particular subgroups of *S*s. The problem of the interactions of experimental conditions with personality characteristics is thus seen to extend beyond the realm of hypnosis and must similarly be addressed to the entire body of experimentation which attempts to manipulate performance by means of verbal instruction.

SUMMARY

Forty undergraduates, twenty relatively susceptible to hypnosis (*T*) and twenty relatively unsusceptible (*UT*), as determined by the Stanford Hypnotic Susceptibility Scale, learned two sets of ten nonsense syllables presented on a memory drum. Three groups were run: one group was hypnotised before presentation of the second list, another was merely exhorted to do better on the second list, and a control group received both lists under identical conditions, with neither hypnosis nor exhortation. Only differences due to susceptibility classification rather than experimental condition were significant. The differences in performance between *T* and *UT* *S*s manifested in this and other studies may be related to personality differences manifested in reactions toward instructions per se, regardless of their content.

REFERENCES

Glaze, J. A. The association value of nonsense syllables. *J. genet. Psychol.*, 1928, **35**, 255–267.

London, P. and Fuhrer, M. Hypnosis, motivation, and performance. *J. Pers.*, 1961, **29**, 321–333.

Rosenhan, D. and London, P. Hypnosis in the unhypnotisable: A study in rote learning. *J. exp. Psychol.*, 1963, **65**, 30–34. (a)

Rosenhan, D. and London, P. Hypnosis: Expectation, susceptibility, and performance. *J. abnorm. soc. Psychol.*, 1963, **66**, 77–81. (b)

Schulman, R. E. and London, P. Hypnosis and verbal learning. *J. abnorm. soc. Psychol.,* 1963, **67**, 363–370.

Slotnick, R. and London, P. Influence of instructions on hypnotic and nonhypnotic performance. *J. abnorm. Psychol.,* 1965, **1**, 38–46, 70.

Weitzenhoffer, A. M. and Hilgard, E. R. *Stanford Hypnotic Susceptibility Scale.* Palo Alto: Consulting Psychologists Press, 1959.

Weitzenhoffer, A. M. and Hilgard, E. R. *Stanford Hypnotic Susceptibility Scale: Form C.* Palo Alto: Consulting Psychologists Press, 1962.

Young, C. An experimental study of mental and physical functions in the normal and hypnotic state. *Amer. J. Psychol.,* 1925, **36**, 214–232.

SOURCES

Chapter

1	*Science,* Vol. 133, No. 3463, pp. 145–1486, 12th May, 1961.
2	From a Thesis submitted to the faculty of the University of North Carolina in partial fulfilment of the requirements for the degree of Master of Arts in the Department of Psychology, 1947.
3	*Journal of Experimental Psychology,* Vol. 43, pp. 75–79, 1952.
4	*Psychological Bulletin,* Vol. 52, No. 4, 1955.
5	Journal of Experimental Psychology, Vol. 51, No. 2, February 1956.
6	*Revue du Son,* January-February, 1959.
7	*Voprosy Psikhologii,* No. 1, p. 65, 1962.
8	*Journal of Mental Deficiency Research,* Vol. 6, June, 1962.
9	*Journal of the Sleep-Learning Association,* October 1965.
10	*Voprosy Psikhologii,* No. 2, p. 87, 1964.
11	*Voprosy Psikhologii,* No. 2, pp. 98–103, 1964.
12	*Voprosy Psikhologii,* No. 1, p. 143, 1965.
13	*Voprosy Psikhologii,* No. 4, p. 130, 1965.
14	*Voprosy Psikhologii,* No. 4, p. 133, 1965.
15	*Czeskoslovenska Psychologie,* roc IX, c.1, pp. 40–50, 1965.
16	A Paper presented to the 4th Interdisciplinary Conference for Experimental and Clinical Study of Higher Nervous Functions, Marianske Lazne, Czechoslovakia, 1965.
17	*British Journal of Anaesthesia,* Vol. 37, p. 544, 1965.
18	*Voprosy Psikhologii,* No. 3, p. 147, 1965.
19	A personal communication to the Editor.
24	'Hypnopaedia and Language Learning' by Brian Dutton, Birkbeck College, London. From *Journal of the Sleep-Learning Association,* April 1966. 'Report of a Test . . .' from Journal of the *Sleep Learning Association,* 1965.
28	A Thesis submitted to the Faculty of Wesleyan University, 1953.

Appendix

II	*Journal of Clinical and Experimental Hypnosis,* Vol. 3, pp. 215–221, 1955.
III	*Journal of Personality,* Vol. 4, No. 1, 1966.

RECOMMENDED LITERATURE FOR FURTHER READING

Ian Oswald. *Sleeping and Waking* (Elsevier).

N. Kleitman. *Sleep and Wakefulness* (Chicago University Press).

G. G. Luce and J. Segal. *Sleep* (Heinemann)

The C.I.B.A. Symposium of Sleep.

I. P. Pavlov. *Lectures on Conditioned Reflexes* (Lawrence and Wishart); *Selected Works* (Foreign Languages Publ. House, Moscow).

K. I. Platonov. *The Word as a Physiological and Therapeutical Factor* (Foreign Languages Publ. House, Moscow).

N. O'Connor. *Recent Soviet Psychology* (Pergamon Press).

E. D. Adrian. *The Physical Background of Perception* (Clarendon Press).

I. M. L. Hunter. *Memory* (Pelican).

W. Grey Walter. *The Living Brain* (Pelican).

Journal of the Sleep-Learning Association.

RECOMMENDED MONOGRAPHS AND ARTICLES

J. G. Jenkins and K. M. Dallenbach. Obliviscence During Sleep and Waking, *American Journal of Psychology,* 1924, Vol. 35, 605–612.

E. B. van Ormer. Sleep and Retention, *Psychological Bulletin,* 1933, Vol. 30, 415–439.

E. A. Graves. The Effect of Sleep Upon Retention, *Journal of Experimental Psychology,* 1936, Vol. 19, 316–322.

H. Davies, P. A. Davis, A. L. Loomis, E. N. Harvey and G. Hobart. Electrical Reactions of the Human Brain to Auditory Stimulation During Sleep, *Journal of Neurophysiology,* 1939, Vol. 2, 500–514.

C. W. Simon and W. H. Emmons. EEG, Consciousness and Sleep, *Science,* 1956, Vol. 124, 1066–1069.

R. L. Williams, H. W. Agnew Jr., W. B. Webb. Sleep Patterns of Young Adults: an EEG Study, *Electroencephalography and Clinical Neurphysiology,* 1964, Vol. 17, 376–381.

H. L. Williams, D. L. Tepas and H. C. Morlock. Evoked Responses to Clicks and Electroencephalographic Stages of Sleep in Man, *Science,* 1962, Vol. 138, 685–686.

A. L. Loomis, E. N. Harvey, G. Hobart. Brain Potentials During Hypnosis, *Science,* 1936, Vol. 83, 239–241.

M. Jouvet and D. Jouvet. A Study of Neurophysiological Mechanism of Dreaming, *Electroencephalography and Clinical Neurophysiology,* 1963, Suppl., Vol. 24, 133–154.

R. J. Berger. Experimental Modification of Dream Content by Meaningful Verbal Stimuli, *British Journal of Psychiatry,* 1963, Vol. 109, 722–740.

J. A. Deutsch and D. Deutsch. Attention, Some Theoretical Considerations, *Psychological Review,* 1963, Vol. 70, 80–90.

Helen C. Beh, P. E. H. Barratt. Discrimination and Conditioning During Sleep as Indicated by the Electroencephalogram, *Science,* 1965, Vol. 147, 1470–1471.

H. Weinberg. Evidence Suggesting the Acquisition of Simple Discrimination During Sleep, *Canadian Journal of Psychology,* 1966, Vol. 20, 1–11.

K. Bowers. Hypnotic Behaviour, The Differentiation of Trance and Demand Characteristic Variables, *Journal of Abnormal Psychology,* 1966, Vol. 71, No. 2.

E. R. Hilgard and C. T. Tart. Responsiveness to Suggestion Following Waking and Imagination Instructions and Following Induction of Hypnosis, *Journal of Abnormal Psychology,* 1966, Vol. 71, No. 3, 196–208.

U. J. Jovanovic. Einige Ergänzungen des elektroenzephalogafschen Schlafschema, *Medizinische Klinik, Sonderdruck,* No. 53, 31st December, 1965.

INDEX

A

B

C

D

E

F

H

I

K

L

M

N

O

P

R

S

T

U

V

W